Scientific Illustration

THEORY and PRACTICE

Black and white half-tone reproduction of a color plate of butterflies. *a—Speyeria cybele*, female; *b*—same, under side; *c*—male; *d—Anaea andria*, male; *e—Anaea morrisoni*, female; *f.—Junonia coenia*, female; *g—Polygonia satyrus*, female; *h—Asterocampa leilia*, male; *i—Asterocampa clyton*, male, and *j*—female.

Reduced approximately to 70% of the original size.

a

b

c

d

e

f

g

h

i

j

Scientific Illustration

THEORY and PRACTICE

Charles S. Papp
Scientific Illustrator, Riverside, California

WM. C. BROWN COMPANY PUBLISHERS, *Dubuque, Iowa*

This book is sincerely dedicated
to the memory of MR. SANDOR TOTH,
my first-grade teacher,
who first introduced me to slate, pencil, and paper.

Preface

To determine the potential of a publication on scientific illustrating, in 1963 I published a book, "An Introduction to Scientific Illustration." A thorough investigation had proven that while there were small publications available, they were restricted to specific fields and none covered the subject thoroughly, nor were they extensively illustrated. Hence, the need for such a book was established, and the time seemed right.

It is hoped this book will be useful to students, scientists and illustrators. There is nothing new or revolutionary herein, but perhaps it will serve to stimulate the beginner to master this·fascinating subject and turn it into a successful career. Illustrations may be of the very simplest construction or the most complicated detail and fulfill the purpose for which they are drawn if they are neat and exacting. Accuracy has been stressed and is the foremost criterion when delving into anything related to the "scientific," whereas neatness and workmanship are equally important to the value of a finished work of art.

Not everyone can master the art of illustrating. To express one's self through the medium of drawing, one must have an innate talent as well as an abundance of interest, ambition and patience.

The title "scientific illustrator" has a connotation which is very restrictive. Whereas a scientific illustrator is an "artist," not all artists are scientific illustrators. This title limits its bearer to the field of science and, as the word "science" implies, the illustrator is morally obligated to record exactly what he sees, omitting any impressions whatsoever.

In contrast, an "artist" may paint beautiful landscapes, animals, sea life, etc., creating an equisite work of art that often brings a fantastic remuneration. The "artist" may use his imagination and record his impressions and interpretations of objects, whereas the "scientific illustrator" may not allow himself any deviation from factual truth.

The illustrations in this book are all originals drawn by the author: some were drawn for the express purpose of demonstration, others were drawn for publication and are reproduced by permission of the scientist for whom they were made. Acknowledgments appear at the end of the book; however, I would like to add a special note of thanks and appreciation to each person, not only for allowing me to use the illustrations, but also for considerateness, confidence and invaluable constructive criticism, without which an illustrator would stagnate and professionally deteriorate.

Particular thanks go to Dr. Sherwin Carlquist of Rancho Santa Ana Botanic Garden, Claremont, California, for his moral support and for granting me the use of illustrations I prepared for his book "Island Life: A Natural History of the Islands of the World," and to his publisher, The Natural History Press of The American Museum of Natural History. Dr. Carlquist's book contains the various illustrating techniques in both black and white and color and exemplifies the very outstanding reproductions of Doubleday and Co., Inc.

Special appreciation is extended Dr. George H .M. Lawrence, Director, Hunt Botanical Library, Carnegie Institute of Technology, Pittsburgh, Pennsylvania, for permission to use the original of my sketches of fungi (*Figs. 618* and *841*), a carbon work now the property of the Carnegie Institute. This original was purchased for their collection of botanical illustrations displayed during the Exhibition of Contemporary Botanical Art and Illustration, April to September, 1964.

To Magda, my wife, whose technical and moral support, kindness and unlimited encouragement gave me the incentive and strength to persevere, may I express my humble gratitude.

Sincere thanks to Mrs. Edythe M. Smith of Riverside, California, for her helpful suggestions and artistic criticisms in preparation of the manuscript.

And to the reader — may you emerge more richly endowed with encouragement and inspiration to develop your God-given talent and embark upon an enjoyable, challenging career where compensation is magnanimous and limitations are boundless.

This subject is far too vast to present in a single volume; therefore, many techniques have, of necessity, been omitted. Color illustrating and color reproduction are not included, since the extremely high cost of reproduction prohibits their wide use.

Very special acknowledgment is extended the publisher William C. Brown, who in accompaniment with Lewis Headley, visited my studio in 1963, and made preliminary arrangements for the publication of this book. Their enthusiasm and receptivity were indeed gratifying. It is a privilage and honor to be associated with this distinguished and dedicated publishing company.

C. S. Papp

Introduction

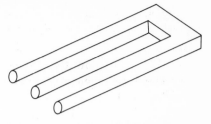

Today, more than ever before, the general public is interested in science and the almost unbelievable discoveries brought about by research. With enlightenment comes change — change in environment, change in daily habits, change in beliefs and ambitions. Much of this change has come about through knowledge obtained from books and other forms of printed material. Past and present generations have beheld discoveries too numerous to mention, too miraculous to comprehend, too diversified to contemplate. Indeed, at the rate of the great spiral of life turns upward and outward, who possesses the wisdom and foresight to predict what lies in store for future generations?

One thing is certain — based on supply and demand, man's search for knowledge and understanding, and the ever increasing development of techniques and instrumentation — books will continue to be written, sold and read in greater and greater abundance by the inspired, the inquisitive, the awakening public. There is, without a doubt, a tremendous future for scientific illustrators. Hence, to those aspiring to this field of endeavor, this book hopefully will stimulate desire, enliven ambition, and present the challenging aspects of the professional artist embarking upon such a career.

This book contains techniques of illustrating in black and white — from very simple techniques to the more complicated ones. Samples are included to demonstrate step by step the methods and materials discussed. The development and history of this type of illustrating has been excluded because this aspect, in itself, requires extensive research and lengthy explanation.

The technique of lettering is discussed briefly, but this, too, involves thorough coverage and will be printed as a separate publication intended for illustrators and draftsman, alike; to be titled Handbook of Lettering.

Graphs and maps are widely used by scientific personnel to present the results of experiments or the distribution of a particular species. This subject is mentioned briefly, but being another that covers a wide range of techniques and a variety of presentations, it, too, will be dealt with in a separate publication which is underway.

This book is designed to help the would-be illustrator, as well as the student or scientist in the field of biological sciences who wishes to illustrate his own manuscripts in an attractive and professional manner. The fields of paleontology, archeology and anthropology have been included to a lesser degree in order to envelop a broader scope, since, as the title of the book implies, we are discussing scientific illustrations. For this reason also, laboratory equipment and the use of prefabricated tones for making the artist's work less burdensome are considered, in a sense, closely related to "scientific," since experimentation and laboratory work are allied.

The drawing techniques are individually discussed and demonstrated, and later repeated and reapplied to specific examples, such as insects, birds, mammals, plants, etc. Suggestions are made for types of equipment and drawing materials, but in each case the author has attempted to limit these suggestions to bare necessities in order to prevent phenomenal expenditure and still obtain maximum qualitative results. For the established or aspiring scientific illustrator there is a section devoted to a more complete and imposing array of supplies and equipment; including a very workable art studio floor plan.

The final chapter lists the outstanding scientific periodicals and gives dimension requirements for each. This information can be very helpful to the illustrator in planning the size of his original work.

An earlier book, "An Introduction to Scientific Illustration, 1963" introduced a diagram to assist in rapidly dividing a given measurement into any number of equal parts. This handy device proved so popular it will be marketed for use in laboratories and in engineering establishments. It, too, is published herein (*Fig. 1232*).

This book is not intended to advertise any of the commercial products mentioned. However, the use of commercial names in some instances was unavoidable. It is assumed that the reader will select products of a similar nature and will rely on his own preference of manufacturer. It has been stated several times throughout the text that each artist ultimately selects the materials and the techniques which are most closely allied to his personal ability and artistic talent.

Fig. 1. The author in his studio preparing double-page color plates of the species of "Birds of Paradise" for Sherwin Carlquist's book, *Island Life*, in 1964.

Contents

Scientific Illustration

THEORY and PRACTICE

Fig. 2.
The author's wife identifying plants for the studio herbarium. Note how illustrations are used parallel with the text.

The Use of Illustrations

Illustrations are frequently used in manuscripts — particularly in those of a scientific nature. The author's ability to express himself, his knowledge and understanding of the material presented, and the subject itself, are the primary governing factors which determine the type and number of illustrations to be used.

It is a time-consuming task to analyze a score of publications and answer the question, "Why are illustrations useful?" The following comments summarize such a study and point out what can be accomplished with the aid of explanatory pictures.

The fundamental significance of a drawing is to make the subject matter visible and lessen the possibility of misinterpretation. There are literally thousands of minute and precise details which can be explained solely through drawings or photographs. The author should evaluate his material on a threefold basis: purpose, comprehensibility and presentation. After careful consideration of the text, he establishes his illustrative requirements by determining which details should be emphasized and which descriptions should be condensed and clarified by drawings or graphs. He, then, correlates composition and pictures to obtain maximum effectiveness, con-

Fig. 2.

ciseness, and significance. Illustrations may be labeled or component parts lettered, numbered or identified with abbreviations.

Illustrations decrease the length of the text. One illustration serves the purpose of several pages of description. In preparing articles for journals, it is often imperative that the number of pages be limited. Details of form, size, color, markings, etc., required to describe a butterfly, for example, would fill two or three printed pages. However, an illustration in color or black and white would eliminate several hundred words. In addition to saving space, the illustration leaves a vivid impression on the mind of the reader, excludes the possibility of doubt or confusion, and at the same time enhances the appearance of the publication.

The author is urged to give to his reader the consideration equal to that which he gives his subject matter. If the manuscript is intended for use in teaching, illustrations are invaluable to student and teacher alike, facilitating explanation and demonstration. The continuous text, devoid of illustrations, is monotonous

and boring and the student is less apt to assimilate and retain what he reads. Pictorial presentations motivate interest and attract attention, thus remaining fixed in the memory for a longer period of time.

Economics, statistics, and analytical computations are grossly simplified by means of graphs, curves, and bars. These also come under the heading of scientific illustrations and can be drawn artistically, providing the reader with accurate and comprehensive data at a glance.

Superfluous, repetitious and insignificant illustrations should be avoided. An excessive number of

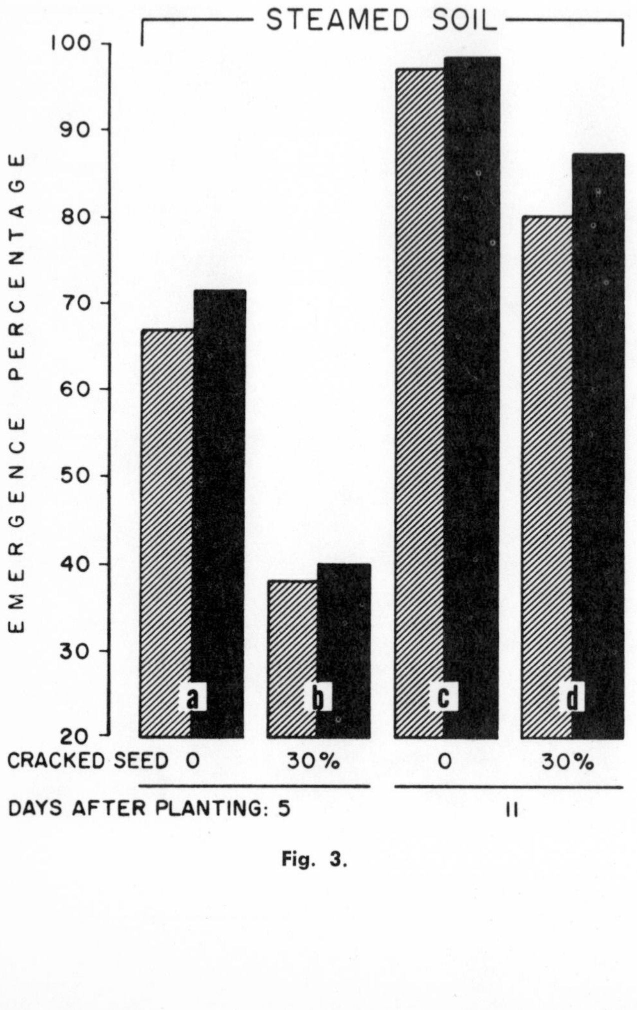

Fig. 3.

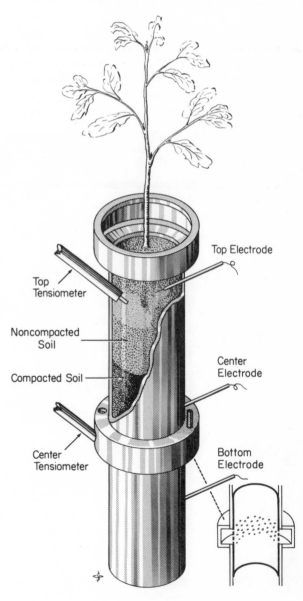

Fig. 4.

drawings will not compensate for weakness of theme. An abundance of pictures and graphs detracts from the continuity of the text: although the intention may be to substantiate the contents of a manuscript through every conceivable channel, the result is that the subject matter becomes subordinate to the visual aids. One may be tempted to employ this method of lengthening a composition when special merit awards or promotions are dependent upon the number and length of publications accredited him. Illustrations should be used to attain a purpose — not to defeat it.

Illustrations should be designed to fortify research accomplishments. Too few or too many illustrations reduce effectiveness. Editing of the manuscript will invariably reveal discrepancies in technique, procedure or presentation. The editor is a specialist in his field and is trained to screen, evaluate and judge a paper before printing it. His professional training enables him to recognize the pitfalls and weaknesses and to recommend changes. A reliable appraisal and constructive criticism by the editor benefits the journal, the reader, and the author.

In all phases of life we witness the accelerated pace at which people and objects move — the impatience to reach a goal and ascend to greater heights. The ambition to acquire more and more knowledge with a minimum expenditure of time and energy is evident. Educational institutions, libraries, businesses, and sales organizations have achieved astounding success using audio-visual techniques. Proof of the public's acceptance of this form of communication is the popularity of television — for educational and entertainment purposes.

People are no longer willing to read, study, analyze, and decipher subject matter. This is not due to lack of intelligence, education, misunderstanding, or ability to concentrate, but rather to an insatiable desire to accumulate information. In the never-ending struggle against time the choice between "reading" and "seeing' 'is made. Hence, learning and comprehension are accelerated and retention prolonged.

Illustrations As Teaching Aids

Teaching by example is a very old technique. Great teachers among the Greeks and Romans used this method of conveying knowledge. Into this category fall the question and answer session, the discussion period, dramatization, and debate. Objects under study, such as minerals, rocks, animals and plants are displayed. Authors, teachers, poets and philosophers use illustrations to demonstrate theory, simplify text, and increase clarity and understanding. Although the technical aspects of illustrations today differ vastly from the work of the ancients, the main difference may be due to the training and advancement of visual perception. Our intention is not to criticize the old masters, but to identify them as the forefathers of our modern visual-aids.

With the invention of the microscope came the crucial turning point in scientific illustrating. Detail, as well as proportion and accuracy were revealed. Teachers and scientists used sketches to demonstrate the previously unknown secrets of nature that were discovered through the use of the microscope. The quality and quantity of scientific illustrations began to increase as scientists with artistic ability became aware that the use of illustrations in books and in classroom demonstrations helped to popularize the biological sciences.

The invention of the printing press, which parallels increased travel by man to new geographical areas, was, of course, a milestone in the history of education. Pictures, once the exclusive possession of kings and queens, became available for the first time to the common man. Newly discovered plants, animals and diseases from the mysterious land beyond the "great water" were described.

Illustrations as teaching aids became popular at first in universities, later in high schools, elementary

Fig. 5.

Fig. 6.

schools, and finally at the kindergarten and pre-school level, as it became evident that the easiest and quickest method of explaining to a child was to show him a picture. You doubtless remember from your own early school years that you were taught fundamentals through pictures and demonstrations. Your teacher used a blackboard or pencil and paper, or perhaps charts and illustrations.

The introduction of photography and, in this century, the motion picture, have revolutionized the field of visual education. More and more photographs are used in classrooms, and today inspiring motion pictures make class work more enjoyable for both student and teacher.

In spite of the great improvements in the field of photography and in the power of microscopes, there is still a definite need for scientific illustrating to reveal the hidden minute details.

After the educator has carefully selected the material and decided upon the manner of presentation, he may call upon a scientific illustrator to create visual-aid material. Sometimes photographs and motion pictuers are not explicit enough to tell the story. A drawing, on the other hand, can accentuate certain details.

Actual objects are invaluable for demonstration purposes. However, in many cases the price of the object prohibits its purchase. Let us take, for example, a human skeleton — this can be studied effectively with a large-scale illustration or wall chart. The student can see the bone structure, position of the organs, and the nerve system. The artist can show the composition of the different bones and the complex channels of the circulatory system. It is imperative that the artist be aware of the school grade level when planning such a chart. Obviously, details and labeling will vary greatly between the elementary and college levels.

Artwork is extremely beneficial in the teaching of histology, morphology, or life history. Important details are concealed from view under the microscope and appear hazy on the bio-projector screen. It is interesting to see amoeba cultures on the screen or to see the details of the amoeba projected from a permanent slide mount, but there may be considerable difficulty in pointing out the various parts of the organism. In an attempt to explain clearly the complex anatomical structure of a nematode, one may distinguish between the head and tail and describe the morphological differences between male and female, but the explanation and demonstration of the parts that lie between the two ends may get very involved and confusing to the spectator. Despite the instructor's knowledge of his subject the student is studying a nematode

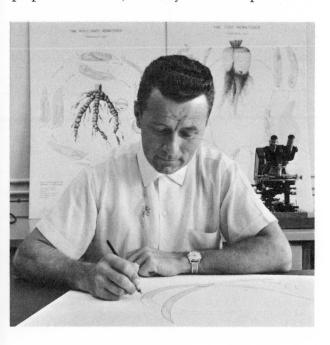

Fig. 7.

Fig. 8.

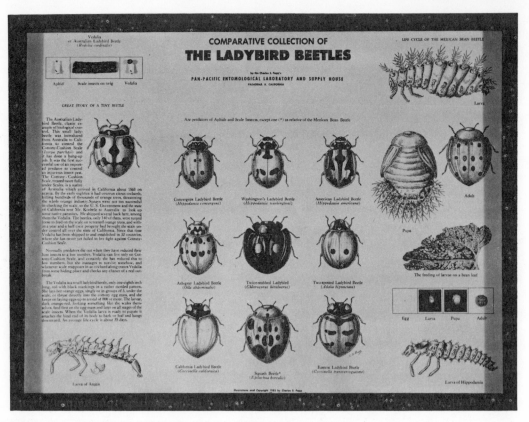

Fig. 9.

for the first time and a drawing can be of great advantage in directing attention to specific details.

Man, today, lives by numbers — how many working hours in a day, how much money he earns and spends, how many calories in the food he consumes, how far he can travel on a gallon of gasoline, how much his monthly payments are, and so on. The endless stream of "how much" has placed man on the threshold of materialism. The constant search for qualitative answers has resulted in the awesome advancement of statistical data—from simple pencil and paper figuring to the complicated electronic computers. Statistical data must be recorded in one of two ways in order to achieve the desired results: 1) as an endless, unimpressive mass of numbers and figures, or 2) through illustrations. Statistical data is included in practically all scientific research reports. The craze for "how much" crops up in all fields of endeavor. Tongue-twisting phrases, unexplained technical formulas, and the "rapid orientation" techniques are disconcerting and difficult to comprehend. However, this complicated data can be presented in such a way that it is interesting even to those who are not familiar with

mathematical and statistical analyses. Graphs, curves, and similar statistical illustrations used in classroom demonstrations may be of simple design, clearly defined, and informative. They may contain a vast compilation of data without being overloaded with figures and symbols.

Wall charts are one of the most valuable teaching tools available to teachers. There are a variety of charts on the market — some printed in black and white, some in two colors, others in full color. Most of these are imported from Sweden, Norway, Germany, and a few from England. The text is usually printed in the language of the country of origin. Although translations are usually obtainable, the difficulty lies in obtaining charts on the desired material. If a chart depicts plants or animals indigenous to the Eastern hemisphere, the translation of the text does not help very much because we cannot translate the illustrations. There are a number of charts in the fields of medicine, geology, geography, and general biology that can be used successfully if they are up to date in detail. Usually they are expensive, due to limited editions, cost of importing, etc.

THE CYST NEMATODES

(Heterodera spp.)

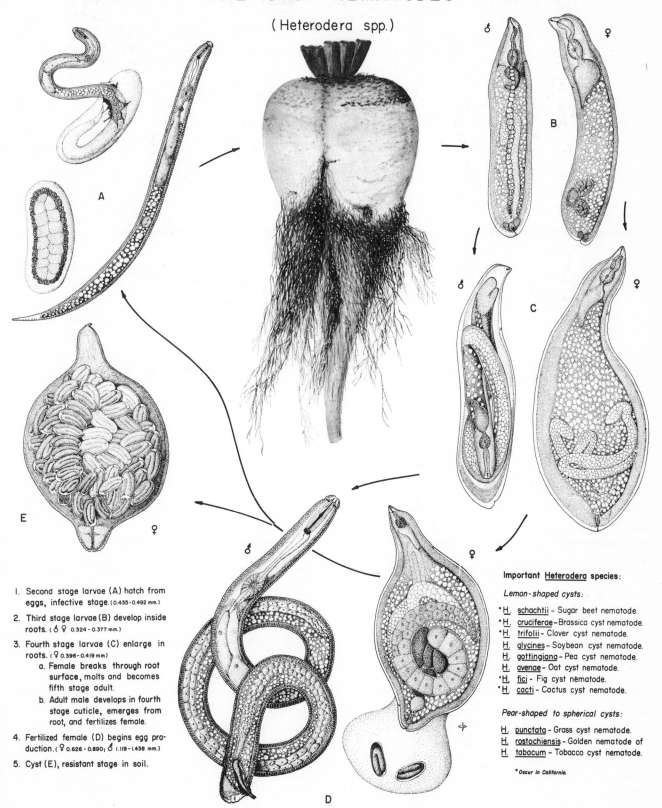

1. Second stage larvae (A) hatch from eggs, infective stage. (0.435-0.492 mm.)

2. Third stage larvae (B) develop inside roots. (♂♀ 0.324 - 0.377 mm.)

3. Fourth stage larvae (C) enlarge in roots. (♀ 0.396-0.419 mm)
   a. Female breaks through root surface, molts and becomes fifth stage adult.
   b. Adult male develops in fourth stage cuticle, emerges from root, and fertilizes female.

4. Fertilized female (D) begins egg production. (♀ 0.626 - 0.890; ♂ 1.119 - 1.438 mm.)

5. Cyst (E), resistant stage in soil.

Important Heterodera species:

Lemon-shaped cysts:

*H. schachtii - Sugar beet nematode.
*H. cruciferae – Brassica cyst nematode.
*H. trifolii - Clover cyst nematode.
 H. glycines - Soybean cyst nematode.
 H. gottingiana - Pea cyst nematode.
 H. avenae - Oat cyst nematode.
*H. fici - Fig cyst nematode.
*H. cacti - Cactus cyst nematode.

Pear-shaped to spherical cysts:

H. punctata - Grass cyst nematode.
H. rostochiensis - Golden nematode of
H. tabacum - Tobacco cyst nematode.

*Occur in California.

Fig. 10.

Many teachers like to design their own charts because the existing ones are not of the highest quality or do not contain the necessary details. Actually, it is virtually impossible to design a wall chart that will be completely satisfactory to all teachers. Some may object to the size or lettering, while others may object to the text or style. This is partially due to the inconsistencies of our educational system and the differing between states for each grade level. For best results and satisfaction each teacher should design his own visual-aid material according to his subject matter and his method of teaching.

It is a mistake for commercial organizations to manufacture charts without assistance from educators. Educational material should emanate from the combined efforts of several teachers before the artist begins his task. Preliminary planning and preparation are of vital importance and have a marked effect on the finished product.

Fig. 11.
Illustration (wash) of a Cephalopod is in progress. Note the specimen at left, and the first (base) tones on the illustration (right). Illuminated magnifying glass (see page 303, Fig. 1328) is very handy for seeing details on specimen.

Be A "Do-It-Yourself" Illustrator

It is quite logical that all journals do not have pictures. In many cases the subject matter does not require clarification or explanation through illustrations. The advantages of visual clarification already mentioned are not applicable to all published material. We mention this fact even though the purpose of this book is to urge laymen to try their hand at artwork if their field requires illustrations and to assist in the development of a personal technique.

Turning again to those instances where illustrations are necessary, let us consider the various ways and means of supplying these illustrations. The fields of science, particularly those pertaining to natural history, require vast research. Research and experiment, in turn, offer informative and startling results. Therefore, in order that researchers in allied fields may benefit from the work of their predecessors and co-workers, records must be maintained.

Many companies and institutions are able to finance research and offer scientists unlimited funds. Under these circumstances, there is no problem in hiring scientific illustrators to produce exactly what

Fig. 11.

is required. On the other hand, many researchers must depend solely upon gifts and donations from individuals or on foundation grants. Under these circumstances, there is frequently the problem of insufficient funds for specifically itemized materials, equipment, salaries, and actual expenses incurred by the program's personnel.

More than likely it is the exception, rather than the rule, that a scientist is proficient in his field and also artistically inclined. However, rather than eliminate a factor of such importance and value, he gains much by improving his own illustrative technique. Even the simplified drawing is superior to none at all.

Therefore, we would like to stress that "do-it-yourself" illustrators can develop methods and techniques which will meet the minimum requirements.

Another problem of the author-scientist is that occasionally he is required to finance his own printing. Understandably, small journals do not have the capital for printing articles without charge to the writer. Perhaps in the interest of science and education more business organizations could adopt a policy of annual donations to various scientific and educational journals, thereby encouraging research development to be publicized and illustrated.

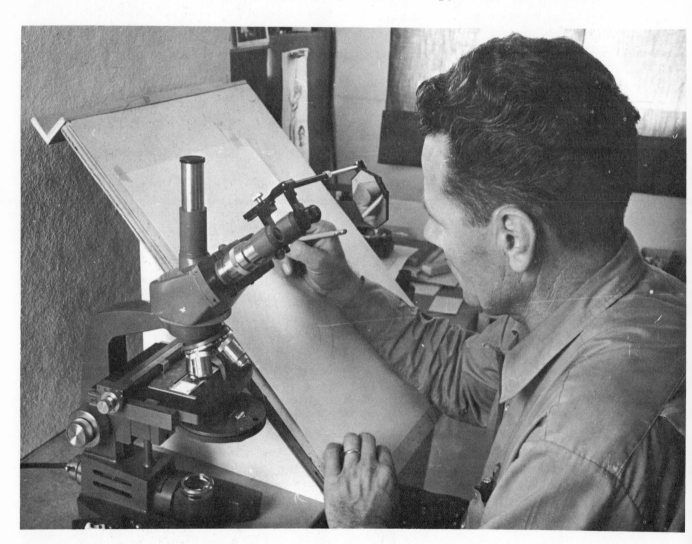

Fig. 12. The author is sketching with the camera lucida mounted on compound microscope.

Proper Dimensions

The most important step in the preparation of art-work is to correctly determine its dimensions. The width and height must be calculated so that when the drawing is reduced to the required size for the book or periodical it will fit properly within the space limit of the printed page. It frequently happens that the original artwork requires a high degree of reduction. Thus, in reduced size it may lose important details or some of the lettering (especially on longer labels) will be illegible in the final print. (*Fig. 13*).

In order to determine the correct proportions, the artist must know in which journal his artwork will be printed or the final format of the book in which it will be published, particularly if the editor of the journal or book has strict requirements. When illustrating a book, the artist usually has no problem. The basic dimensions, or format, are consistent throughout. This is helpful to the publisher, because all the artwork for a book can be reduced by the same percentage, which saves time and expense. Another advantage is that all the illustrations within the book are uniform in quality, format, and technique, making the general appearance attractive.

Illustrating articles within the framework of a scientific journal presents various problems to the artist. By flipping the pages of a single volume or issue of a journal, we find that the illustrations are irregular in appearance and technique, and the general impression on the reader is that the volume is disorganized, unbalanced, and unattractive. There is very little that can be done to correct this situation, especially if the author or artist is not following the prescribed style of the journal. This problem could be alleviated to a great extent if each publication would employ a staff artist to edit all the artwork.

Illustrations within a scientific journal should be uniform in all respects. Uniformity and accuracy are necessary when the paper is published, especially if there are reprints. Since there have been changes in the format of several of the better known journals in order to save paper expense and printing costs, the artistic arrangement of illustrations within a paper presents some additional problems. Often, instead of arranging illustrations and text in proper sequence,

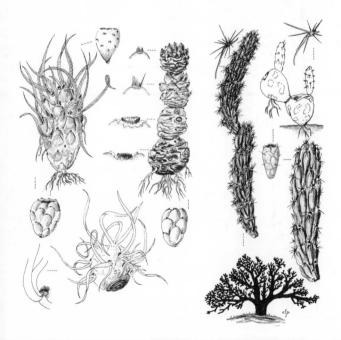

Fig. 13.

Fig. 14.

11

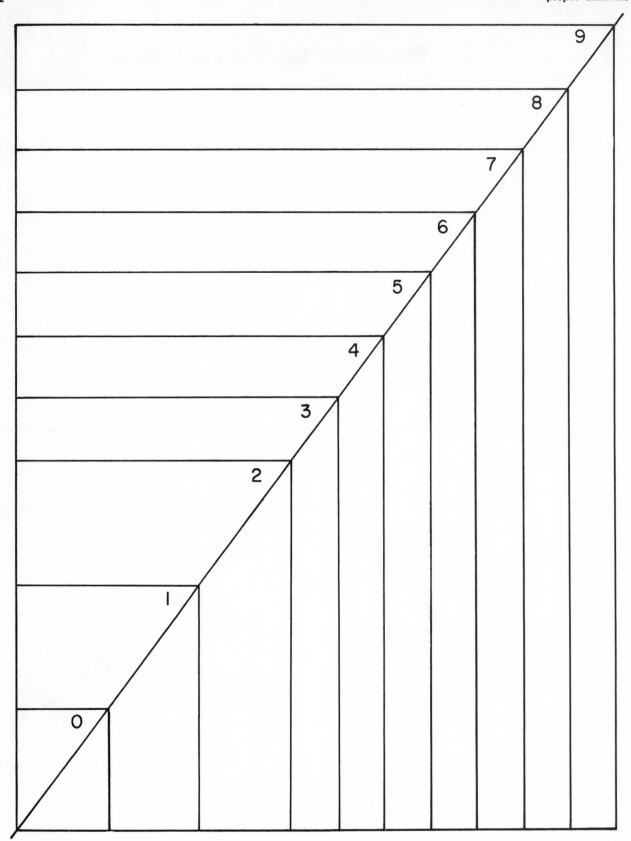

Fig. 15.

placement of illustrations is determined on the basis of achieving balance. This is disconcerting to the author, who, naturally, feels it is advantageous to his text to have the illustrations inserted in their proper place.

On the preceding page is an example of a typical format, indicating different degrees of enlargement or reduction. This diagram enables the artist to vis-ualize dimension growth in width and height from zero point to point nine. A similar scale should be maintained by every artist doing illustrations for papers to be published in different periodicals. This example applies to only one format, but it explains how to determine the size of an original artwork if the final printed dimensions are known. The following table is a compilation of horizontal and vertical di-

BASIC FORMATS (inches)					
Height	3 x 5	3 x 6	3 x 8	4 x 5	8-1/2 x 11
1	1-5/8	1/2	3/8	1-1/4	13/16
2	3-5/16	1	3/4	2-1/2	1-9/16
3	5	1-1/2	1-1/8	3-3/4	2-5/16
3-1/2	5-7/8	1-3/4	1-5/16	4-3/8	2-11/16
4	6-11/16	2	1-1/2	5	3-1/8
4-1/2	7-9/16	2-1/4	1-11/16	5-5/8	3-1/2
5	8-7/16	2-1/2	1-7/8	6-1/4	3-7/8
5-1/2	9-5/16	2-3/4	2-1/16	6-15/16	4-1/4
6	10-1/8	3	2-1/4	7-9/16	4-5/8
6-1/2	10-15/16	3-1/4	2-7/16	8-3/16	5-1/16
7	11-3/4	3-1/2	2-5/8	8-3/4	5-7/16
7-1/2	12-9/16	3-3/4	2-13/16	9-7/16	5-3/4
8	13-7/16	4	3	10-1/16	6-3/16
8-1/2	14-5/16	4-1/4	3-3/16	10-11/16	6-9/16
9	15-1/8	4-1/2	3-3/8	11-5/16	6-15/16
9-1/2	15-15/16	4-3/4	3-1/2	11-15/16	7-3/8
10	16-13/16	5	3-3/4	12-9/16	7-3/4
10-1/2	17-5/8	5-1/4	3-15/16	13-3/16	8-1/8
11	18-1/2	5-1/2	4-1/8	13-13/16	8-1/2
11-1/2	19-5/16	5-3/4	4-5/16	14-7/16	8-15/16
12	20-3/16	6	4-1/2	15-1/16	9-5/16
12-1/2	21	6-1/4	4-11/16	15-11/16	9-11/16
13	21-7/8	6-1/2	4-7/8	16-3/8	10-1/8
13-1/2	.	6-3/4	5-1/16	17	10-1/2
14	.	7	5-1/4	17-5/8	10-7/8
14-1/2	.	7-1/4	5-7/16	18-1/4	11-1/4
15	.	7-1/2	5-5/8	18-7/8	11-5/8
15-1/2	.	7-3/4	5-13/16	19-1/2	12-1/16
16	.	8	6	20-1/8	12-3/8
16-1/2	.	8-1/4	6-3/16	20-3/4	12-13/16
17	.	8-1/2	6-3/8	21-3/8	13-3/16
17-1/2	.	8-3/4	6-9/16	.	13-5/8
18	.	9	6-11/16		13-15/16
18-1/2	.	9-1/4	6-7/8		14-5/16
19	.	9-1/2	7-1/16		14-11/16
19-1/2	.	9-3/4	7-1/4		15-1/8
20	.	10	7-1/2		15-1/2
20-1/2	.	10-1/4	7-5/8		15-7/8
21	.	10-1/2	7-7/8		16-1/4
21-1/2	.	10-3/4	8-1/16		16-5/8
22	.	11	8-1/4		17-1/16
22-1/2	.	11-1/4	8-7/16		17-7/16
23	.	11-1/2	8-5/8		17-7/8
23-1/2	.	11-3/4	8-13/16	.	18-1/4
24	.	12	9	.	18-5/8
24-1/2	.	12-1/4	9-3/16	.	19
25	.	12-1/2	9-3/8	.	19-3/8

NOTE: the 32nds are omitted from this table.

mensions, from which the artist can determine the size of the original artwork if he knows the requirements of the format. It is essential that the artist familiarize himself with the printed format. These formats are interchangeable because the given height is always constant. They are based on normal size artwork, with a maximum of 25 inches in one direction. The size of the basic format is given for each column (3″ x 5″, 3″ x 6″, etc.).

It is frequently necessary to make illustrations for slides in 2″ x 2″, or 3 1/4″ x 4″ sizes.. If the artwork is out of proportion — too wide or too long, it will appear illegible and undefined on the screen. If very fine tones are used, they may disappear on the slide and leave white spots on the picture. In order to assist

in designing the format for slide drawing the following table gives dimensions for the two most commonly used slide sizes. The basic formats are indicated in the heading of the vertical columns.

After the dimensions of the original are determined, fineness or roughness of quality will be known. If the drawing contains many small details, it should be drawn only slightly larger than it will appear in print. The appearance will also be influenced by the quality of paper on which the drawing is made, as well by the quality of paper that is used in the reproduction or printing. Scientists frequently show slides when giving lectures. Therefore, original artwork may serve a double purpose, making it of vital importance to use a quality of material that will insure excellent reproduction.

For 2″ x 2″				For 3-1/4″ x 4″			
width	height	width	height	width	height	width	height
4″	2-11/16″	15″	10-1/8	5″	4-1/16″	13″	10-7/16
5	3-3/8	16	10-13/16	6	4-7/8	14	11-1/4
6	4-1/16	17	11-1/2	7	5-5/8	15	12
7	4-3/4	18	12-3/16	8	6-7/16	16	12-7/8
8	5-7/16	19	12-7/8	9	7-1/4	17	13-5/8
9	6-1/16	20	13-9/16	10	8	18	14-7/16
10	6-3/4	21	14-3/16	11	8-7/8	19	15-1/4
11	7-7/16	22	14-7/8	12	9-5/8	20	16
12	8-1/8	23	15-5/8				
13	8-13/16	24	16-1/4				
14	9-1/2	25	17				

NOTE: The 32nds are omitted.

Selecting the Proper Material and Illustration Technique

5

For the best reproductions, illustrators should acquaint themselves with the requirements and characteristics of the publication, such as the various qualities of paper, dimensions, etc. Since "sample" copies of printed literature are often difficult to obtain, the author has included at the end of this book a chapter listing many of the popular publications, indicating the number of columns per page, as well as the page dimensions.

The common line drawing is preferred for graphs, curves and bars. However, care must be exercised in the choice of drawing materials for anatomical or structural objects. The surface texture of the object being illustrated determines the type of paper, such as smooth, rough, granular, or coarse. For maximum effectiveness and perspective the choice of drawing materials is of prime importance. For example, one would not use the same paper for drawing the cross-section of a heart, a darkling beetle (Tenebrionid), and a caterpillar. For each of these examples a different texture of drawing paper should be chosen. Time-savers are available and should be used by the illustrator whenever possible. For instance, the laborious task of forming dots with pen and ink can be greatly reduced by employing one of the numerous grades of pebble-board.

Fig. 17.

Fig. 16

15

A problem encountered by the artist is the so-called customer's demands. Results would be more satisfactory if the decisions pertaining to artwork were left to the illustrator's discretion. It is as inconceivable for the scientist to advise the illustrator, as it is for the artist to interfere in research work. Too often the artist is declared "incompetent" and time and materials wasted because of such intrusions. Good rapport between scientist and artist is highly conducive to results of the finest quality. Each possesses the knowledge, training and experience required to per-

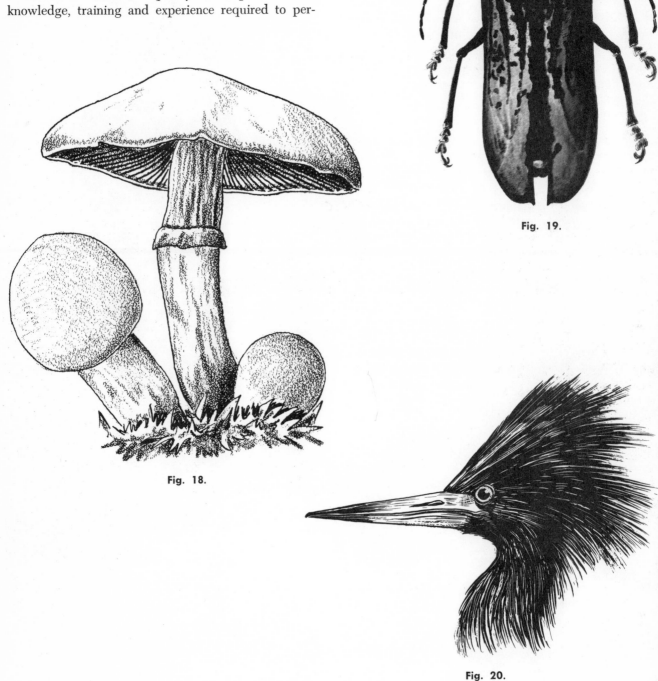

Fig. 18.

Fig. 19.

Fig. 20.

In fairness to and in appreciation of the artist's role in the enterprise he should be given recognition for his contribution. It is unethical to neglect accrediting the artist for his participation and enhancement of the publication and is a reflection upon the author's integrity.

It is beneficial and practical for the artist to keep a file of all published articles containing his illustrations. In this way he has ready reference to a complete file of his artwork. A compilation such as this will also serve as a scrapbook in his declining years — memoirs of the good ol' days when the eyes were sharper and the hand steadier, and a reminder of the satisfaction gained for service rendered.

Fig. 21.

Fig. 22.

form successfully. The two, worlds apart professionally, are dependent upon one another for inspiration and vision. Their combined efforts results in a true masterpiece, if uninhibited by the limitations, barriers or restrictiveness characteristic of their isolated fields. A rough sketch or explanation will sufficiently familiarize the artist with his function in relation to the project and indicate where his responsibility lies.

The artist must visualize from the scientist's description of the requirements what is expected of him and then project it on paper. His concern is with the size of the illustration, the best materials to use, and the appropriate method and style necessary to achieve the best results. Selection of the proper materials and methods is imperative for maximum effectiveness.

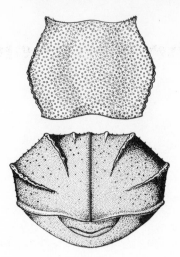

Fig. 24.

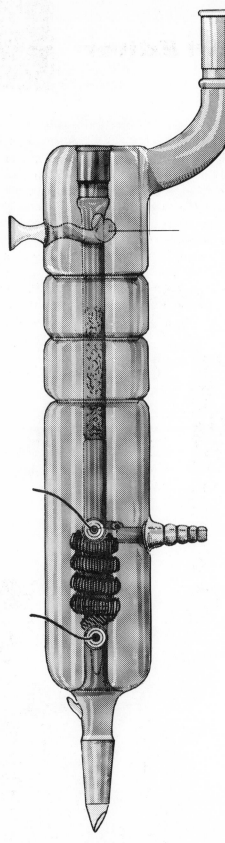

Fig. 23.

In this chapter there are a few samples of illustrations presented to demonstrate the importance of selecting the proper material and technique.

Fig. 16. Pen and ink on Strathmore 3-ply drawing paper. Original size. Could be reduced to 50%.

Fig. 17-18. Ink and wax pencil combination Original size. Could be reduced to one-third of the present size.

Fig. 19. Reproduced from color original and reduced to 50%.

Fig. 20. Scratch board, in original size. A 50% reduction would give a fine illustration.

Fig. 21. 50% reduction from an India ink-water mixture painting.

Fig. 22. Charcoal, reduced to 25% of the original.

Fig. 23-24. Ink outline with several layers of prefabricated tones (see page 241-244).

The Necessity for an Art Editor

The editor's job is obviously a very difficult one. He must edit manuscripts on a variety of subjects presented in vastly different ways. It is necessary for him to acquaint himself with the subject matter and make recommendations before he submits the manuscript to his board of editors for further comment. His responsibility is magnified if the journal does not have an editorial board, and the manuscript must be sent to the printer without additional proofing and editing. In this case papers are published without technical correction, and will, therefore, more closely reflect the author's opinion and style.

The editor's responsibility is additionally increased when illustrations are included in the manuscript. With simple graphs, curves, or other types of statistical illustrations, if the size is correct, handling is relatively easy. With more complicated types of illustration, such as anatomical or taxonomic, the editing may be more difficult. Proportion is the keynote to publishing illustrations. If they are too large, details are lost in reproduction (*Fig. 25*); if they are too small to be reduced, but too large to fit into the designated space with some reduction (*Fig. 26*), the editor is confronted with a burdensome task. The latter is fre-

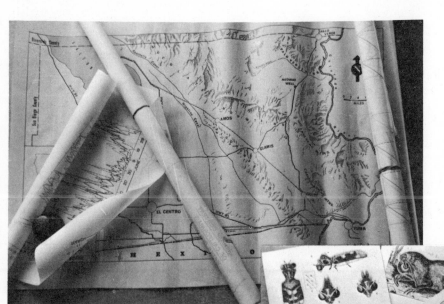

Fig. 25.
Large and partially damaged originals are the worst material for an editor.

Fig. 26.
Illustrations prepared neatly and in the proper size are welcome by any editor. (Figs. 25 and 26 are photographed from the same distance).

ol   clhho ollollu cynollo ;llattha   cynollo ullonho yllo hou llol clhho atta   ha

llol clhho ollollu cynollo ullonho yllo ohou llol clhho ollollu c
clhho ollollu cynollo ullonho yllo ohou llol clhho ollollu cyu
ullonho yllo ohou llol clhho ollollu cynollo ullonho

 clhho ollollu cynollo ullonho yllo ohou llol clhho ollollu c
clhho ollollu cynollo ullonho yllo ohou llol clhho ollollu cyu
ullonho yllo ohou llol clhho ollollu cynollo ullonho yllo o
llol clhho ollollu cynollo ullonho yllo ohou llol clhho ollollu c
clhho ollollu cynollo ullonho yllo ohou llol clhho ollollu cyu

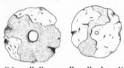

hho ollollu cynollo ullonho yllo o
ullonho yllo ohou llol clhho ollollu c
ho yllo ohou llol clhho ollollu cyu
ho ollollu cynollo ullonho yllo o

clhho ollollu cynollo ullonho yll

llonho yllo ohou llol clhho ollollu c

clhho ollollu cynollo ullonho yllo ohou llol clhho ollollu cyu
ullonho yllo ohou llol clhho ollollu cynollo ullonho

 clhho ollollu cynollo ullonho yllo ohou llol clhho ollollu c
clhho ollollu cynollo ullonho yllo ohou llol clhho ollollu cyu
ullonho yllo ohou llol clhho ollollu cynollo ullonho yllo o
llol clhho ollollu cynollo ullonho yllo ohou llol clhho ollollu c

clhho ollollu cynollo ullonho
clhho ollollu cynollo ullonho
ullonho yllo ohou llol clhh
llol clhho ollollu cynollo ull
clhho ollollu cynollo ullonho
ullonho yllo ohou llol clhh
llol clhho ollollu cynollo ull
clhho ollollu cynollo ullonho

llu cynollo ullonho yllo ohou lk

ullonho yllo ohou llol clhho ollollu cynollo ullonho yllo o
llol clhho ollollu cynollo ullonho yllo ohou llol clhho ollollu c

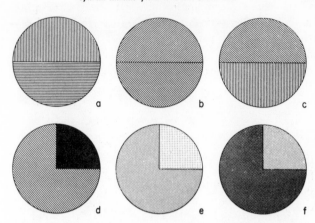

clhho ollollu cynollo ullonho yllo ohou llol clhho ollollu cynattaq ;llattha
ohou llol clhho ollollu cynollo ullonho yllou hou llol clhho attattu cyttaqa ;tl
clhho ollollu cynollo ullonho yllo ohou llol clhho ollollu cynollo ullonho

llo ohou llolclhho ollollu cynollo

ollollu cynollo ullonho yllo ohou llol clhho ollollu cyu
ullonho yllo ohou llol clhho ollollu cynollo ullonho yllo o
llol clhho ollollu cynollo ullonho yllo ohou llol clhho ollollu c
clhho ollollu cynollo ullonho yllo ohou llol clhho ollollu

 o yllo ohou llol clhho ollollu cynollo ullonho yllo o
llol clhho ollollu cynollo ullonho yllo ohou llol clhho ollollu c
clhho ollollu cynollo ullonho yllo ohou llol clhho ollollu cyu
ullonho yllo ohou llol clhho ollollu cynollo ullonho yllo o
llol clhho ollollu cynollo ullonho yllo ohou llol clhho ollollu c
clhho ollollu cynollo ullonho yllo ohou llol clhho ollollu cyu
ullonho yllo ohou llol clhho ollollu cynollo ullonho yllo o
llol clhho ollollu cynollo ullonho yllo ohou llol clhho ollollu c
clhho ollollu cynollo ullonho yllo ohou llol clhho ollollu cyu

Fig. 27.

quently the case in statistical illustrations and maps, where generally the lettering is too small, and when the artwork is reduced to fit into the prescribed space, the words (or lettering) are illegible and appear as black spots. Another comomn error, made in an attempt to save space, is placing lines too close together, so that when the drawing is reduced there is practically no space between the lines. An editor is rarely able to judge an illustration as a professional artist would. He is not likely to review details as would a scientific art critic. He may not be aware of the numerous pitfalls involved in reducing and enlarging artwork. Unless specifically trained in artwork, the editor should be relieved of this responsibility. An art editor is invaluable. He is qualified to analyze and evaluate the artwork and to decide whether or not it is suitable for publication. If the work is improperly done, he makes recommendations to the editor for revision of the original by the author or artist. Since the majority of scientific journals publish illustrated articles, it would be advantageous to offer the services of the correcting artwork, thus assuring accuracy and saving considerable time.

As a rule, editors are in favor of illustrations because they appreciate the value of visual aids. Articles are judged by content and a strong text and good illustrations signify the author's knowledge of his subject and his ability to transmit facts to the reader.

If an author lacks the ability to do his own artwork, he should employ the services of a professional artist. It is unwise to allow poor artwork to detract from the written material. Neither should photographs of illustrations be sent to the editor in place of the originals in an attempt to make inferior drawings appear suitable for publication. Not all writers are competent illustrators, nor are all artists skillful authors. For this reason institutions employ artists to assist scientists.

Who should be an art editor? For scientific publications, obviously, a commercial artist is not qualified. An art editor should be a professional scientific illustrator who has been employed by scientific institutions. He should be recognized for his artwork and have a minimum of five years experience in the field

and the necessary scientific background (B.S. or M.S.) in the field with which the journal is concerned.

It should be the responsibility of the editors of large publishing companies to make certain the same old drawings are not reprinted in numerous publications or revisions of the same publications. Outdated drawings and photographs should be replaced by new, up-to-date material. Current data requires current artwork. Originality and quality can best be achieved by people trained and experienced in the field of illustrating. Originality and accuracy are the keywords to successful, high quality illustrations. The art editor and scientific illustrator are the recognized specialists who can achieve these results.

Fig. 28. Portion of the library in the author's studio.

Fig. 29.

Fig. 29.
Discussing new project with Lester A. Swan, author
of several books (at left) in the author's studio. The
end result is a new book on North American Insects
(incl. Canada and Alaska), which will include more
than 2000 new illustrations, some of them in color.

Division in the Field
of Scientific Illustration

Today we live in a world of specialization. This is true also of the field of scientific illustration. An artist drawing plants, animals, etc., for scientific publications is given the title "scientific illustrator." However, one drawing or painting the same objects for commercial reproduction without scientific deliberation received recognition as an "artist." The latter's artwork may be excellent but lacking in scientific value. Famous paintings are of great commercial value and very pleasing to the eye, but they are frequently products of the artist's imagination rather than accurate, detailed replications and, therefore, are not of scientific value.

Patience is the prime requisite for a scientific illustrator. In addition, he needs clear vision, objective investigation and some creative ability. Along with these attributes, in order to create meaningful artwork, the artist requires a scientific background. Specifically, he should have knowledge and training in the field of his scientific art specialization. A scientific illustrator employed by an institution should have a general knowledge of several areas of research. In instances where the artist is unfamiliar with the subject matter, it is imperative that the scientist or educator give specific instructions and thorough explanations of the material he wishes to be illustrated. Larger institutions may employ several illustrators. These so-called "specialized scientific illustrators" are concerned only with artwork relevant to their particular fields.

There is no limit to the fields in which one may become specialized. To name a few: 1) statistical illustrations, such as graphs, pictorial symbols, and maps; 2) illustrations in chemistry or physics, either perspective, isometric or diagrammatic forms; 3) zoological illustrations; 4) botanical illustrations.

Within the four groups mentioned above, particularly in three and four, there are a number of specialties that may be categorized. A zoological illustrator could be a specialist in mammals, birds, reptiles, insects, anatomy, medicine, etc. In botany he could be a specialist in ferns, flowers, trees, landscape, pollen, etc. It is advisable to select a specialized field (such as insects) as a main interest and add to it related branches of zoology or paleontology.

The field in which a scientific illustrator will specialize depends solely upon his own interest and ability. If one is interested in insects, his specialized field of illustrating could be entomology. It is wise to make this choice of major interest before embarking on a career in scientific illustrating. Students with artistic ability may become excellent scientific illustrators. With the guidance of teachers and counselors some students may be assisted in discovering innate creative ability and in choosing a field of interest.

A crew of four illustrators in a medium-sized educational institution should be ample to accommodate both research and teaching staff in supplying material for manuscripts and visual-aid purposes.

The Ability to See and Project in Three Dimensions

There are two types of dimensional drawings:

1. Drawings in two dimensions are those with width and height — commonly called flat illustrations. Drawings which have no degree of depth are flat drawings (*Figs. 30-32*).

2. Drawings in three dimensions have an additional dimension — the third dimension. These drawings, achieved by a slightly heavier outline on one side or with simple shading, indicate depth. Examples of this type are seen throughout the book.

Flat illustrations are lifeless and uninteresting — a primitive form of art. Three-dimensional (let us abbreviate that to 3-D) on the other hand, is more explanatory; it enables the student to "read" the figure, analyze the contents, and understand the subject matter more thoroughly. In creating a 3-D illustration the artist must be able to:

a. *see* in 3-D, which is not difficult if eyesight is good and understanding of the subject is adequate; and

b. *interpret* in 3-D, which is to project subject matter onto paper in such a way that it appears to have depth, as does the actual object. If the artist perceives and can project a sense of depth, he is able to produce 3-D illustrations.

Some artists specialize in 2-D or flat drawings and do an excellent job simplifying a complicated structure. Often the work is detailed and painstaking and clearly signifies order and proportion. Others specialize in 3-D drawing; they produce an object by viewing hundreds of slides in their sequential order.

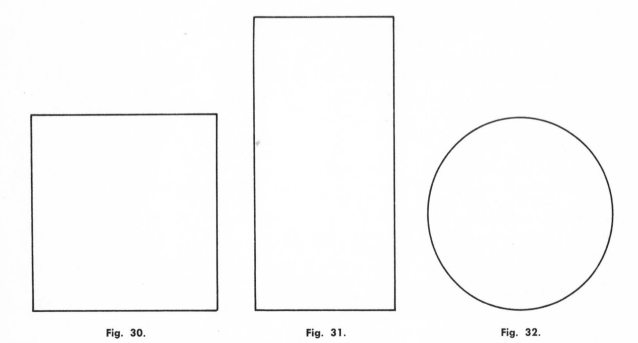

Fig. 30.   Fig. 31.   Fig. 32.

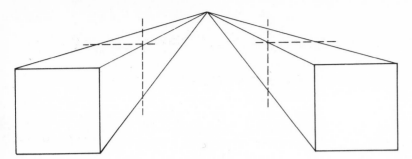

Fig. 33.

placing the horizon point in another position, you will see a drastic change in the angles. Because of the change in your imaginary focal point the two objects now appear quite different. Look at *Figs. 30-32* again and compare them with those you have just drawn. Now you have the feeling of depth. You have just drawn the outline for a city street with a block of houses, or a long pipeline. The next step is to set a limit on your depth lines. You must stop some place in front of the vanishing point, as indicated by the broken lines in *Fig. 33*. After you have practiced this

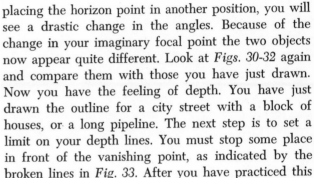

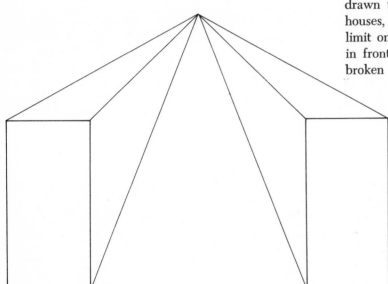

Fig. 34.

Outlining an object first makes 3-D drawing much easier. Examine the three shapes illustrated in *Figs. 30-32*. They are flat. Try to visualize those forms within space. Take pencil and paper and draw two identical shapes (*Figs. 33-35*) on the same level. Now draw a perpendicular line in the center of the two shapes and select a point some place on this line. This will be the horizon point, sometimes referred to as a "vanishing point." Now, if you will draw lines from this point to the inner corners of the two identical shapes, your forms will become perfect 3-D shapes. If you imagine yourself standing between the two objects, with the horizon point your eye level, this is the image you would get of the two objects on either side of you. Now, if you will repeat this whole procedure,

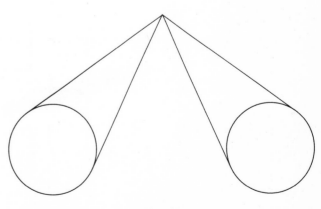

Fig. 35.

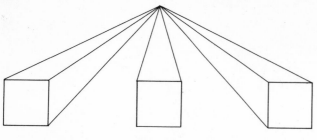

Fig. 36.

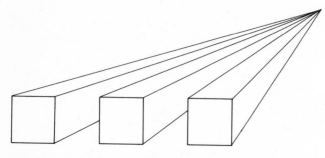

Fig. 37.

several times, let us place a third object of the same shape between the two we already have. Again, place a point of focus and extend lines from this point as shown in *Fig. 36*. And now draw three squares on the same level and place your imaginary eye level to the upper right, and again draw the connecting lines. Here you have changed the view of the objects, as shown in *Fig. 37*.

You are now familiar with the technique, so practice changing the eye level for various perspectives. After you have mastered this preliminary step, try putting the objects on different levels, changing the vanishing points repeatedly (*Fig. 37*). Now you are ready to try still another step. Introduce new and varied shapes following the procedures in the sequence illustrated in *Figs. 38* and *39*. You are now at the stage where you can combine previously used angles and shapes and create your own 3-D drawings.

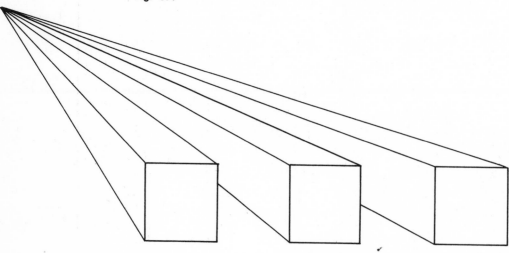

Fig. 38.

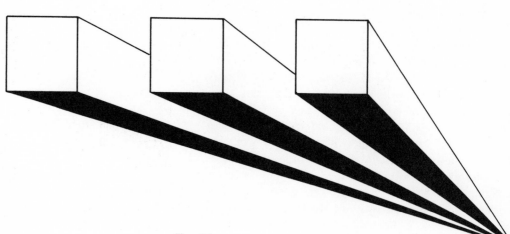

Fig. 39.

With different combinations in varied positions (*Figs. 40-42, 44*) you may create an untold number of designs. Keep practicing changing your eye level and placing the vanishing point in different locations. Introduce new shapes (*Fig. 43* and *45*). By combining the views of *Figs.* 37 and 38 you have achieved a block outline for a cut-out. Place yourself in front of the closest vertical edge of *Fig. 46* and lay out your vanishing points in both *A* and *B*, following the directions given in *Figs.* 37 and 38. If you cut off the length of those sides, the result will be the frame illustrated in *Fig. 46*. This fame was used to complete the illustration in *Figs. 515, 558* and *559*.

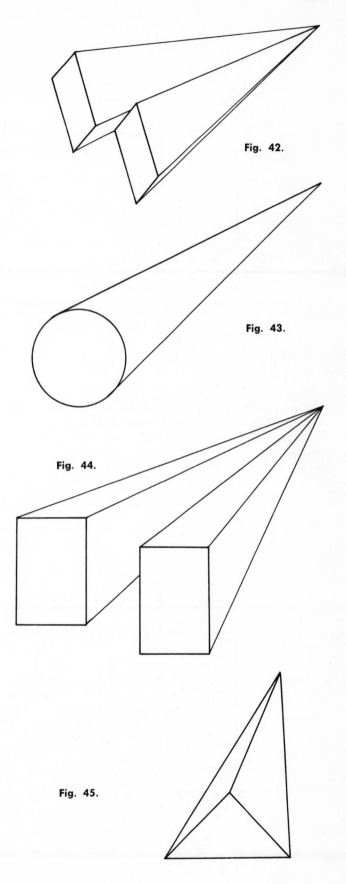

Fig. 42.

Fig. 43.

Fig. 44.

Fig. 45.

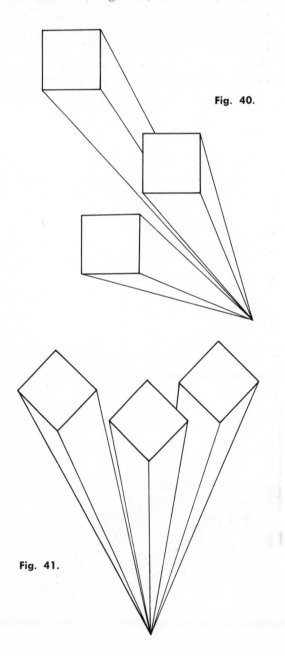

Fig. 40.

Fig. 41.

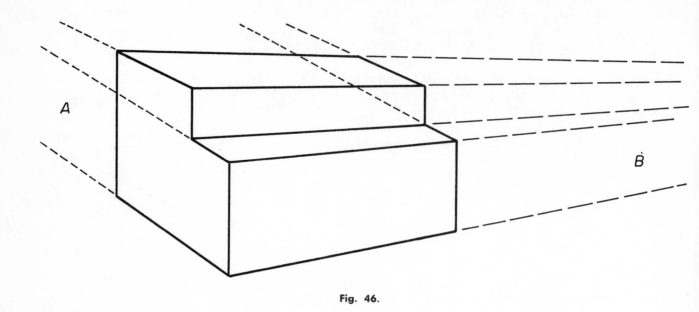

A

B

Fig. 46.

By placing the horizon at different heights and moving the vanishing point from place to place, you vary the structure of your block outline. As in *Fig. 47,* the horizon is elevated in comparison to the previous sketches and the vanishing point is placed in the center (*a*). Can you find the obvious, but barely visible mistake in the left half of *Fig. 47*? Correct it on your own practice sketches.

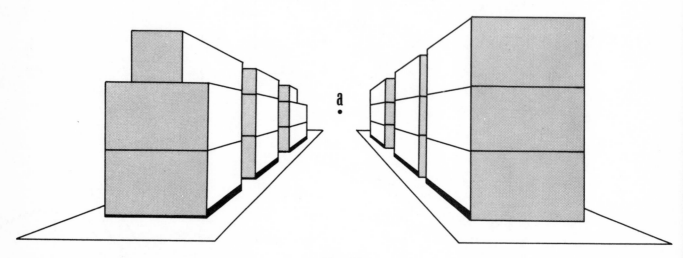

a

Fig. 47.

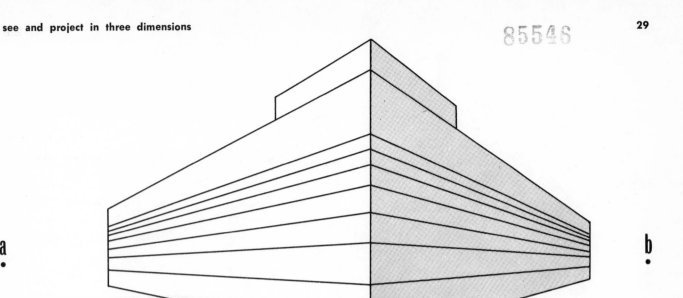

Fig. 48.

Now, reverse the situation. Set two vanishing points, and imagine yourself in the center of the picture, as in *Fig. 48*. This is how the general layout for the corner of a city block is done. These blocks will be the basic outlines for a variety of illustrations (such as plant anatomy drawings, for example).

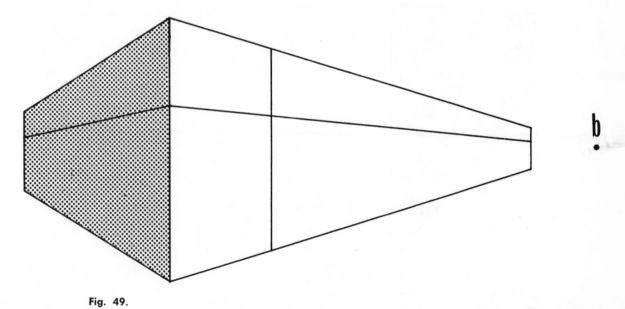

Fig. 49.

Move away from the center, keeping the eye level at the same height, and use two vanishing points, *a* and *b*. You will arrive at a new form (*Fig. 49*). This provides a very convenient form to frame any plant anatomy work.

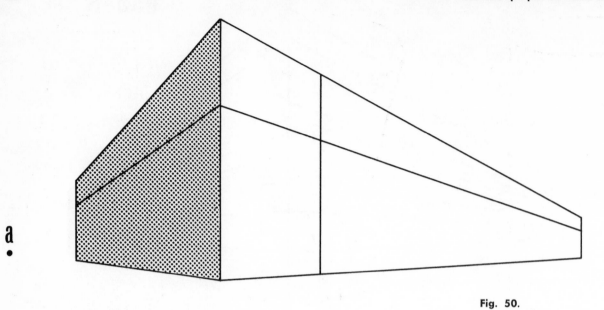

a

b

Fig. 50.

Lower your horizon (as if lying on the ground) and use the same blocked area as in *Fig. 49*, with the two lowered vanishing points. The result will be a view as in *Fig. 50*.

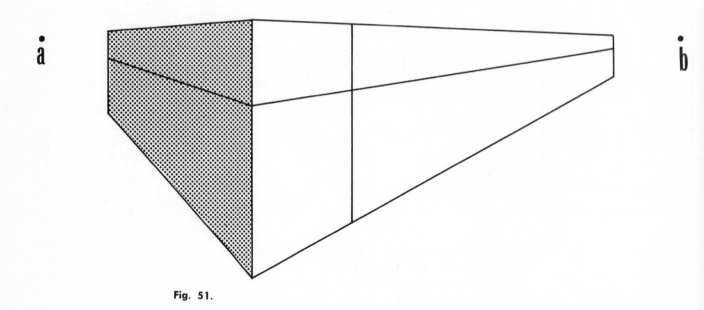

a

b

Fig. 51.

Now, if you elevate yourself (your eye level) to the top of the block and keep the same two vanishing points *a* and *b*, the result will be exactly opposite, as seen in *Fig. 51*.

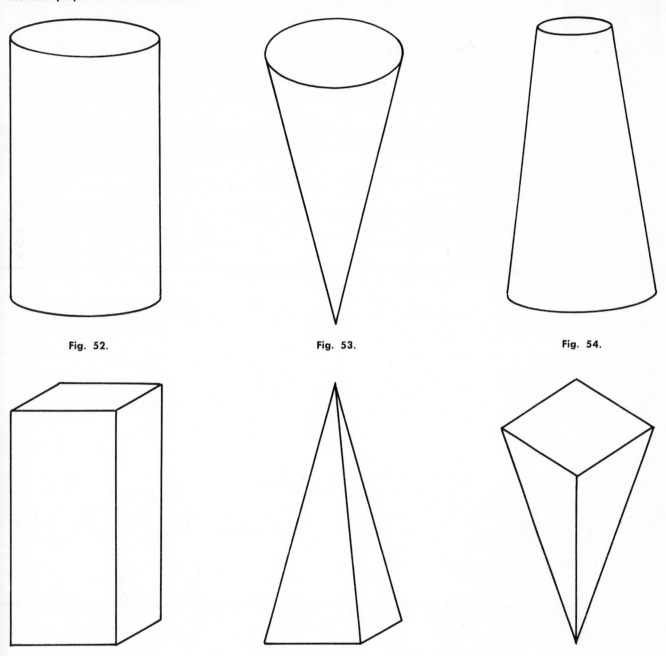

Fig. 52. Fig. 53. Fig. 54.

Fig. 55. Fig. 56. Fig. 57.

You have learned the fundamentals of 3-D drawing and realize the limitless forms and shapes and
angles that can be drawn. There are six forms illustrated in *Figs. 52-57*. For practice try to arrange those
forms individually and in groups, as outlined above.
Make up your own combinations and try as many
variations as you can think of. Repeat this procedure,
starting at the beginning and practicing each phase a
step at a time until you reach the stage where you
can interpret depth on paper.

Illustration Techniques

With time and practice you will soon develop your own technique — the one most suited to your individual taste and ability. Each artist has his own personal approach to artwork and devises his own system or technique. Some prefer India ink line drawings, others use pencil and ink combination, while still others may like the pencil, carbon, or wash method. If you aspire to scientific illustrating, it is well to become acquainted with and adept at most of the popular techniques. A scientific illustrator employed by an institution must yield to the likes and dislikes of the scientists, rather than adhere to his own preferences. The artist determines the style which will most advantageously simulate an object, and he prudently endeavors to reflect the scientist's suggestions. Remember, if you will, illustrations should enhance the article and impress the reader, in addition to their primary purpose of clarifying the text.

There is a great deal of satisfaction in doing a job well and a rewarding sense of accomplishment, indeed, if the person for whom services were rendered is completely satisfied. The greatest attributes a successful artist may possess are creativity, sound judgment in selecting the proper materials and technique, and an abundance of patience.

In this chapter we will discuss black and white illustrations. As a reminder, it is stressed that drawings can be reproduced either by line cut (*Fig. 58*) or by half-tone (*Fig. 59*). In the figures which follow there will be a notation of the most suitable method of reproduction to use in each technique described.

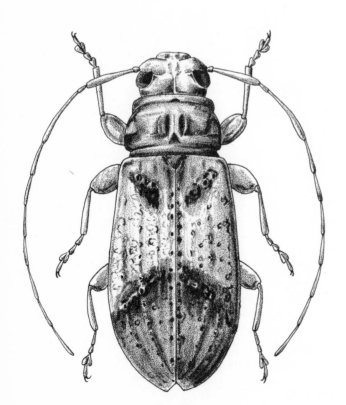

Fig. 58.

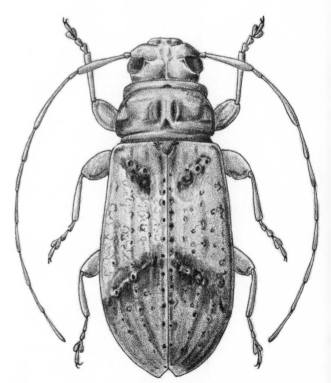

Fig. 59.

A. LINE DRAWINGS

What is a line drawing? An illustration composed of sharp, distinct lines of black India ink on white paper is termed a line drawing. Light or faded lines will not reproduce satisfactorily (*Fig.* 60). When minute details of scientific significance are present, it is of utmost importance that they reproduce sharply, otherwise the illustration may be worthless. This is especially true of taxonomic drawings where the presence or absence of setae is the determining factor for identifying the species (*Fig. 61*).

Line drawings consist of lines and dots (*Fig. 62*). The lines (*a*) and the dots (*b*) should be solid black, distinct, and clearly separated from one another, regardless of the technique used. Shading effect may be achieved by gradually decreasing the thickness of lines or dots, or by decreasing the distance between them.

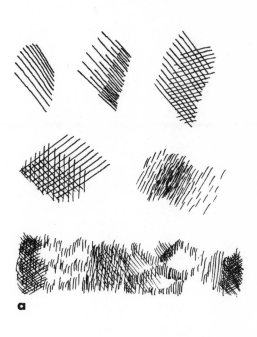

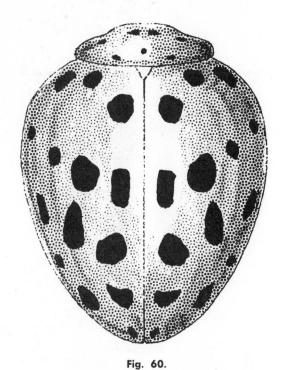

Fig. 60.

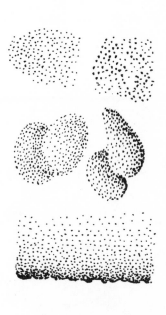

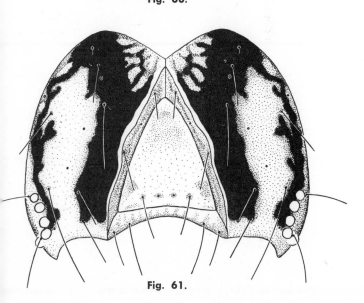

Fig. 61.

Fig. 62.

(*a*) An attractive illustration may be created by using a few solid lines with additional lines for shading effect. Do not use dots and lines for shading within the same object (*Fig. 63*).

Fig. 63.

(*b*) Dots may be used effectively in an illustration. Outlines should be solid lines, as should also specific details, such as setae. In dot drawings shading is composed of smaller dots. Again, it is stressed — do not use dots and lines for shading within the same drawing (*Fig. 64*).

© 1965 Sherwin Carlquist

Fig. 64.

Method (*a*) is faster; however, method (*b*), using dots or stippling, is more attractive and looks more professional, especially for shaded areas.

Color patterns on certain specimens, such as on insects and mammals, must show up in drawings. In the line drawing method (*a*) dark areas may be drawn solid black. If a highlight is desired, leave that area white (*Fig. 62, a*). Highlights on dark areas where stippling or dots are used may be bordered with a few dots, indicating that those areas are also black (*Fig. 62, b*).

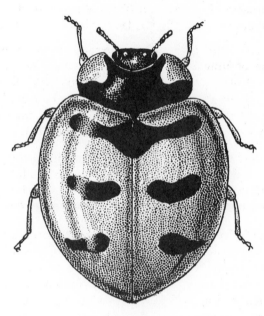

Fig. 65.

Any of the better quality paper may be used in line drawings. The harder surfaced paper is preferable. Strathmore two- or three-ply smooth or medium-smooth drawing paper is excellent for this purpose. Its weight and texture are conducive to drawing ease, and pencil markings are removed easily. Avoid the use of a razor blade to remove marks. "Snopake" is preferred for corrections. Thinner may be added to Snopake to make the proper consistency for smooth corrections, especially if lines or dots are to be placed over the corrections. Pelican black India ink is our choice, and our preference of pens is the crowquill. They are durable and inexpensive. Drawings of this type do not require a protective coating (Krylon). To avoid fingerprints, smudges and dirt, cover the illustration with a piece of tracing paper.

B. PENCIL DRAWINGS

Illustrating solely with pencil is not considered to be one of the better techniques. This method is used mostly by amateurs who are unfamiliar with other illustrating techniques. There is little difference in the quality of pencil drawings regardless of the type of pencil used — whether an ordinary inexpensive pencil or the best quality art-shop brand. One must use extreme caution in order to prevent fingerprints and smudges.

There are two elemental ingredients in pencil drawings: (*a*) solid lines of varying thickness and sharpness (*Fig. 66*), and (*b*) continuous shading with uniform or gradually weakening tones (*Fig. 67*).

(*a*) *Solid lines* are of special importance in this type of drawing. Outlines should be light (with a pencil of at least a 4-5 degree harder lead than the rest of the illustration). Outlines may be erased after the drawing is completed, whereas the internal detail may be blocked out by shading (*Fig. 66f*).

(*b*) Shading should be uniform in quality. Some artists prefer soft tones (*Fig. 67a*), while others favor hard tones (*Fig. 67b*). Whichever you choose, be consistent throughout the illustration (*Fig. 69*).

The type of drawing paper is important. Our preference for smaller (up to 5″ x 5″) illustrations is the two-ply Strathmore paper. For larger drawings (up to 10″ x 10″) the three-ply Strathmore medium-rough or smooth surface drawing paper has proven very satisfactory. For originals larger than 10″ x 10″, hard illustration board is preferred.

Uniform shading can be achieved on these and similar types of drawing paper. For shading, use the same pencil that is used for the final outlining. Keep the paper free of fingerprints, particularly if tones or shading are to be implemented. Fingerprints will show up on the finished drawing in spite of shading effects. (*Fig. 68a*, arrows).

Shading should be uniform in tone, even if depth is to be registered by changing the density of darkness. Irregular or untidy shading will be visible in any reproduction (*Fig. 68b*).

In the next chapter we will describe another pencil drawing technique. This chapter is placed in between two line drawing procedures in order to emphasize, that in this method, we do not use smudging to achieve shading (*Figs. 90-96*). For this technique,

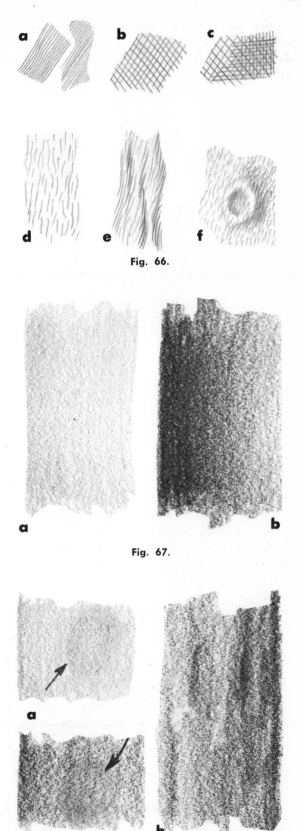

Fig. 66.

Fig. 67.

Fig. 68.

shading effects are created by pencil lines of different density. This distinguishes it from other methods and, if mastered, some very exceptional illustrations may be produced. It is especially adaptable for illustrating mammals, reptiles and birds.

Mammals' hair can be drawn by this technique much better than with any other. To draw hair the artist should have several pencils of the same hardness, sharpened and ready for use, to produce even, uniform lines (*Fig. 69*).

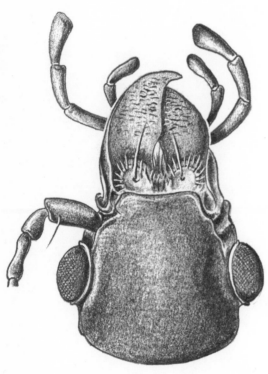

Fig. 69.

The pencil is useful in drawing reptiles, where scales of varied dimension are involved.

The detailed construction of individual feathers of birds may be illustrated effectively by this method.

This technique, necessitating time, effort, talent and patience, produces outstanding drawings.

It is recommended that such illustrations be carefully cleaned and protected with Krylon spray. This type of illustration can be reproduced only by halftones.

C. PENCIL-INK COMBINATION

This technique, although restrictive, is probably the fastest method. It is adaptable for illustrating insects, reptiles, plants and fossils, as well as semitechnical illustrations in other fields of research.

Special paper must be used for this type of drawing — the so-called coquille board or pebble board, possessing a rough surface. Select the pattern of coarseness and structure according to your requirement (*Fig. 70*).

Fig. 70.

Outlines are drawn first with a No. 1 or No. 2 pencil, then blackened with India ink, using a crowquill pen with very light pressure. Do not erase mistakes. Cover them with very thin Snopake. Shading is accomplished through the use of a wax pencil of any hardness, regulating the pressure to achieve dark and light shades. Caution must be taken in shading, especially darker areas, as the wax cannot be removed without disrupting the uniformity of the granules. If an error is made without damaging the paper, an application of thin Snopake may be used.

After investigation and use of the several different coquille board surfaces you will discover that this technique saves a great deal of time and enables you to produce fine artwork. The density of dots may not be regulated, as by stippling (*Fig. 116*), but their size may be regulated by using heavier pressure on the wax pencil.

This technique reproduces best in line cut (*Fig. 71*); however, in some cases half-tone reproductions are also satisfactory (*Fig. 59*). Spray the artwork with Krylon spray to protect it.

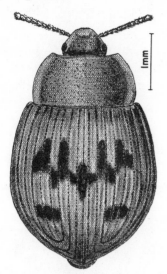

Fig. 71.

D. THE WASH METHOD

Under this category fall illustrations made with brush and any water soluble material. Frequently these drawings are reproduced in black and white, and therefore, the originals are done in black and white. There are several types of paint which may be used for this purpose, such as water soluble tempera, or diluted India ink.

For the beginner, Pelican India ink thinned with water has proven very successful. *Figs. 271, 275-281* were made with India ink and water mixture.

Mix your four basic shades (ranging from light gray to black) in separate containers (*Figs. 72a-72d*). Keep the drawing paper adequately moist while applying shading. On a dry base, the shading will be uneven and separated from the background by a definite line (*Fig. 73a*), whereas, on a moist base it will blend smoothly and uniformly (*Fig. 73b*).

Highlights should be added with wihte cover ink. Sometimes these highlights require only a small dot, as in eyes (*Fig. 74a*). On a slightly gray base, a prominent white line will create highlights (*Fig. 74b*).

If the drawing is small (no larger than 5″ x 7″), the three-ply Strathmore drawing paper is adequate. However, for best results you are urged to use heavier illustration board.

Fig. 72.

Fig. 73.

Fig. 74.

This method of illustrating does not require a protective spray because the colors are solidly bound to the paper and will not smudge. Reproduction is done in half-tone only.

E. ILLUSTRATIONS ON SCRATCH BOARD

The most attractive line drawings are done on scratch board, which is a heavy sheet of paper with a fine coating of soft substance giving it a smooth, even finish on one side. Scratch board is available in black or white. Two or three types of scalpels are required to scratch the inked surface. It is suggested that while learning and practicing this technique you use the white scratch board.

Mark a small area, about 2″ x 2″ and cover it with Pelican India ink evenly and lightly. Let it dry thoroughly — about five minutes in normal temperature (*Fig. 75*). Take a scalpel and ruler and lightly draw a series of parallel lines (*Fig. 76*). Now, cross these lines with another series of lines drawn at a ninety degree angle, using very light pressure. Note the intersection of the lines. They should be smooth. If you let the ink dry thoroughly and did not use too much pressure on your scalpel, the corners will be sharp and smooth. If, one the other hand, the ink was not completely dry or your pressure was too heavy, the intersections will be fuzzy and torn. Vary the pressure as needed (*Fig. 77*). Add still another series of intersecting lines, handling the scalpel gently and lightly, and examine the area with a hand lens (*Fig. 78*).

Now, try freehand scratching. Start with straight, short lines and then try longer lines, depicting hair on a dark background (*Fig. 79*).

Lightly paint another square with India ink. This time try some curved, intermingling lines of varying length and thickness. Try to duplicate the flow or ruffled-look of a short-haired animal (*Figs. 80, 81*).

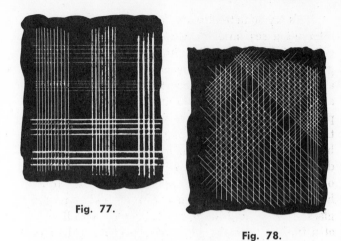

Fig. 77.

Fig. 78.

Fig. 79.

Fig. 80.

Fig. 75.

Fig. 76.

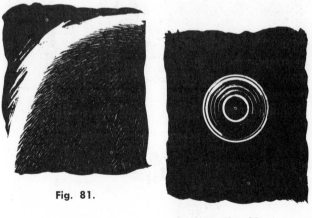

Fig. 81.

Fig. 82.

You may introduce other tools for scratch board drawing. If you have circular forms to draw, such as a large eye, you may use an ordinary compass (*Fig. 82*).

Let's try something easy for the first drawing, for example, a sea lion. Make the outline (*1*) and indicate the folds of skin (*2*) with a pencil on white background (*Fig. 83*). Cover evenly with India ink (using a brush) the areas you want dark. Let the ink dry about five to ten minutes (*Fig. 84*). Using a crowquill pen, connect the black areas with thin lines, following the flow of fine fur (left part of *Fig. 85*). When you have finished the preliminary scratching, check for details, especially around the eyes and mouth. Work out a gradual shading by applying cross lines. It will help you if you will examine *Fig. 85* with a reading glass. After several hours of scratching you will arrive at a finished drawing (*Fig. 86*), reduced to half the original size.

Fig. 83.

Fig. 84.

Fig. 85.

Fig. 86.

When your drawing is finished, clean it with a soft eraser. If you have made any mistakes on the black surface, cover it again with India ink and start over. No protective coating is needed for this type of illustration. It may be reproduced with line cut. Do not make your original more than three times the allotted published size.

This, as we mentioned earlier, is a very attractive method of illustrating. As you practice and develop this technique, you will be aware of how much pressure is required to make sharp lines. You will learn how to make very fine lines, how to vary the thickness without creating fuzziness, and how to achieve shading effects. Highlights may be whitened, as on the head of a bird (*Fig. 87*). The white areas on the feathery parts are left white, and the dark areas, darkened. The margins of these areas are carefully "molded" together with the scalpel. When making larger bird drawings, never leave the outline as a solid line (*Fig. 87*).

A very interesting and delicate subject to draw is the marine Globigerina, composed of hundreds of white and black lines (*Fig. 88*). The three-D effect is accomplished by leaving one side slightly darker (*Fig. 88 — right side*).

The scratch board can be used in many ways (*Fig. 89*). Solid outlines with somewhat rougher stippling for shading, or outlines composed of fine dots the same size as used for shading. Or, as discussed earlier, the variation in length and thickness of lines.

Fig. 88.

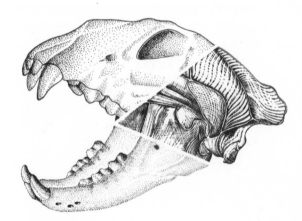

Fig. 89.

Fig. 87.

The greatest advantage of scratch board drawing is the ease of correcting mistakes. Do not scrape off the coating. Do not use Snopake. A sharp (new) razor blade has proven practical to gently shave a smooth area. If this is done smoothly and uniformly, a fine pen and fresh thin ink may be cautiously used on the re-smoothed surface, using very light pressure.

F. SMUDGING TECHNIQUE

This method, while very similar in appearance to the pencil technique, is less difficult and takes less time. With a little practice you can easily master it. Corrections are easy to make and the illustrations have a neat, photographic appearance. Practically any type of soft pencil may be used and any grade of paper, ranging from inexpensive mimeograph paper to the most expensive types. Here again, our preference is Strathmore or, for larger originals, the heavier illustration board. Smooth, glossy-finish surfaces should be avoided.

Let's learn this technique by drawing a homopterous insect with very peculiar external characteristics. Do the outline carefully with pencil. Note in *Fig. 90, 1* how the finished outlines are inked. Do the elevated, net-like design (represented with double lines) by adding another line parallel to the basic outline. Examine *Fig. 90, 2* carefully to see how these lines join correctly. Between these elevated lines there is a membranous surface. To show depth it is necessary to shade one side of these elevated sections (*Fig. 91, 3*). After inking the double lines the next step is shading. Use a soft pencil. Start with the darkened (or shady) area of the membranes, making them dark and gradually lighten your touch and shading as you move down the paper. Leave about one fourth of each cell white (*Fig. 91, 4*). After this is finished use a fine pointed smudger (Stump) to smear the graphite (or carbon) from the darker area toward the lighter area, using a light pressure. Very slight smudging is required in the lightest area, leaving some of the white area white (*Fig. 91, 5*).

Complete your drawing, following the procedures mentioned above, i.e., outlining in ink, penciling, and

smudging. For darker body parts use more graphite or carbon. For an irregular marmorated appearance, lightly use a soft- pointed eraser to gain this effect (*Figs. 92, 93*). Your eraser will be a helpful aid in your artwork on hard surface paper, but it will not work on glossy surfaces.

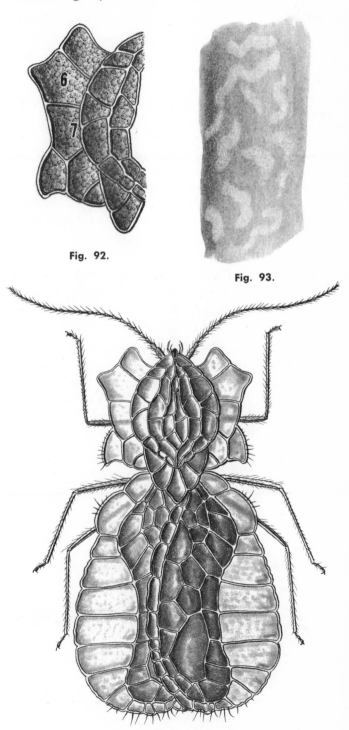

Fig. 92.

Fig. 93.

Fig. 94.

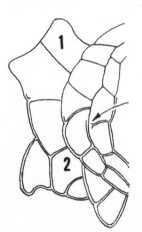

Fig. 90.

Fig. 91.

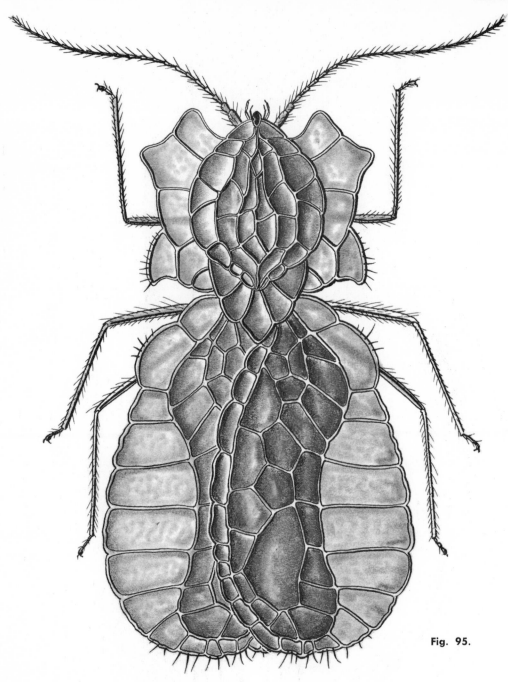

Fig. 95.

Eighty percent of the original drawing in *Figs. 94* and *95* have inked outlines. Pencil can replace ink, but care must be taken not to smudge the drawing, especially when cleaning (*Fig. 96*). When placing setae or hair on an illustration, do it with a sharp pointed pencil and with a precise stroke. If the whole surface is characterized by a uniform pattern, this pattern may be added by using artificial tones on lighter shading (*Fig. 92*).

Carbon pencil (Wolff's) is also very useful in making this type of illustration. It is darker and softer than graphite. It is more sensitive to pressure applied in shading and is "dirtier" to work with. This pencil may be used for outlining, as well as shading. Stumps of varied points should be used to smear the carbon powder on the paper. Highlights may be added by using a soft eraser (*Figs. 93, 94*). Drawings must be thoroughly cleaned, especially at the edges of the outline (*Fig. 95*).

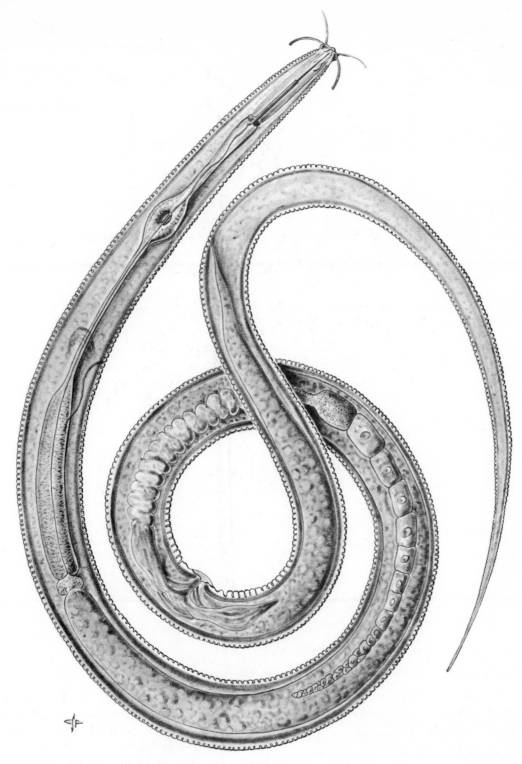

Fig. 96.

Originals of this type require Krylon protective spray and are reproduced only with half-tone process (see samples). Compare with line cuts (*Figs. 60-62*).

G. ILLUSTRATING WITH PREFABRICATED TONES

There are numerous prefabricated tones available to the artist which enable him to do attractive artwork with less effort and less artistic skill. These products are sold in most art shops. They are acetate sheets with patterns printed on one side, and the other side covered with wax, enabling it to be placed securely on the required area without the use of glue or special materials.

The procedure for using these aids is to, first, outline your drawing with pencil (*Fig. 97*). Then, ink over the outline and carefully remove pencil marks from paper. Cover the surface with the required tone and cut around the outline with a sharp blade applying even pressure. Cut out highlights, using a ruler as

a guide, and peel off excess areas. Use these same cut outs on the dark (shaded) portions of the object. If you wish to make the shaded areas darker, use additional layers of the same tone pattern. If the highlight is too light, use tone strips of lesser density (*Fig. 98*).

If, for example, you want to show a hole inside of a tube, you would have to ink in the outline, as well as the opening. Apply tones, cutting out highlights, and reverse the shading on the inside of the hole, creating a 3-D effect (*Fig. 99*). To register visible differences in composition, use a darker (or solid) tone for one layer, and a dotted tone for the other layer. If, you want to indicate different material within the same composition, use various tones with the proper shading (*Figs. 100-102*).

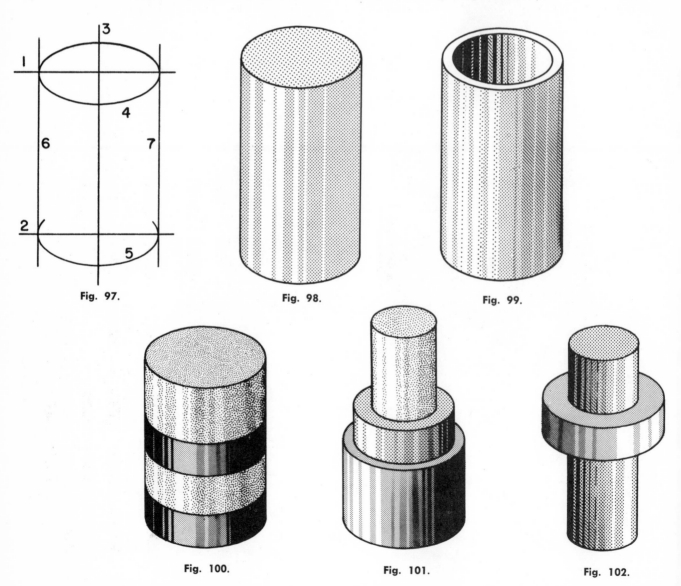

Fig. 97. Fig. 98. Fig. 99.

Fig. 100. Fig. 101. Fig. 102.

Corrections are not difficult to make. If there is an error in the outline, gently lift the tone off and scrape off the wax with a blade. Cover the outline with Snopake, and ink in the corrected outline. You are now ready to cover the area with tone again. A word of advice — after erasing be very careful to clean particles away, otherwise they may stick to the tone and will be embedded in your illustration. These particles will also show up in reproduction.

When all the tones are in place, put a piece of tracing paper over your drawing and press the tones smoothly to the paper with the flat surface of your fingernail.

Keep your tone sheets in a cool place. Do not discard small pieces; they may come in handy later. Always replace the protective sheet on the waxed side of the tones. These sheets are comparatively expensive and should be handled and stored with care.

Cover the finished artwork with a protective sheet and avoid extreme temperatures — or photograph it immediately. Heat causes the tones to shrink, leaving white lines visible around cut sides.

On page 233 you will find additional information and numerous suggestions regarding this form of artwork. Illustrations made with this technique reproduce well in line cut. Do not spray artwork with protective Krylon spray.

You are encouraged to use this technique, as it is very effective and less difficult than others. Refer to *Figs. 103* and *104* when practicing this technique. The paper best suited to this type of artwork is two- or three-ply Strathmore drawing paper for larger originals; heavy white drawing board is also good.

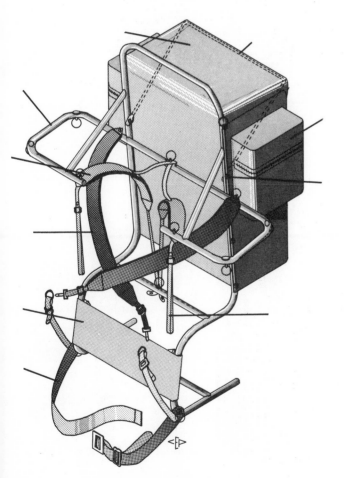

Fig. 103.

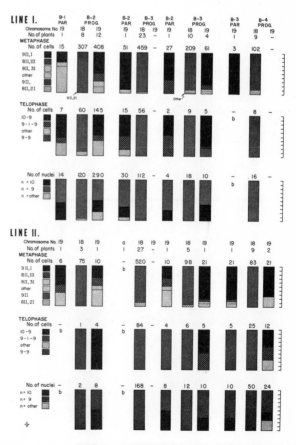

Fig. 104.

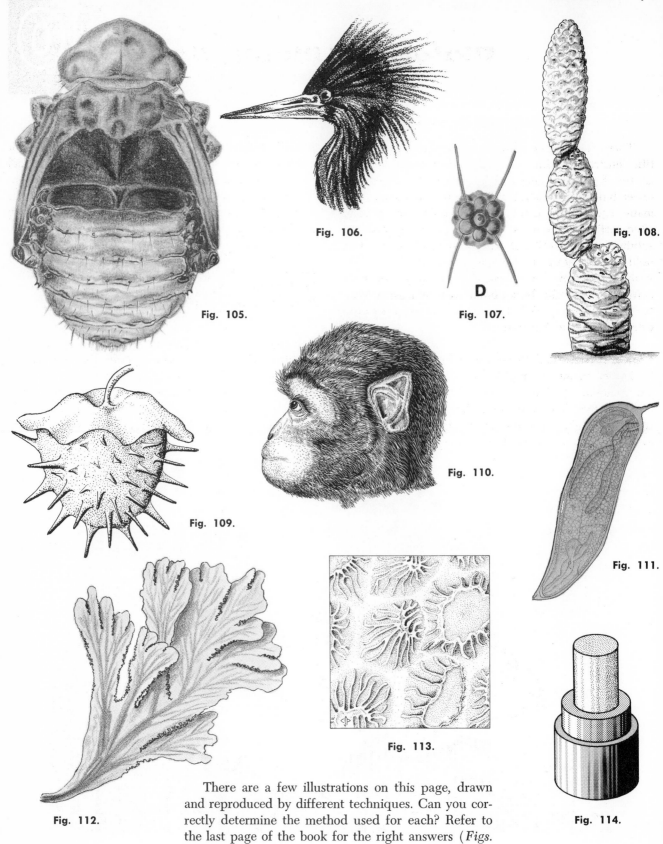

Fig. 106.

D

Fig. 107.

Fig. 108.

Fig. 105.

Fig. 110.

Fig. 109.

Fig. 111.

Fig. 113.

Fig. 112.

Fig. 114.

There are a few illustrations on this page, drawn and reproduced by different techniques. Can you correctly determine the method used for each? Refer to the last page of the book for the right answers (*Figs. 105-114*).

Biological Illustrations

There is no other field in the profession of scientific illustration with as widespread or broad a scope as the field of biology. Proportionately, there are fewer biological illustrators than any other kind. The many specializations of this profession have been cited earlier. Those divisions, having many specialized subdivisions, make it noteworthy to mention that this field of illustrating surpasses all others insofar as versatility, exactness, and scientific training are concerned. A scientific background with at least a Master's degree is required of an artist who aspires to the title of biological illustrator.

Within this field there are artists who specialize in insects, mammals, reptiles, birds, plants, anatomy, etc. Academic training in one of these chosen fields is imperative. The average scientific illustrator possesses the ability to draw graphs, maps, animals and plants but, having possibly a high school diploma or junior college degree in general education, he is not academically equipped to enter the field of biological illustrating. A minimum requirement for a person entering this field is the study of science leading to at least a Master's degree and several years' experience in illustrating.

It is far superior to specialize in one phase of science than to dabble with many. If the words "quality above quantity" apply anywhere, they most certainly apply to biological illustrating.

In the pages which follow there will be information and illustrations concerning several specialized divisions within this enormous field. The decision is left to you. Act wisely, weighing carefully your background in the sciences and your artistic ability. Any of these fields offers a challenge, and above all, any one of them will be a lasting and interesting lifetime profession.

Fig. 115.

A. ILLUSTRATING ANIMALS

It is futile to try to estimate the number of animals known to science. It is sufficient to say there are numerous classes and orders and within these, thousands of families and genera. There are some families with one or two genera, others with hundreds of genera. One genus may have only one species, while another may have as many as a thousand. The scientific classification of the animal kingdom distinguishes the fields from which a scientific illustrator may choose his speciality; mammals, birds, reptiles, insects, etc., including macro- or microscopic creatures.

Thanks to the advancement of science and printing techniques there are numerous publications and books with illustrations of animals. Artwork of biological illustrators, as well as some extraordinary work of amateurs, has contributed to the present status of printed matter. The greatest advantage of artwork is that one good illustration is as significant as several hundred words.

Animal drawing is often very difficult for the beginner. To simplify as much as possible the burdensome preliminaries, an accumulation of practical ideas acquired during years of experience will follow. Do not get discouraged. We learn through trial and error, and, as stressed throughout preceding portions of this book, illustrating involves a great deal of patience and perseverance.

From the illustrations and discussions which follow, choose the subject of greatest interest to you and select the technique that best conforms to your artistic ability.

Fig. 117.

Fig. 116.

a. Illustrating Birds

There is probably nothing more disheartening to an illustrator than to have to draw a beautiful colored bird in black and white. However, if you consider the high costs of color printing, you will agree with the publisher. Obviously, colored illustrations are much more appealing, but in the light of practicability and the fact that black and white drawings are used much more frequently, the following pertains, essentially, to black and white techniques.

The general structure of the bird will indicate the best method to use in drawing it. The *smudging* method (*Fig. 118*), *pencil and ink* on various types of pebble or coquille board (*Fig. 119*), *scratch board* (*Fig. 121*), or the *wash method* (*Fig. 120*) are the various choices. The technique to follow also depends upon the method in which the work will be reproduced, e.g., line cut or half-tone, and, furthermore, upon the preference of the author, the editor, the publisher, and finally, upon the artist's ability.

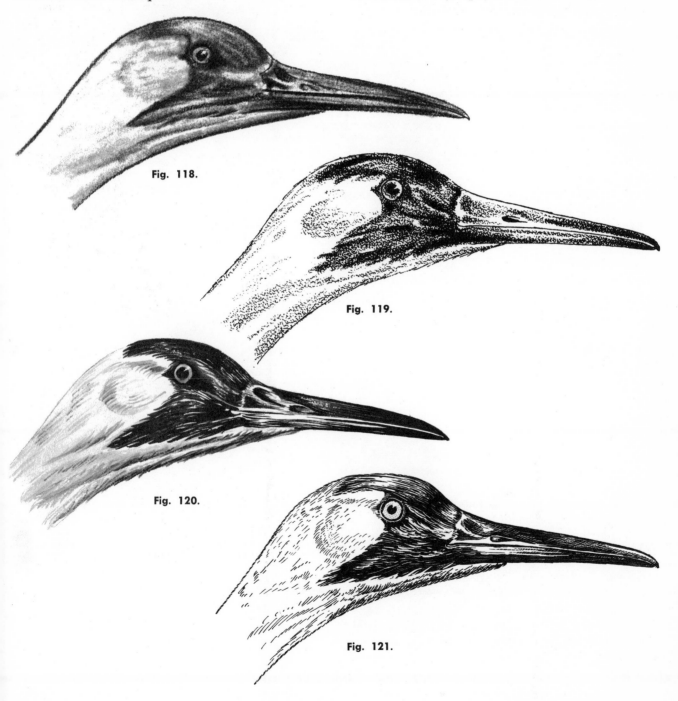

Fig. 118.

Fig. 119.

Fig. 120.

Fig. 121.

Assuming you know which method of drawing you are going to use, the next step is to study your specimen. If the bird is alive, its natural contour and characteristics are not distorted or influenced by a taxidermist (*Fig. 122*). However, usually the artist is compelled to work from mounted specimens, in which case the end product may not be true to life (*Fig. 123*). In this instance the author's assistance is required; he is able to point out discrepancies. If you have sketched an outline, he can correct it or explain how it should be changed. Or, another alternative is to refer to illustrations or photographs of live specimens in scientific publications.

Fig. 124.

The word "science" is synonomous with knowledge. Therefore, a scientific illustration must divulge truth. Analyze and scrutinize your specimen throughly. The most minute detail must not tbe overlooked. It is essential to draw an exact replica of a beak, for instance, because the slightest defect may change its identity from one species or family to another. The striking characteristics (*Fig. 125*) are easy to distinguish, but the very minor details are those which require critical detection and precise recording.

Fig. 122.

Fig. 123.

The artist should always do his first outline on a heavy, inexpensive drawing paper that will withstand erasing. When this outline is completed and checked by the author for accuracy, make a tracing of it on transparent paper. The transferred image will be the basis for the finished product.

If you must show the bird perched on a branch or some other object, be careful it is not tilting unnaturally good in (*Fig. 124*). Also, in drawing a background setting, be certain to capture the proper habitat or environment. In drawing from a skin not mounted, it is essential to obtain the exact contour and dimensions.

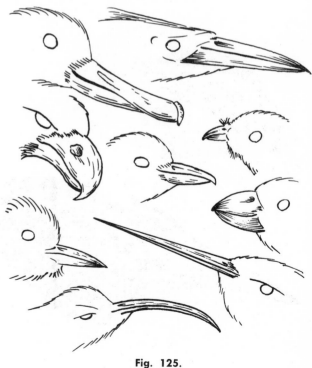

Fig. 125.

Also study the eyes. As a rule these are not difficult to draw. However, if you are drawing from a mounted specimen, it is well to investigate available literature or obtain the author's verification. The most common specimens have a simple eye structure (*Fig. 126*). After you have finished drawing the eye, put "life" into it by adding highlights (reflection) properly.

The structure of the legs (*Fig. 128*) is also very important, especially the scaly characteristic which should be realistically represented. Proportion and dimension should be considered. In black and white drawings very little shading is required on the legs of a bird. A slightly heavier pressure on the shady side is sufficient to achieve the 3-D effect. If the leg is

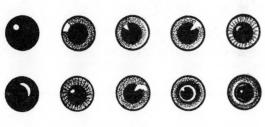

Fig. 126.

The shape of the head is of importance. Capture the contour and the placement of feathers in their relative size and direction, especially around the eyes. Here again, the more common ones (*Fig. 127*) are not difficult to draw. However, to be scientifically perfect, the artist must be very critical and draw exactly what he sees.

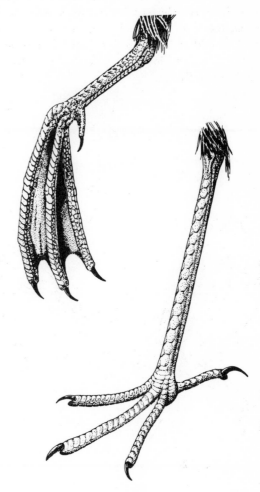

Fig. 128.

Fig. 127.

large, as in the case of hawks or eagles, shading is required within the entire surface. Observe the claws — their length, shape and color in relation to the rest of the leg. Bear in mind that when working with black and white it is necessary to translate the original colors in various depths of gray, as well as black and white.

The smudging method is very satisfactory for drawing birds, and is faster than other methods. Background composition is also faster and easier (*Fig. 124*).

It is more time consuming to draw a bird using pen and ink. These drawings are composed of an assortment of thin ink lines (*Figs. 129-130*). The crow quill drawing pen No. 102 produce fine, uniform lines and works especially well on Strathmore drawing paper. This is recommended for smaller birds, such as the hummingbird, particularly (*Fig. 131*), and in some cases for larger birds.

The scratch board method is laborious but well worth the time and effort. As you know, this technique consists of nothing more than carving into the paper. It may be necessary to experiment with different body parts on a separate piece of scratch board until you are thoroughly accustomed to it. Learning this technique and perfecting it will be very gratifying, since it is the most provocative of all black and white illustrating (*Figs. 121* and *132*).

Fig. 129.

Fig. 132.

Fig. 130.

The ink and pencil combination method on roughly surfaced pebble or coquille board is very adaptable to bird drawings, and is reproduced in line cuts. This technique requires less detail work than those already mentioned but can result in very effective artwork. Selection of paper, i.e., the pebble board (*Fig. 133*) or the rougher coquille board (*Fig. 134*), is dependent upon the characteristics of the species you are drawing. The granulation of these boards should be related

Fig. 131.

Fig. 133.

Shading on birds should be considerably darker than other parts. The legs require very little shading. The eyes should be of solid India ink (the same as the outline), leaving the highlight white. If the eye is multicolored, indicate coloring by light shading (*Fig. 126*). The same principle applies to the beak. If it is dark, cover with India ink, leaving white highlight. When the beak is light colored, use light pencil shading (*Figs. 135, 136*).

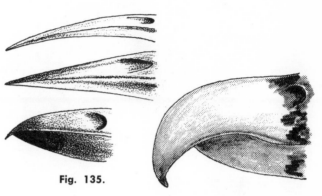

Fig. 135.

Fig. 136.

These same factors apply to the wash method. Density of darkness is the prime concern. However, much finer shading details may be achieved with this method not only for the eyes (*Fig. 137*) and beak (*Fig. 138*), but for the entire bird (*Fig. 139*). As in the smudging method, here again it is relatively easy to compose an attractive background by adding a few decisive lines in dark tone and some lighter shading. Wash illustrations can be reproduced in half tones only.

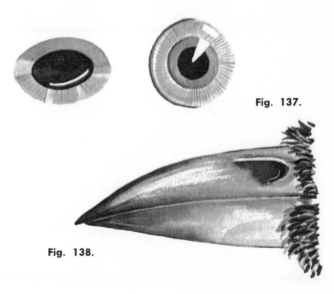

Fig. 137.

Fig. 138.

Fig. 134.

to the size of the original, as well as the size of the finished (printed) reproduction. If you prefer doing your originals four or five times larger than the reproductions, use rougher coquille board.

Fig. 139.

b. Illustrating Mammals

Drawing of mammals seems to be favored by professional and amateur artists alike. The numerous external characteristics, the vast differences in sizes and forms, and the dissimilarities in the color, density, length and texture of the fur make this illustrating specially very interesting and challenging.

Art schools seldom engage in the study of animal paintings. The preferred mammalian species seems to be the Homo sapiens, male and female, clothed and unclothed. The requirements for a true scientific illustrator far surpass this training.

Illustrating mammals is not easy to learn. Live specimens make the best models, since products of taxidermists are not always accurate. If you must work from a stuffed (mounted) specimen or from a skin, check details carefully with the author. Also seek, photographs of live specimens.

Mammals are either entirely or partially covered with fur. This is the outstanding external characteristic of the species. It is not always necessary to draw individual hairs, as shading may be used to gain that effect. Smudging (*Fig. 140*) or rough surfaced coquille board (*Fig. 141*), or wash method (*Fig. 142*) are commonly used and are entirely acceptable. These processes will be discussed before going into the detailed, truly scientific techniques for drawing mammals.

Starting with a pencil sketch on ordinary sketching paper, after checking and rechecking for accuracy in proportion and stance, transfer it to tracing paper and from there to the final illustration paper. These will be the preliminary steps for practically anything you draw.   The smudging method is probably the quickest way to achieve a photograph-like illustration. The smudged surface will reflect shaded areas of the animal and the general contour but will not indicate the

condition or characteristics of the fur which covers the creature (*Fig. 140*). An effect of fur may be brought out by adding soft pencil marks within the shaded areas. If the animal is multicolored, this is interpreted in the first smudging stage by varying the degree of color depth or in the later stage when adding fur density with pencil. Compare *Fig. 140* and *Fig. 144*. Light hairs were added with a fine brush, using Grumbacher, Gamma No. 3 gray cover color with occasional white ones. The addition of hair changes the appearance of the illustration, giving a more true-to-life impression.

The wash method can be used for mammals. Most any base black color thinned with water is appropriate, such as Pelican India ink reduced in varying degrees of shades. Or the conventional black colors available in tubes are equally acceptable. A set of good brushes ranging from size No. 000 to No. 10 should be in every artist's possession. You will find

Fig. 140.

Fig. 142.

Fig. 141.

Fig. 143.

many uses for brushes No. 000 to No. 2, especially. You will also need a fairly large supply of small dishes for mixing varying shades and two larger ones for rinsing your brushes. Keep plenty of water on hand.

Mammals may be illustrated merely by using different shading (*Fig. 142*) or, preferably, by adding hair (*Fig. 144*) which *greatly* enhances the drawing. Hair may be added with pen or a fine brush, depending upon the density and length and also upon the size of the original artwork. Black lines in the darker shaded areas will produce the hair effect, and a few strokes of gray with intermingling white lines will create indirect light reflections.

width of the lines and their shading against the background tones; produced with pen or fine brush, using various dilutions of India ink. Drawings done with this method are reproduced in half-tone.

Ink and pencil combination technique adapts itself well to drawing mammals. It is an easy and fast method and is quite satisfactory for semi-scientific or popular publications. The surfaced paper, pebble boards containing thousands of dots (*Fig. 147*) or coquille boards having lined surfaces (*Fig. 148*), simplify and hasten the artist's job. On one of these surfaced ma-

Fig. 147.

Fig. 144.

Being familiar with the smudge and wash methods, you realize that the general appearance is very similar. Detail is accentuated after the shading process by adding lines (*Fig. 145*), softer grades of pencil for darker areas (*a*), harder pencils for lighter areas (*b*), soft pencil for short, spine-like strokes (*c*), and white ink for shading the individual hairs (*d*). The wash method offers greater flexibility, reflects more lifelike objects, and brings out detail and accentuation more sharply. Note in *Fig. 146* the style of strokes, the

Fig. 148.

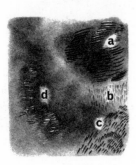 

Fig. 145.   Fig. 146.

Fig. 149.

Fig. 150.

terials try drawing a mammal without first making an outline as you have previously been instructed, using shading effects to achieve a 3-D appearance (*Figs. 147* and *148*). Either darken the eyes with India ink or make them two-toned, not forgetting the white highlight. With a sharp pencil add lines indicative of hair (*Fig. 149*). Drawings made by this technique are reproduced by line cuts.

The scratch board method is excellent for drawing mammals. You are familiar with this technique and ready to try your first scratch board drawing of a mammal. In *Fig. 150* you will see a scratch board drawing of a tenrec. After the outline is completed, blacken the animal except for the head. Give the ink ample time to dry (20 minutes), then with a rough scalpel scratch the spines. The 3-D effect noted in *Fig. 150* was accomplished by regulating the density

of the lines. You will also observe spines crossing each other. After scratching in the lower layer of spines these were added with India ink and then given highlight by scratching away the background on one side. This same procedure was used and is more evident under the ear (*Fig. 150*). The face is composed of short, extremely fine scratch lines placed more sparsely than on the body thus denoting a marked variation in texture and composition. The eye is solid black with a spot of highlight to give it life, and the ear sharply outlined in moderately dark background. The longer hairs on the head were added with crow quille pen, and the background scraped away to make the whiskers more prominent.

A reduction to 57 per cent of the original size is shown in *Fig. 151*.

Fig. 151.

Fig. 152.

In *Fig. 152* is a drawing of a Tandraka. This animal is covered with spines with an intergrowth of soft hair. The technique used here is the same as in *Fig. 150* for the tenrec; inked area scratched to form spines, white portions filled with stronger India ink lines, the face shaded with short, thin lines in such a manner as to create a 3-D effect. The soft, thin lines representing hair were added last, and the hair shading accomplished by scratching away background. Stippling is used in this drawing around the mouth and lower jaw to represent depth.

In *Fig. 153* the same drawing is shown in a 57 per cent reduction.

Fig. 153.

Fig. 154.

Fig. 155.

Fig. 156.

Fig. 157.

It may be discouraging to the beginner to see the quantity of lines required to make a drawing. When you get further along you will discover that it is not as difficult as it looks. When starting a drawing, plan where you will want dark and light spots. Since we are presently discussing mammals, we must concentrate on drawing hair. The density of hair determines to what extent you achieve the 3-D effect. The following illustrations represent the basic steps to follow:

Figure 154: Make a complete outline of the animal's body with a soft pencil, using light strokes. Mark the location of the eye, ear and mouth.

Figure 155: Cover the body with India ink, leaving white a small area for the eye and the extreme lower portions of the animal, which will be bordered by the ground. Stripe these latter white areas with slanted, thin black lines (pen and ink).

Fig. 158.

Fig. 160.

Figure 156: Mark with a thin pencil line the lighter and darker areas. With a few short, fine strokes throughout the body indicate the direction of the fur growth. Then, starting at the nose make scratch marks with a scalpel toward the tail. While working on the head, add the few heavier and longer lines representing the whiskers. With fine, short, dense lines create the image of the ear. After you have proceeded to the area behind the shoulder the rest of the drawing is easy.

Figure 157: Place the animal on the ground and indicate the habitat (holes, shadows, ground cover, etc.). Just a few lines will accomplish this in some cases.

When the drawing is completed, set it aside and return to it later to do finer corrections and to increase the 3-D effect.

Figure 158 illustrates a Limnogale and demonstrates this technique in a larger animal with dense, comparatively short fur. You will note that the lines (in *Fig. 159*) are somewhat longer, not quite so fine and dense as in *Fig. 157*. The preliminary step in making this drawing is the same as presented in *Fig. 83*, etc. Then the shaded areas are connected as in *Fig. 85*, by using a scalpel and scratching the hairs into the black background, after which the silhouette is drawn with a fine coquille pen on the white background. Compare *Figs. 158* and *86* for shading. Areas you wish to highlight require more scratch lines in order to reduce the depth of the inked areas. A simple setting of grass, water and rock add the finishing touches (*Fig. 160*).

Fig. 161.

When drawing an animal that is not unicolorous, such as the little Australian phalanger (*Figs. 161, 162*), after completing the outline, ink in only the areas which are dark, leaving the spots white. A scalpel is used to scratch in hairs, as you have previously been instructed. Hair lines are added to the white portions with India ink and pen. Note the edge of the dark spots — how the density of lines reduces the marked contrast and blends the two colors. *Fig. 161* is a reproduction in the original size, whereas *Fig. 162* is reduced 50 per cent. The twig on which the animal rests is done with the same scratch board technique.

Fig. 162.

Fig. 164.   Fig. 165.

© 1965 Sherwin Carlquist

Fig. 163.

Fig. 166.   Fig. 167.

Note the characteristics of the husky *Sarcophilus* in *Fig. 163.* This species serves as an excellent example of a dark colored animal with coarse, rough fur, having white bands across the chest and rump. This is a 50 per cent reduction of the original. The lighting effect is different in this illustration, giving the appearance of a photograph taken in the shade. To achieve a 3-D effect, highlights were added to give the fur a more or less shiny appearance. The two white bands were accentuated by leaving the surrounding areas slightly darker, using finer fur lines in those areas, and by applying fine black lines in the white band portions. You will note that the white on the chest is less contrasting and more delicate in appearance than that on the rump. These techniques are more clearly defined in *Fig. 164* (a white area on a dark background similar to the chest of a *Sarcophilus*), and in *Fig. 165* (representing the hair formation on the rump).

The fur on longer-haired animals is not measured in inches or centimeters, but is drawn in proportion to the size of the species. An example of one of these mammals is the Schoinobates (*Fig. 168*). Observe the variations of hair length within a species, as well as the difference in texture between the hair on the back and that on the tail. For detailed study of the techniques used, *Fig. 166* shows the shorter coarse hair structure, wider at the base than on the tip. *Fig. 167* shows a variety of longer, slightly wavy hairs similar to those on the tail of the Schoinobates. Those on the black area were scratched with a scalpel, while the ones on the white were done with pen and ink. Too many wavy hair lines drawn parallel to one another appear artificial, so avoid this error and change the direction of the hairs originating from the same area (*Figs. 167, 168*). Parallel lines are sometimes neces-

Fig. 168.

Fig. 170.

Fig. 169.

The pencil drawing technique for drawing mammals is very similar to the scratch board method. While lines are made on scratch board with scalpel or pen and ink, with pencil drawings the effect is achieved by using different grades of pencil. It is advisable to have at least three pencils of varying hardness, a good pencil sharpener, and a piece of fine (0 or 00) sandpaper fastened to a piece of wood or heavy cardboard (about 2 x 6 inches) readily available for maintaining a good point. It is convenient to have this sandpaper block attached to your drawing table.

The first step is to make an outline with very light strokes with a hard pencil. Remember that these outlines will not be erased and you will not want them visible when your drawing is completed (*Fig. 171*).

sary, such as in portrait paintings of humans, especially the hair of a woman (*Fig. 169*). In this sketch you see the immediate impact of an orderly hairstyle (done with carbon pencil). However, this will not be applicable to mammal drawings unless you are asked to draw a combed long-haired dog.

The scratch board technique is very desirable for hairy creatures. Another good example is the long-haired gorilla reproduced at 50 per cent of the original size in *Fig. 170*. All parts except the face were painted black on the scratch board, then the white lines were scratched in with a sharp pointed scalpel following the natural placement of the hairs. The cross-etching around the eye and the rest of the face is the same as demonstrated in *Figs.* 78 and 79.

Black scratch board is available in art stores under the trade name "Essdee," for large originals. This material is of high quality, is made in England, and comes in 19 x 24 inch pieces.

All illustrations made on scratch board are reproducible as line drawings.

Fig. 171.

Next, lay out the lighter areas, which, as already discussed, will be the areas exposed to light and those of a lighter color. Whichever the case, faintly outline these portions and indicate in which direction the hairs will be arranged (*Fig. 172*).

Now, you are ready to work out the details. You have studied your specimen adequately to determine shaded spots and highlights. It does not matter at which end of the animal you start. If the animal is facing to the left and you are right-handed, you will probably become accustomed to working on the head first. A word of caution: avoid fingerprints on the paper. It is suggested that you wash your hands frequently. Grease spots will cause trouble when adding the fine hair lines and will show up in the reproduc-

tion. In this instance, let's work from the head, placing the hairs in the correct position and work back toward the other end. Also add a few lines throughout the body as an indication of the direction they naturally grow (*Fig. 173*). Do not hesitate to turn your paper from time to time if this enables greater freedom of movement.

With this step completed (*Fig. 174*) you are ready to add the finishing details. Perhaps the darker areas are not dark enough. If so, with a softer pencil and light strokes increase the density of hair. If accidentally, it should turn out too dark and you think the individual hairs will not show up, apply thinned white cover ink with a fine drawing pen. When you have finished with your corrections and touch-up work,

Fig. 172.

Fig. 173.

Fig. 174.

Fig. 175.

your drawing is complete and is ready for coating. Use Krylon clear spray and cover your drawing lightly. *Fig. 175* is reproduced in original size, and *Fig. 176* (with background added) is a 50 per cent reduction of the original. Illustrations drawn by this technique are reproducible by half-tone.

Shading for this type of drawing may be accomplished by using a stump with a very scant amount of charcoal powder in it. The original (*Fig. 175*) has a primitive quality to it; however, the 50 per cent reduction (*Fig. 176*) improves its appearance. This technique is well adapted to semi-scientific publications.

If you find the pencil method too slow, the *smudging* technique may be applied. As mentioned earlier (*Fig. 140*), this type of drawing is adequate if there are no exacting minute details to illustrate.

Fig. 176.

The first step is a general outline, preferably very light lines with a soft pencil. If you are using Wolff's carbon pencil, the outline requires an extremely light touch with a somewhat dull point. These lines must blend into the internal portion of the figure (*Fig. 177*).

Next, indicate the darker (or shaded) and lighter areas. Those may be roughly outlined by applying light strokes with a carbon pencil and a stump (smudger) having just a trifle of carbon powder on it. Cover the shaded areas lightly, having first tested the stump on a piece of paper to determine the density of color. When it appears correct, apply a few sharp strokes to the shaded portions of your drawing, blending them into the outline and around the highlights. If your shading is too dark, lighten it with a soft (kneaded) eraser (*Fig. 178*).

The elephant, a large and relatively hairless mammal, serves as an excellent subject to introduce an interesting art material called velour. This paper, with a very soft velvet-like coating, readily lends itself to the smudging technique. *Figs. 181* and *182* are composed of neutral light gray with Blaisdell No. 623-T soft charcoal pencil for smudging (a French smudger was used), highlights were added in white pastel and color pastel for the background.

It is recommended that you work from left to right (opposite, if you are left-handed), keeping your fingers free of dirt and grease (a piece of tracing paper may be used to avoid unwanted fingerprints). Apply the desired shade of color to highlight areas (*Figs. 179* and *180*). Upon completion of the mammal, add background details. A background indicative of the natural habitat adds distinction and authenticity and

Fig. 177.

Fig. 179.

Fig. 178.

Fig. 180.

Fig. 181.

is rarely omitted. A possible exception may be an illustration of a fish (*Fig. 359*). In adding background start at the top of your picture with the sky down to the horizon line (*Figs. 33-41*). Now, reverse the direction by dropping to the bottom of the drawing and filling in the ground shading and details. Upon completion of the background, cover the picture with a piece of paper the exact dimensions of the illustration and erase around the edges of the paper so that your artwork will have a sharp outline. Check your artwork once again, make any final embellishment, and then spray the finished product with Krylon clear spray. *Fig 181*. is reproduced in its original size; *Fig. 182* is reduced 50 per cent. It is customary to cut around the drawing and mount it on a sheet of heavier paper. Illustrations drawn with this technique can be reproduced in halftone.

Fig. 182.

Fig. 183.

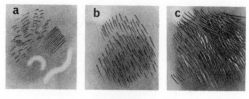

Fig. 184.

Fig. 185.

The combination pencil or ink and smudging method which incorporates the techniques discussed and illustrated (*Figs. 171-182*) creates a very interesting and effective drawing. *Fig. 183* is reproduced in its original size. Compare this with *Fig. 181*. Detailed structure may be seen in *Fig. 184*. The hairs were added with pencil, as described in *Figs. 175* and *176*. For this work it is suggested that you have five or six sharpened pencils of the same grade of hardness accessible, as well as diluted India ink for drawing scattered darker hairs in the lighter areas and gray or white ink slightly diluted for placing light hairs in the darkest areas. Ink may be applied with a fine (No. 0 or 00) brush. If the white hairs appear to be too much of a contrast, you may lightly apply a smudger (stump) to soften the effect after the white ink has completely dried. Such changes in shading will affect the illustration when it is reduced and printed (*Fig. 185*).

This drawing technique is reproduced in half-tone, resulting in a very clear, detailed photographic appearance.

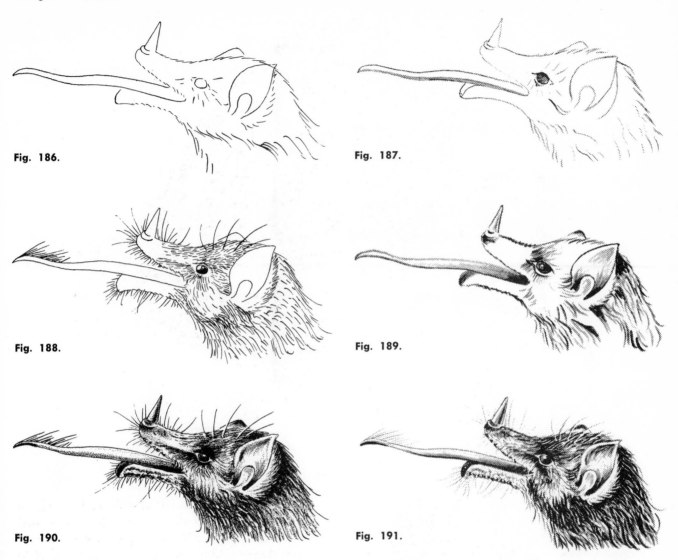

Fig. 186.

Fig. 187.

Fig. 188.

Fig. 189.

Fig. 190.

Fig. 191.

Perhaps the fastest method of illustrating is that which is done on so-called "repro" boards, also known as coquille boards. Two important types of this material were used in the following illustrations in order to demonstrate their usefulness and the technique involved. *Figs. 186, 188* and *190* were drawn on stipple board. *Figs. 187, 189* and *191* were drawn on pable board. If the original is made in a smaller size, as the figures demonstrated here (these have been reduced to 75 per cent of the original size), India ink is recommended for use in drawing the outlines (*Fig. 186*). If the mammal's fur is moderately long, the outline should include the hairy silhouette. Where the hairs are short (such as on the head), the outline may be a solid line.

The second step is to determine the shaded areas, using a black wax pencil. After adding a few charac-

teristic shade markings with very light lines you will be ready to start on the detailed finishing work (*Figs. 188-189*).

Starting at the darker areas work gradually toward the lighter ones. If you want a highlight in a dark area, work around it and go back to it after all the darker sections are completed. With this method individual hairs are not represented; however, an attempt is made to follow the same general direction of the "hair flow" and to create a definite impression of a hairy animal. Upon completion of the artwork it is advisable to add background, if only a few lines representing grass or a few rocks. This makes the drawing more attractive and adds a touch of realism. Spray completed drawing with Krylon spray (*Figs. 190-191*). Illustrations employing this technique may be reproduced as line drawings.

For an illustration of high quality which may be reproduced by half-tone nothing can surpass a good brush painting, known also as the wash technique. It requires time and patience but very little equipment or materials.

Here again, the first step is to draw an outline with very light pencil markings, indicating the various parts of the body. If the animal is unicolorous, the next step is to cover the entire body surface with a uniform color tone. Or, if the creature is spotted or has contrasting colors, use two color tones (*Fig. 192*).

Now you are ready to introduce shading effects which will establish the 3-D basis in preparation for the next step. It is preferable that the shading be done immediately after the preliminary tone is applied and before it dries, thus allowing the tones to blend smoothly (*Fig. 193*). Use plenty of water and keep your drawing on a slanted drawing board. Do not fasten your paper to the board. You should leave it free so that it can be moved in different positions for greater drawing ease. Prepare your tones in separate receptacles and keep them until your artwork is completed.

After applying the second toning allow it to dry, then, lightly add water to the surface. Remove excess water and now you are ready to complete the shading by adding darker tones. Work out the details around the eyes, mouth, and ears. If you get some areas too dark, apply well diluted white. Be sure the transition from lighter to darker shades is smooth and unbroken (*Fig. 194*). When you are satisfied with the results, let the drawing dry completely.

When you return to it for the final analysis and touch up, observe the details around the eyes and ears. Have your highlights given a complete 3-D effect? You are not drawing individual hairs, but have you with a few superficial strokes achieved the appearance of a coat of fur? (*Fig. 195*) The grayish half-tone background present in *Figs. 192, 193* and *194* were opaqued on the negative of *Fig. 195*. The progression of steps described and illustrated (*Figs. 192-195*) suffices for completed semi-scientific illustration. However, if greater detail is desired, these

Fig. 194.

Fig. 195.

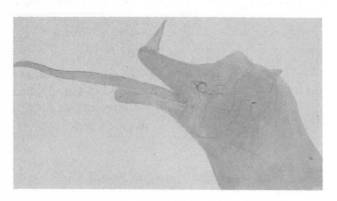

Fig. 192.

Fig. 193.

procedures constitute the basis for an additional step which transforms the artwork into a scientific production. The addition of individual hairs (*Fig. 196*) gives a life-like appearance. Hairs may be drawn with a fine brush (0 and/or 1) or a fine pen, using

Fig. 196.

Fig. 197.

diluted white cover ink in the darkest areas and black or gray in lighter areas (*Figs. 198, 199*). Hair lines should be as natural looking as possible, i.e., straight, wavy, curly, etc. *Fig. 196* is reproduced in its original size; *Fig. 197* is a 50 per cent reduction.

Illustrations made by this technique are reproducible with half-tones only. They have a photographic appearance and are excellent for accentuating details. Skill in this technique is acquired through practice and patience.

c. Reptiles and Amphibians

If you possess tenacity and perseverance, have adequate time and exceptionally good eyesight, you have what is required to illustrate reptiles. The creatures included in this chapter have scales of various sizes, shapes and colors. Drawing scaly objects is a true art, since proportion, size, arrangement, and in some cases the exact number, of scales is of scientific importance, as in the instance of fish (*Figs. 336-360*).

There are several drawing techniques suitable for drawing this group of animals. The choice, however, is dependent upon the characteristics of the species, the artist's ability, and most important, the process of reproduction.

Fig. 198.   Fig. 199.

Lizards and snakes will be classified identically in this discussion, since drawing techniques will apply to both. If you do not have to be concerned with scientific detail, as may be the case in a publication of nontechnical significance, you are free to choose one of the speedy uncomplicated drawing methods (*Figs. 200-203*). These effects were achieved by a simple outline drawing with slight shading and indication of pattern with ink and pen by using lines, with brush creating dark areas (*Fig. 200*), on pebble board (*Fig. 201*), by wash method (*Fig. 202*), and by smudging (*Fig. 203*). However, for greater detail and for drawings of taxonomic importance other techniques must be used. This need is answered by the pen and ink method (*Fig. 204*). Fine coquille board, a fairly detailed pencil outline denoting the pattern of the scales and other surface markings, and India ink served as the basis for this illustration. Shading around the lip region and around the eye sufficiently enhances the drawing to call it finished. However, to make it more appealing to the viewer the outline should be inked and shaded with wax pencil. (*Fig. 205*). In order

Fig. 200.

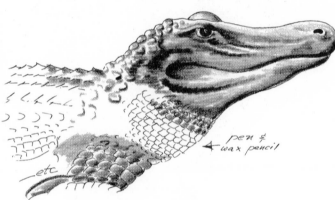

Fig. 201.

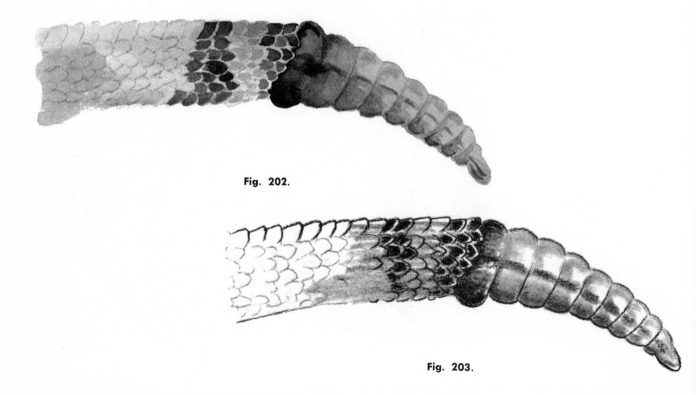

Fig. 202.

Fig. 203.

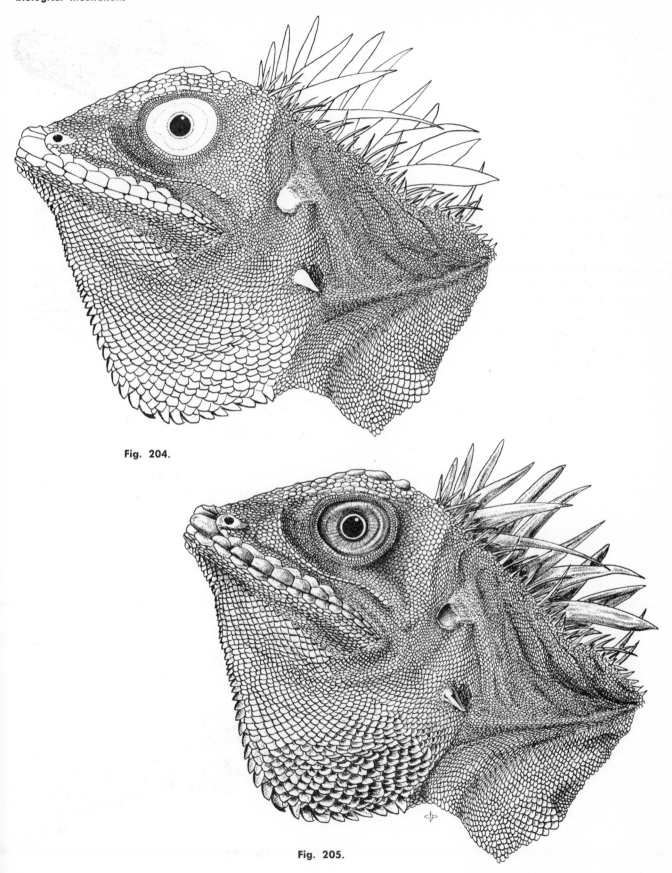

Fig. 204.

Fig. 205.

to demonstrate the difference between *Figs. 204* and *205*, portions of these drawings were reduced to show the grade and density of lines on the original artwork, shown in *Figs. 208* and *210*. Illustrations drawn by this technique may be reproduced as line (*Fig. 206*) or as half-tone (*Fig. 207*) reduced to one-fourth of the original size. Half-tone reproductions are satisfactory when the reduction is great enough to conceal the dotted surface of the paper. Compare the original (*Fig. 210*) with the reduction (*Fig. 206*)

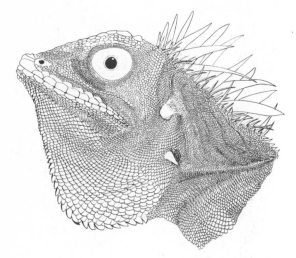

Fig. 206.

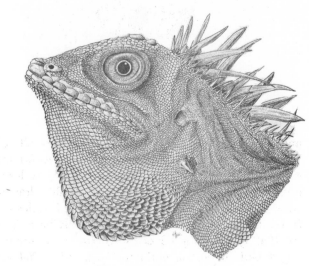

Fig. 207.

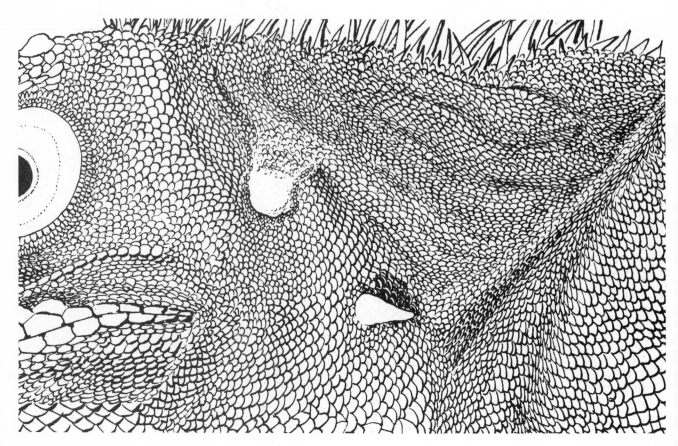

Fig. 208.

der and using the smudging method (*Fig. 211* is reduced to one-fourth; *Fig. 212* is a 50 per cent reduction). Make certain of the process used by a publication for reproducing illustrations before you start a drawing.

Fig. 209.

and observe how the details were scarcely altered. This drawing was reduced to one-eighth of its original size for use on letterhead stationery without losing detail of any significance (*Fig. 209*). If this drawing were to be reproduced in half-tone and the scales had to be distinctly represented, the materials best suited for that type of reproduction would be Strathmore paper with India ink outlines (as in *Figs. 204* and *208*), shading effects accomplished with carbon pow-

Fig. 211.

Fig. 210.

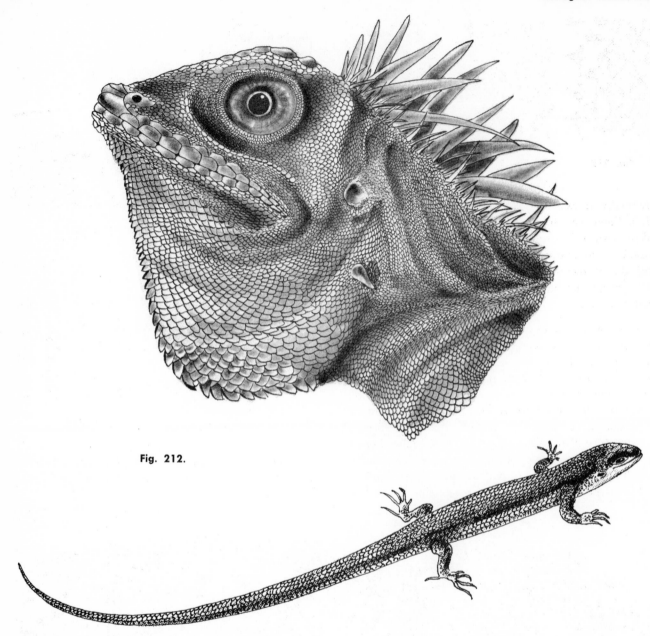

Fig. 212.

Fig. 213.

The prefabricated boards, such as coquille and stipple boards are of great assistance to artists in making the drawing process faster. The general appearance of a creature (*Fig. 213*) is relatively easy to accomplish satisfactorily with these materials.

In *Fig. 205* shading was applied to individual scales. However, in *Fig. 213* the 3-D effect was achieved by registering various densities on the overall surface of the animal. If the artist must indicate a color pattern in accurate detail, as is required for a purely scientific illustration, each scale must be in-

Fig. 214.

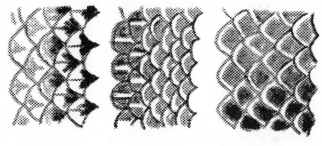

Fig. 215.   Fig. 216.   Fig. 217.

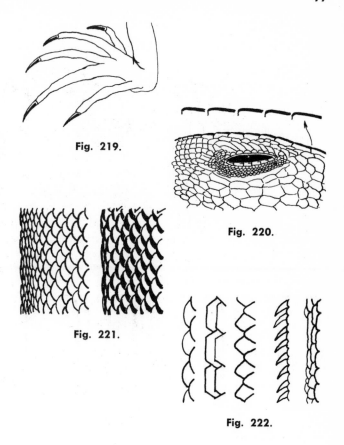

Fig. 219.

Fig. 220.

Fig. 221.

Fig. 222.

dividually drawn and shaded (*Figs. 214, 215, 216, 217*). Each scale must be outlined in pencil and later inked with a fine crow quill pen and India ink. Accuracy is imperative in both the formation of scales and the correct depth of shading tones (*Figs. 214, 218*). Proportion and position of legs (*Fig. 219*) are of importance.

In drawing snakes one must be equally painstaking in capturing the exact proportion and scale pattern. In most cases the scales of snakes are uniform, well defined, and of a relatively obvious color pattern. To draw them correctly it is important to analyze the formation of scales from the view the illustration is to be drawn, i.e., dorsal, ventral or side view. Observe the structure of the scales. Do they join each other or are they separated, do they increase or decrease in size, and are groupings of scales similar or dissimilar? A 3-D effect, as seen in *Fig. 204*, may be accomplished

by reducing the height of scales (*Fig. 221*). Practice drawing various types of scales and combinations of these (*Figs. 220-222*).

Fig. 218.

Illustrating a snake head from dorsal or ventral view requires a perfectly symmetric outline of the two sides of the snake's head. Can you locate the incorrect view in *Fig. 223*? Draw such a head and place the scales within the outline (*Fig. 225*), adding shading (*Fig. 224*). If a color pattern is present, work out the pattern in each scale. Now, draw a segment of a snake (*Fig. 226*) and complete the segment (*Fig. 227*), observing the position of the scales and the proportionate size and structure. Add shading with a wax pencil, or ink and wax pencil to create the pattern (*Fig. 228*). Refer to *Figs. 235-240* for additional patterns and shading.

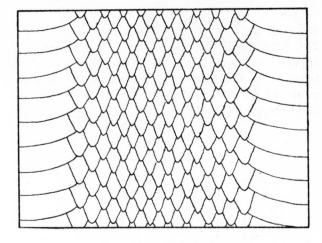

Fig. 227.

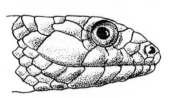

Fig. 223.

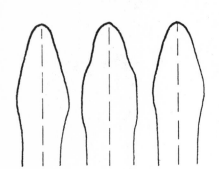

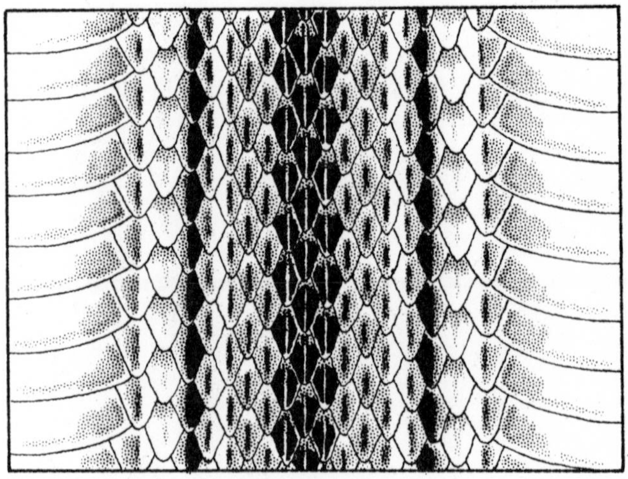

Fig. 224.

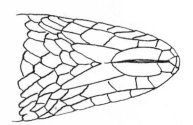

Fig. 225.

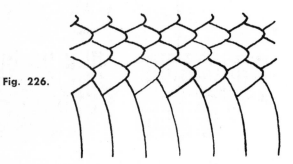

Fig. 226.

Fig. 228.

Fig. 229.

Fig. 230.

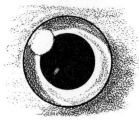

Fig. 231.

Fig. 232.

The eye must be drawn specifically to size, color and position, applying the highlight correctly (*Figs. 220, 229-236*). If the eye is incorrect, the snake will appear lifeless. You have already learned the importance of the eye from preceding discussions and are aware of the life-like quality in a well-drawn and highlighted eye.

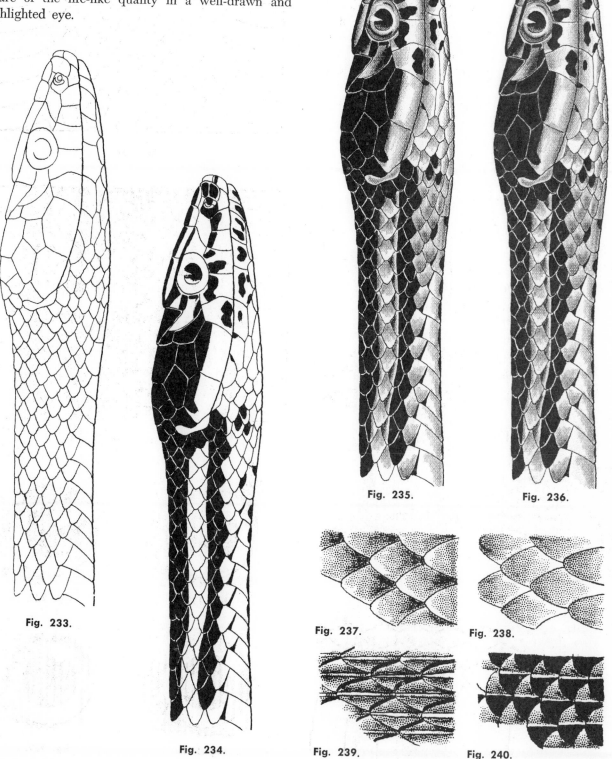

Fig. 233.

Fig. 234.

Fig. 235.

Fig. 236.

Fig. 237.

Fig. 238.

Fig. 239.

Fig. 240.

With a fine pointed scalpel (after the ink is thoroughly dry) start to shade the dark scales. On the white scales, use pen and ink for the dotted shadings (*Fig. 242*). When working with this technique on this particular species, it is suggested that the original be large enough to insure working ease. The portion seen in *Fig. 243* is reproduced in its original size.

Fig. 241.

Fig. 242.

Fig. 243.

The scratch board method of drawing is laborious and slow when drawing reptiles. Its greatest advantage, however, is that you may use dots and lines for indicating tones of color and shading. The first step, as you have been instructed many times, is to sketch your outline on tracing paper first and then transfer it to the scratch board. Ink in the completed outline and cover the dark scales with ink and a brush (*Fig. 241*).

Fig. 244.

Fig. 245.

The smudging method is both appropirate and effective for drawing snakes and is not time consuming (*Fig. 244-245*). One possible disadvantage is that it can be reproduced only in half-tones, while the two proceeding techniques are excellently reproduced in the less expensive line process.

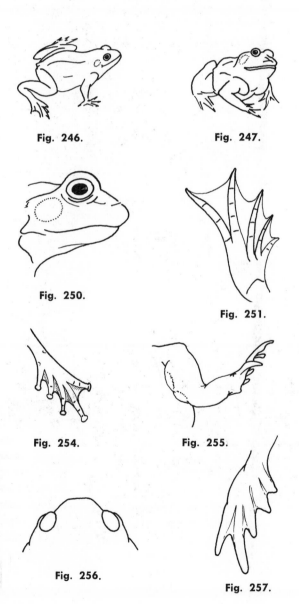

Fig. 246.

Fig. 247.

Fig. 250.

Fig. 251.

Fig. 254.

Fig. 255.

Fig. 256.

Fig. 257.

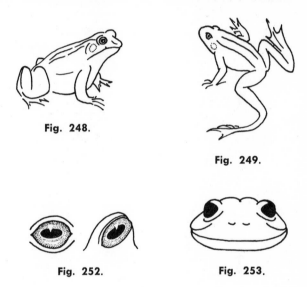

Fig. 248.

Fig. 249.

Fig. 252.

Fig. 253.

We are now ready to draw frogs. This may be a little difficult for the artist who is being introduced for the first time to drawing this creature. By taking one step at a time and familiarizing oneself with the procedure, it will become increasingly easier. The first thing to do is to draw an outline in which is included the 3-D effect (*Figs. 33-57*). If you mastered the three-dimensional exercises covered earlier in this book, you should have no trouble outlining a frog in any position or from any view (*Figs. 246-249*). Observe its head and strive to capture its structure and proportion from several different views (*Figs. 250-253, 256*), the location of the eyes and their shape (*Fig. 252*), the legs (*Figs. 251, 254, 255 and 257*), and above all the color and pattern (*Figs. 260, 264*). The two most commonly used techniques will follow.

Wax pencil with ink outlines is most likely the easiest and perhaps the fastest. Coquille or stipple board is the best material to use. Work out the outlines and ink them with crow quill pen (*Fig. 258*). Cover dark spots with ink (*Fig. 259*). The finishing step is to carefully place shading with a wax pencil. When your artwork is completed, spray with protective Krylon spray (*Fig. 260* is reproduced at nearly half the original size, and *Fig. 261* is the same drawing reproduced in half-tone).

Fig. 260.

Fig. 258.

Fig. 261.

The outline should be worked out, including the pattern and other details, such as the eyes and nose area. Make your outline on tracing paper and when it is completed, transfer it to the illustration paper you have selected. Trace over the outline with the same carbon pencil you are going to use for smudging (*Fig. 262*). When dark colors are present in the pattern, it is best to use India ink, leaving highlights exposed (*Fig. 263*). Add shading with carbon powder, using different sizes of stumps according to your requirement. If your original is large, naturally you would use larger stumps. When the shading is completed, clean paper of excess fingerprints and powder, starting at the outline with a kneaded eraser and blowing

Fig. 259.

off loose particles. After the drawing is free of unwanted debris, spray it with a protective coating (*Fig.
264*). If you are not entirely satisfied with your frog
drawing, practice outlines and shading of selective
body parts (*Figs. 265-270*) until you have gained sufficient proficiency to connect all the pieces and produce a frog to your liking.

The smudging method is another easy way to draw
a frog. It is especially recommended when the surface

Fig. 264.

Fig. 262.

of the frog is not smooth. The tubercles do not present
a problem (*Fig. 269*), because the sharp carbon outline and smudged background may be converted to
tubercles (*Figs. 265, 267, 269*). Work out the details
of the eyes and nose area (*Fig. 266*). The darker pattern may be done with brush and India ink and then
smudged (*Figs. 268, 270*).

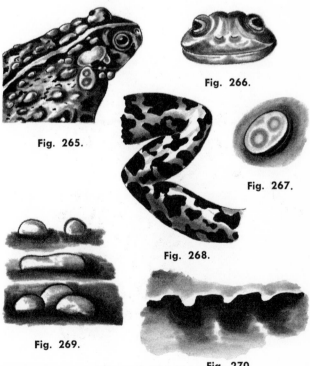

Fig. 266.

Fig. 265.

Fig. 267.

Fig. 268.

Fig. 263.

Fig. 269.

Fig. 270.

d. Illustrating Mollusks and Other Marine Animals

Perhaps there is nothing more interesting or challenging for an illustrator than drawing creatures of the sea. At first glance these forms appear unusually simple. However, delving into the intricacies of taxonomic details you will find their structures and characteristics to be quite involved. There are ways of illustrating squids, polyps and similar sea life without going into minute detail. Such may be accomplished by ink or pencil technique drawn four or five times larger than they will be in print. The illustration may be very attractive and amply satisfactory for nontechnical publications.

We are interested in scientific illustrating, and thus details are vitally important and cannot be overlooked.

Each artist will prefer one method of illustrating to all others. While one may like the wash method (*Fig. 271*), another will favor simple outline drawing,

as demonstrated by the mollusk in *Fig. 273*. Still others prefer the smudging method (*Fig. 272*), while there are those who like the pencil-ink combination technique, using presurfaced paper (*Fig. 274*). Any of these techniques are satisfactory for drawing marine life. There are three factors to be considered when determining the type of artwork: 1) how important is it to include details, 2) how much time do you have in which to complete the drawing, and 3) which method of reproduction will be used by the publication.

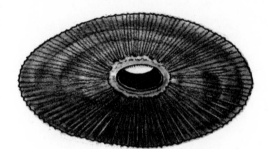

Fig. 272.

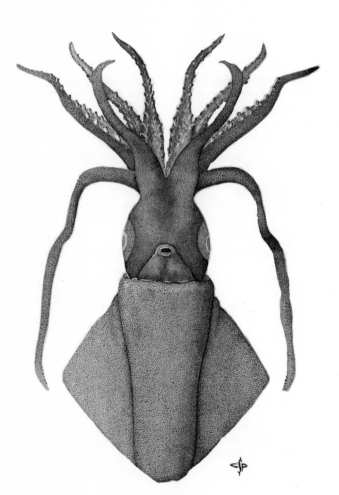

Fig. 271.

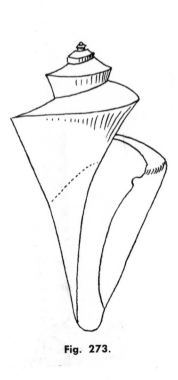

Fig. 273.

Fig. 274.

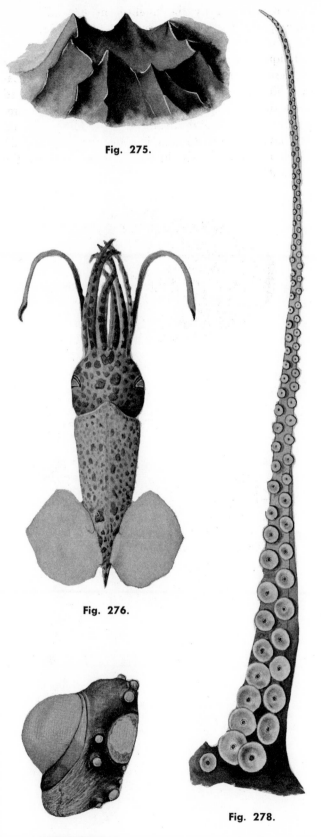

Fig. 275.

Fig. 276.

Fig. 277.

Fig. 278.

When the illustration is accompanying a strictly scientific manuscript, all details should be drawn. It should not be overlooked or considered trivial that a surface of an animal is covered with fine dots (*Fig. 271*). Nor should the illustrator feel obliged to use pebble board and wax pencil. These dots are not placed symmetrically as those on the prefabricated surfaces. Using the wash method, the ground shading is completed, and then tiny dots are applied with India ink and crow quill pen. This is time-consuming, but accurately illustrates the animal's true characteristics.

If time is of the essence, choose the method in which you are most adept. However, do not sacrifice important details and your own reputation as an illustrator in order to save time.

It is important that you know the reproduction technique before attempting a drawing. If the illustration is to be reproduced in half-tone, use the wash or smudge method. If the reproduction is to be of the line type, you may use presurfaced material or line drawings. These are satisfactory both for scientific and semi-scientific journals.

The following illustrations of cephalopods will serve as examples of wash drawings, stressing the very satisfactory application of the technique for this particular type of animal. For many years the stippling method was used. However, it is evident that the wash method is far superior to the stippling method; details are more clearly defined and it takes less time. *Fig. 275* illustrates the mouth opening very clearly; *Fig. 276*, the overall view of the animal; in *Fig. 277* you will note the structure of the eye, the long narrow tentacles in *Fig. 278* and the thick short ones in *Fig. 279*, as well as the perfect specimen in *Fig. 280* and the damaged one in *Fig. 281*.

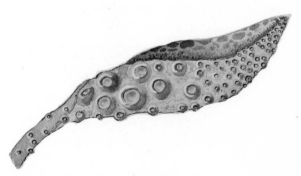

Fig. 279.

Fig. 280.

Fig. 281.

Experiment now with line drawings. First, the outline drawing (*Fig. 284*). This is accomplished by a pencil outline and then inked. Do not make the original more than twice the size of the reproduced size, using Strathmore paper, two- or three-ply smooth and a crow quill pen (*Fig. 282*).

The original should not be more than twice the size of the reproduced size. *Fig. 285* is the original, *Fig. 283* is reduced 50 per cent. It is possible to get a clear reproduction at one-third of the original size with this drawing technique.

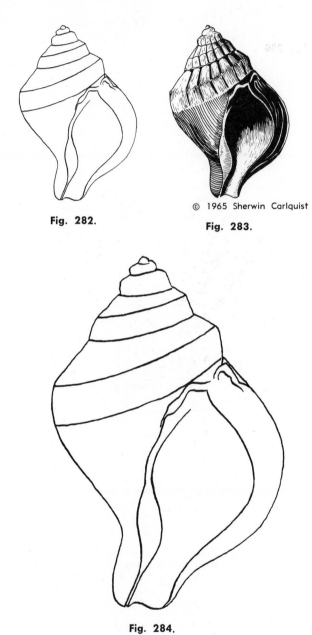

© 1965 Sherwin Carlquist

Fig. 282.　　　　　　**Fig. 283.**

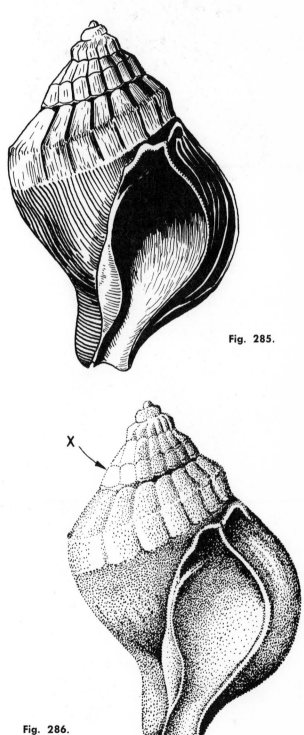

Fig. 285.

Fig. 284.

With this same outline as a basis, you may wish to add line-shading as seen in *Fig. 285*. Use solid black for the extremely dark areas, applying India ink with a brush. The rest of the shading may be done with the same pen with which you inked the outline.

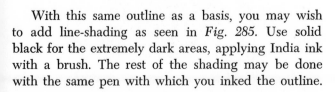

X

Fig. 286.

Stippling may be used for shading, regulating the density of dots, as well as their size by using different pens. When the pencil outline is completed, carry out the stippling effect throughout the entire object (*Fig. 286*), starting with the darker areas first and gradually decreasing in density for the lighter portions. *Fig. 286* is the original size. This drawing would reduce well to 40 per cent of the original size.

Presurfaced paper speeds up shading. For drawing shells coquille board is perhaps the most satisfactory (*Fig. 287*). Make ink outline with crow quill pen, drawing very fine lines with very little pressure. Clean the paper well and with a wax pencil place the pattern and shading. After completing the preliminary shading, with heavier pressure indicate shaded areas.

Be very careful not to puncture the paper, as these will show up in the reproduction. Drawings using this technique will reduce to 30 per cent of the original size. The drawing in *Fig. 287* is a 50 per cent reduction and is reproduced as a line drawing. Note in *Fig. 288* that some of the shaded areas did not reproduce well in half-tone.

This method is recommended for simple, smooth objects as seen in *Figs. 289* and *290*. If you wish to become adept at this method, practice objects as seen in the two figures cited and work out the shading. Then, study *Fig. 291* and practice on this type of shading. If you study the structure of *Figs. 289-290* with a magnifying glass you will find them to be the same as *Fig. 291*. Those tiny little black triangles and the outline are the parts done with ink; the rest is wax pencil. *Fig. 292* is the same drawing reproduced in half-tone. It now looks somewhat flat and the shaded areas have partially disappeared; the whole picture appears gray and without character. Such line drawings should not be reproduced in half-tone. This method of reproduction distorts artwork of that technique.

It is *again* stressed that detailed, impressive illustrations of cephalopods may be accomplished by the wash method. There are many colors on the market under various trade names. It is recommended that you buy the best. Colors in tubes may be mixed in a variety of different shades. Clean away the sealer used by the manufacturer to prevent drying. If you mix more color than is needed, store the remainder in

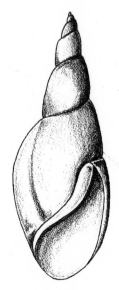

Fig. 287.   **Fig. 288.**   **Fig. 289.**   **Fig. 290.**

screw top jars for future use. It is recommended that you keep a piece of plate glass about 3 x 6 inches available for mixing deeper shades when drawing with colors. Keep plenty of water on hand and work with the surface evenly wet in order to have the shading blend evenly. If your drawing should dry, you may dampen it again with clean water. Complete the preliminary coloring within a surface before attempting lighter, darker and highlighted areas (*Fig. 293*).

Fig. 292.

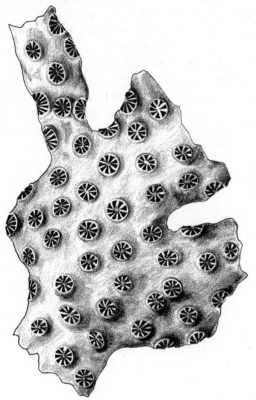

Fig. 291.

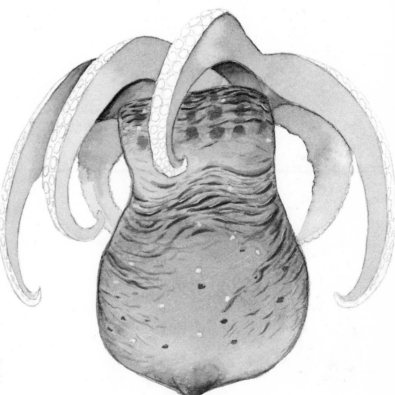

Fig. 293.

Fig. 294.

Fig. 295.

Fig. 296.

Fig. 297.

If there is an area on the body of a creature which is either a very light color or a reflection of light, add a few strokes of diluted white (*Fig. 294*), or if there are white markings on the surface, use white cover ink again (*Fig. 295*). To bring out a 3-D effect on the individual sucking units, place a parallel line to the margin opposite to the shaded area (*Fig. 296*). If the body parts are "milky" in appearance, or somewhat faded and hazy, cover the area with diluted white (*Fig. 297*). All of these details are represented in *Fig. 298*, which is reproduced in 75 per cent of the original size.

Most of your specimens will be preserved in liquid. Some of them may be very old and should be handled with extreme care. Do not keep them out of their containers for long periods of time (*Fig. 299*). Specimens become dried out and distorted when exposed to the air for too long a time. It is best if you study the specimen and observe it under a magnifying glass (*Fig. 300*) first. You will want to first make an outline and later develop details.

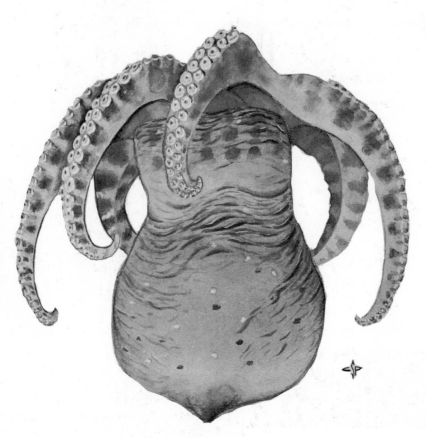

Fig. 298.

Fig. 299.

Fig. 300.

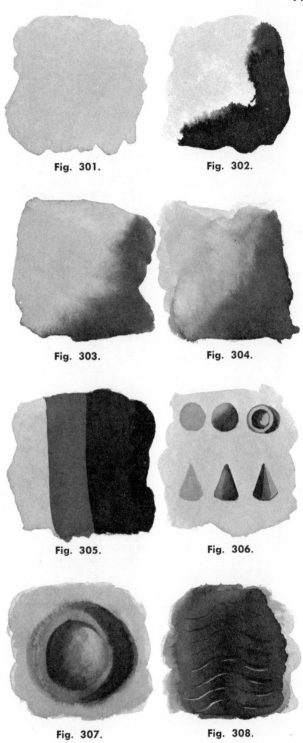

Fig. 301.

Fig. 302.

Fig. 303.

Fig. 304.

Fig. 305.

Fig. 306.

Fig. 307.

Fig. 308.

When you become accustomed to the wash method, it will be a pleasure for you to work with it. It is one of the best techniques and it is possible to make corrections without having them show up in the finished product. There are a few invaluable tricks to this method of drawing. Look at *Fig. 117* again.

This should have been reduced to half of that size for a more finished and professional appearance. Now, look at *Fig. 309;* observe the roughness in its original size; then turn to *Fig. 310,* which is the same drawing enlarged 150 percent to illustrate the composition of the minute details.

Step by step the process will be repeated. After the outline is completed, the basic color tone is applied. This should be a light tone (*Fig. 301*). Before this coat is dry, apply basic shading. If the first application dries before you have blended the second tone (*Fig. 302*), do not become disturbed, merely wet the entire surface again and blend the deeper tone (*Fig. 303*). Remember that the surfaces of animals are not completely evenly colored, so if you get an effect as seen in *Fig. 304,* do not worry about it. As you proceed with your artwork, much of the roughness will disappear. If you desire sharp contrasts of color as seen in *Fig. 305,* place tones adjacent to one another and smooth them with water. Details may be added

(*Fig. 306*), and no matter what the shape or size, they will accentuate a characteristic. To place little suckers on tentacles is quite simple (*Fig. 307*), just remember to set the direction of oncoming light in order to establish the 3-D effect. Highlights on wrinkled surfaces may be done with the logical use of darker and lighter strokes of the brush. For lighter tones, use diluted cover-white (*Figs. 294, 308*) in accordance with the contrasting background color. These steps are all components of the finished drawing (*Figs. 309-310*). If you take a reducing glass and

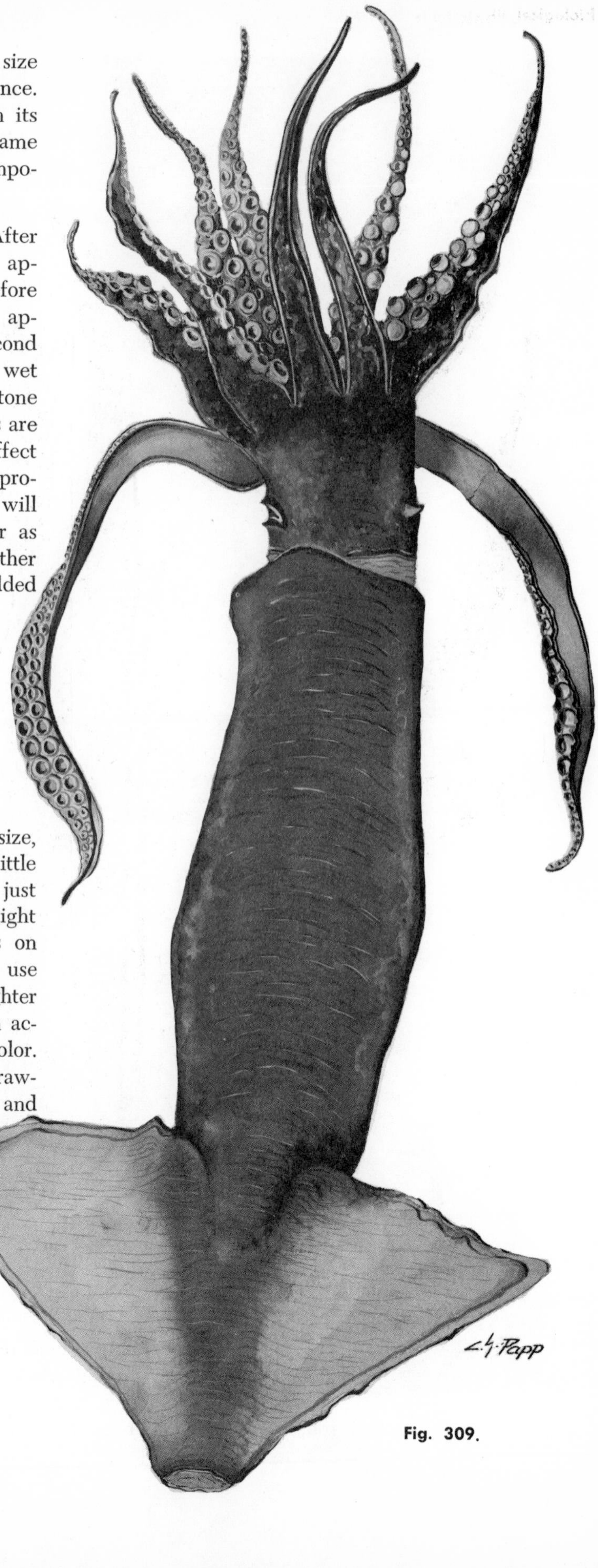

Fig. 309.

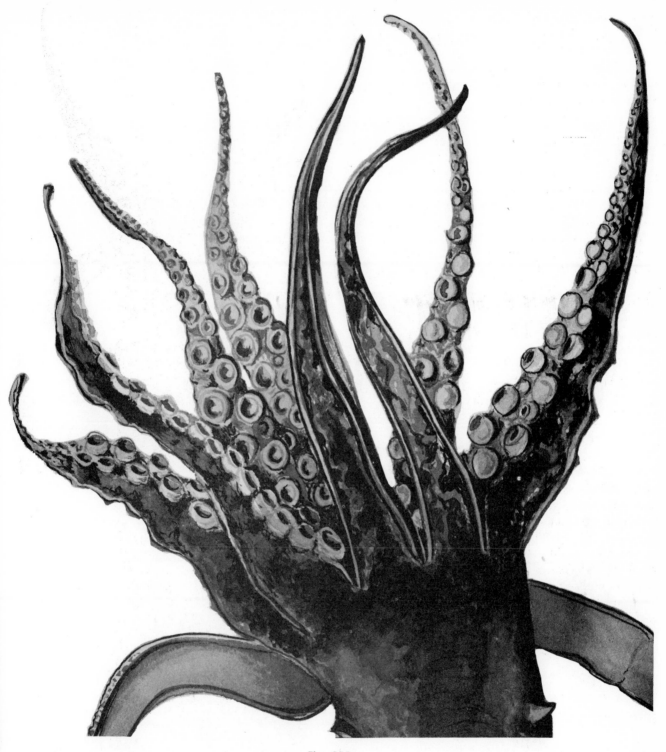

Fig. 310.

observe *Fig. 310* from different distances up to three
feet, you will see the roughness disappear. You should
be able to judge how large your original drawing
should be in relation to the reproduction.

With practice you will develop your favorite technique and learn to judge the size of your originals. *Figs. 311-314* are samples of detailed composition reproduced in the original size. Those will reproduce well at 50 per cent; however, a 75 per cent reduction would be the most convenient size for the reader. *Fig. 316* is the original; in *Fig. 315*, it is reduced to 25 per cent,

Fig. 311.

Fig. 314.

Fig. 313.

Fig. 312.

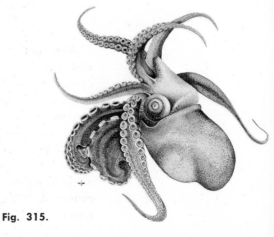

In addition to water colors India ink is an excellent medium to work with, and it reproduces more satisfactorily than any other color. This may be observed in *Figs. 311-316*. The fine details in shading were not lost in reproduction.

Fig. 315.

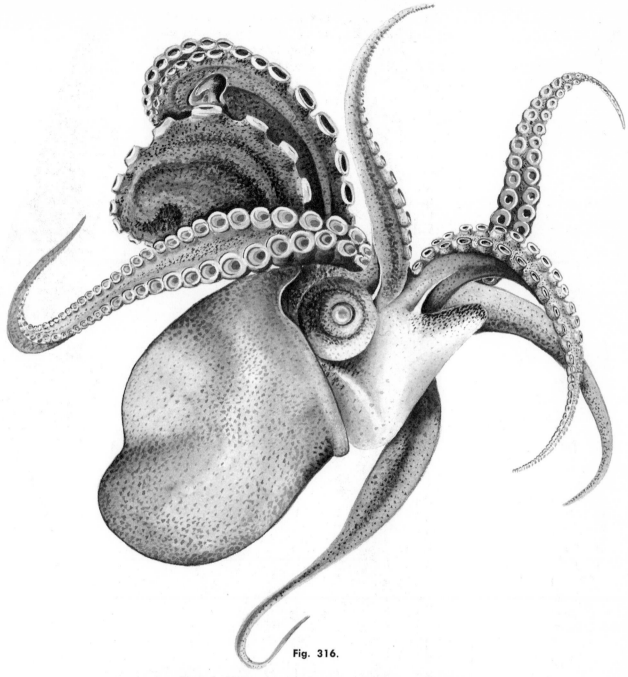

Fig. 316.

For half-tone reproduction another technique which works out very well is smudging. As discussed previously, this method is quite fast, relatively easy to do, and makes impressive artwork. This technique is especially satisfactory for drawing bones (*Figs. 610, 611*), and occasionally adapts itself for drawing marine material. The starfish (*Fig. 321*) is drawn by this method. It is smooth, uniform and quite effective. The ink lines show up in details, and the 3-D effect is well conveyed. If the surface is not unicolorous, a shaded effect may be achieved by using a sharp eraser on

Fig. 317.

Fig. 318.

Fig. 319.

Fig. 320.

the shaded surface. By use of an eraser a pattern may be "carved" into the background tone (*Fig. 317*). Larger portions may be treated the same way (*Figs. 318, 319*), or sharp strokes of white chalk (*Fig. 320*) will create the desired results. This technique may be used only for half-tone reproduction and, therefore, only those specimens which are not too detailed may be drawn this way. Obviously, microscopic animals drawn by this technique would have no scientific value — they would be merely decorative.

Line drawing is preferable for smaller creatures. The features of the species illustrated in *Figs. 322-324* are simply represented with a few lines and dots. *Fig. 325* demonstrates scratch board technique, showing hundreds of needle-like lines to exemplify the structure of a species. Species with sponge-like or wrinkled surfaces should be illustrated by stippling, as shown in *Fig. 326*. The internal texture is stippled, while the outline is an inked line. To represent flexible joints between body parts, as in *Fig. 329*, leave a narrow white line next to the outlined area. (*a*) This will indicate that segments are joined but are movable, whereas the connection between the first segment and the base, (*b*) *Fig. 329*, shows no white line because this joint is solid. Shading is added to give a 3-D effect. *Figs. 327* and *328* are 50 per cent reductions of *Figs. 326* and *329*.

Fig. 321.

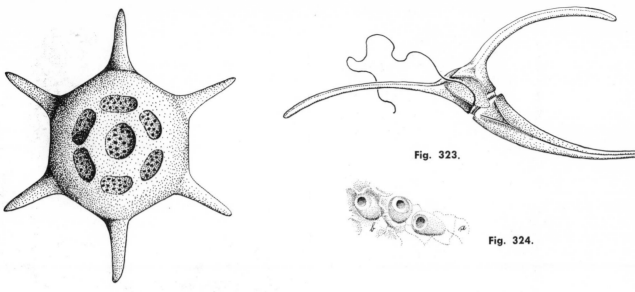

Fig. 322.

Fig. 323.

Fig. 324.

Fig. 325.

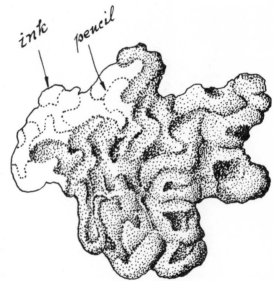

Fig. 326.

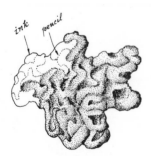

Fig. 327.

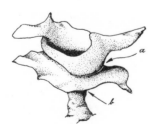

Fig. 328.

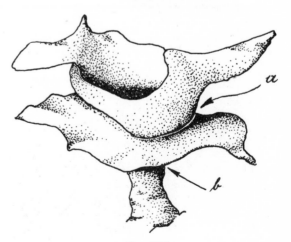

Fig. 329.

e. Illustrating Fishes

Drawings of fish may be effectively drawn by smudging on presurfaced paper or on scratch board. It is again stressed that technique depends upon the scientific importance of the illustration, as well as upon the method in which it will be reproduced.

For semi-technical or for popular publications fish may be drawn in black and white or in color without showing individual scales. Shading added to the fins (*Figs. 330, 331*), around the eye (*Fig. 332*), and to the mouth area (*Fig. 333*) with carbon powder and a stump create a desirable effect. *Fig. 334* is reproduced at 50 per cent of the original size; *Fig. 335* is reduced to one-fourth. This drawing technique will clearly reproduce at a one-tenth reduction. Preserve the original with Krylon spray. Reproduction is done by half-tone process.

Fig. 330.   **Fig. 331.**

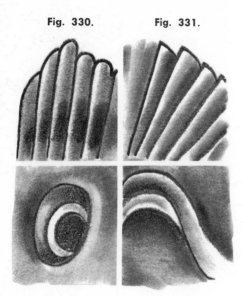

Fig. 332.   **Fig. 333.**

Fig. 334.

Fig. 335.

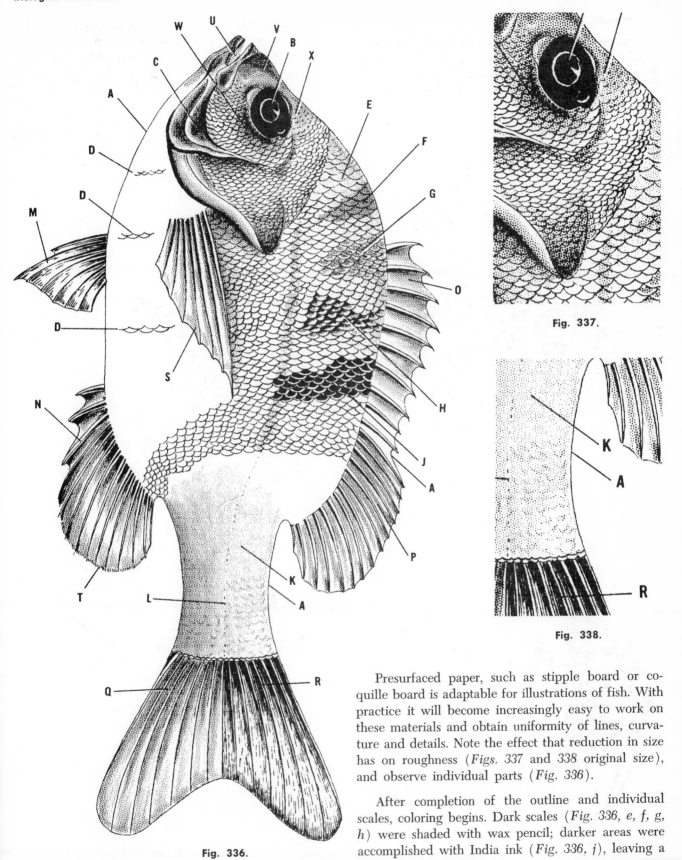

Fig. 336.

Fig. 337.

Fig. 338.

Presurfaced paper, such as stipple board or coquille board is adaptable for illustrations of fish. With practice it will become increasingly easy to work on these materials and obtain uniformity of lines, curvature and details. Note the effect that reduction in size has on roughness (*Figs. 337* and *338* original size), and observe individual parts (*Fig. 336*).

After completion of the outline and individual scales, coloring begins. Dark scales (*Fig. 336, e, f, g, h*) were shaded with wax pencil; darker areas were accomplished with India ink (*Fig. 336, j*), leaving a

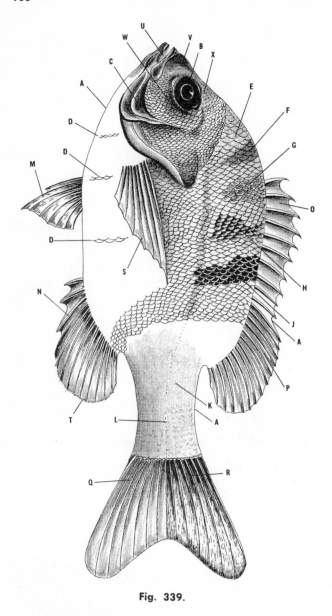

Fig. 339.

Figs. 336-339. At the completion of your drawing clean it carefully and spray with Krylon spray. This technique is reproducible in line cut.

Although mentioned earlier, it bears repeating that this type of drawing reproduced in half-tone sometimes results in a satisfactory picture, but in most cases fine details are lost in reproduction. Compare the line reproduction (*Fig. 339*) with the half-tone reproduction (*Fig. 340*).

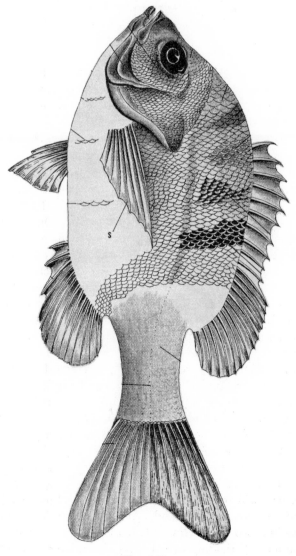

Fig. 340.

white area between individual scales, so as not to disrupt the scale pattern. Observe the technique employed to highlight the eye; a narrow triangular white area within the blackened portion. This is clearly visible in reduction (*Fig. 339*). Compare the grades of shading in the two sizes of reproductions (*Figs. 336* and *339*). The same technique was used here as previously discussed in *Figs. 204* and *205;* the only difference is in paper. Fine coquille board was used for *Figs. 204* and *205,* and stipple board was used in

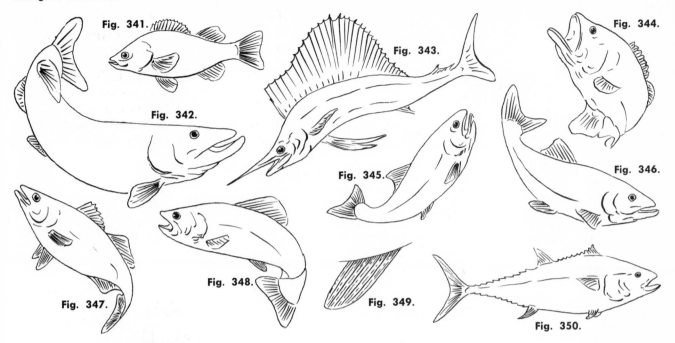

Fig. 341. Fig. 342. Fig. 343. Fig. 344. Fig. 345. Fig. 346. Fig. 347. Fig. 348. Fig. 349. Fig. 350.

In outlining fish there are many positions in which they may be illustrated and it is relatively easy to put life (motion) into these drawings. Examples are given in *Figs. 341-350.*

The scratch board technique is ideal for detailed fish drawings. The explanation of this method was thoroughly discussed and demonstrated (*Figs. 75, etc.*). It has been repeatedly pointed out that this technique is time-consuming and laborious. However, mastery from practice will be forthcoming. Once perfected, it is likely to be the favored technique for the scientific illustrator. Before attempting a complete fish drawing, start with individual details, such as the eye. It is round, shaded, and has light reflection (*Fig. 351*). The fins are delicate, almost transparent and may be represented by lines differing in length and thickness (*Fig. 352*). The lip region is usually smooth and may be defined by a series of lines and shading (*Fig. 353*). Scales are individually drawn and shaded, varying in shape and color. They may be lightened by scratching away some of the ink and leaving the larger position of the surface white (*Fig. 354*), or by covering the surface with ink and scraping lines within the scale area, leaving the outlines sharp but with a tone effect (*Fig. 335*). Combining these techniques to draw a group of scales and introducing curved strokes will result in an effect similar to that in *Fig. 356*. As you practice and experiment with lines and shading, you will develop many interesting combinations of shading which may be adapted to the scratch board technique.

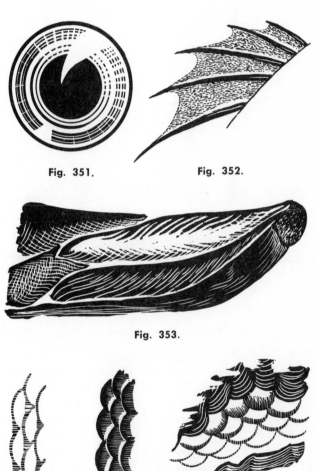

Fig. 351. Fig. 352.

Fig. 353.

Fig. 354. Fig. 355. Fig. 356.

Figures 357 and *358* are reproduced in their original size. Note how the shaded light scales differ from the dark scales on the dorsal part of the fish and how

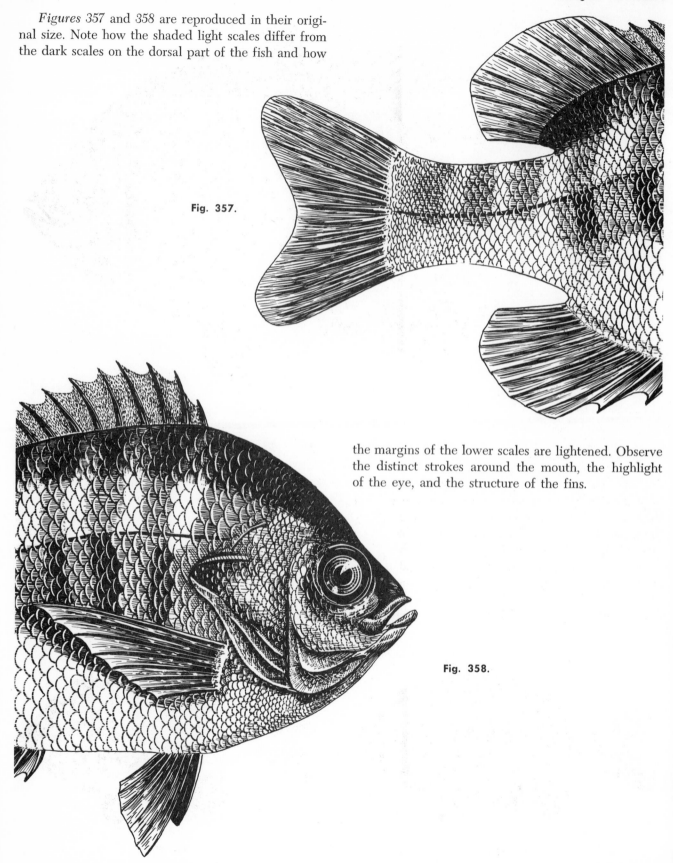

Fig. 357.

the margins of the lower scales are lightened. Observe the distinct strokes around the mouth, the highlight of the eye, and the structure of the fins.

Fig. 358.

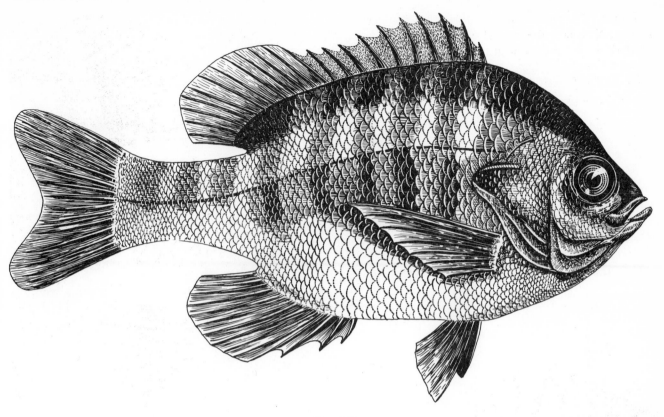

Fig. 359.

In *Fig. 359* the original has been reduced to 75 per cent. The grades of shading are quite visible, the head area and the fins are uniform, and the general shading throughout is smoothly blended. *Fig. 360* is the same illustration reduced to 30 per cent of the original size. Some of the fine strokes have been lost (this depends upon the quality of paper used for the illustration in printing). However, you see the fish in its 3-D effect and if you check details with a magnifying glass, you will be able to determine what was lost in reduction. A 50 per cent reduction (or possibly 40 per cent) would be best for an illustration the size of the original used in this example.

Drawings in this technique reproduce best with line cuts (*Figs. 357-360*). If your original is too large for the prescribed size in a journal and it has to be drastically reduced, the editor may be forced to use half-tone. *Fig. 360* is a line reproduction; *Fig. 361* is done in half-tone.

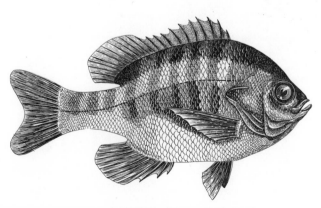

Fig. 360.

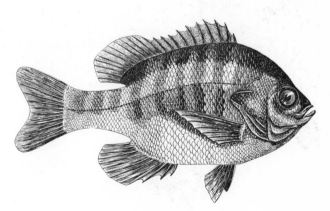

Fig. 361.

Scratch board illustrations are delicate and detailed, making very fine prints. This method is more expensive, but undoubtedly, it is the finest technique for any type of drawing, whether of insects, mammals, crustaceans or fish (*Fig. 366*).

f. Illustrating Arthropods

Arthropods are probably the most difficult of any species to illustrate. Whereas other biological subjects may be drawn with little scientific background, proper training and knowledge of arthropods is required in order to accurately translate structure and detail. The scientific value of such an illustration depends upon such things as the exact location and relative length of setae, the placement of the joints of antennae or tarsi, the flawless form and structure of the creature. Representing taxonomic detail in color is less difficult than when you are limited to black and white. Lack of entomological training is definitely a handicap in illustrating in this field. Therefore, if you are called upon to draw arthropods and do not have the necessary experience, seek as much guidance and advice as possible from the scientist. Reference to textbooks on the subject is extremely beneficial also. A study of

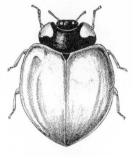

Fig. 362.

Fig. 363.

Fig. 364.

Fig. 365.

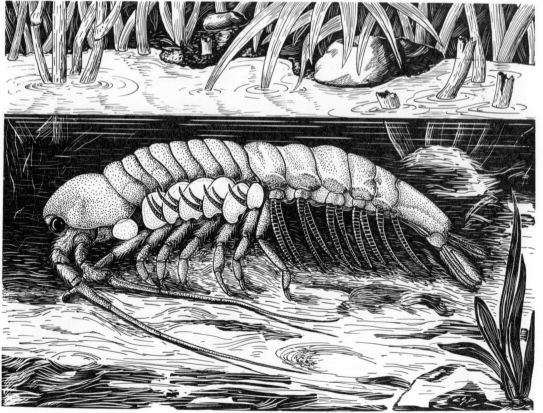

Fig. 366.

© 1965 Sherwin Carlquist

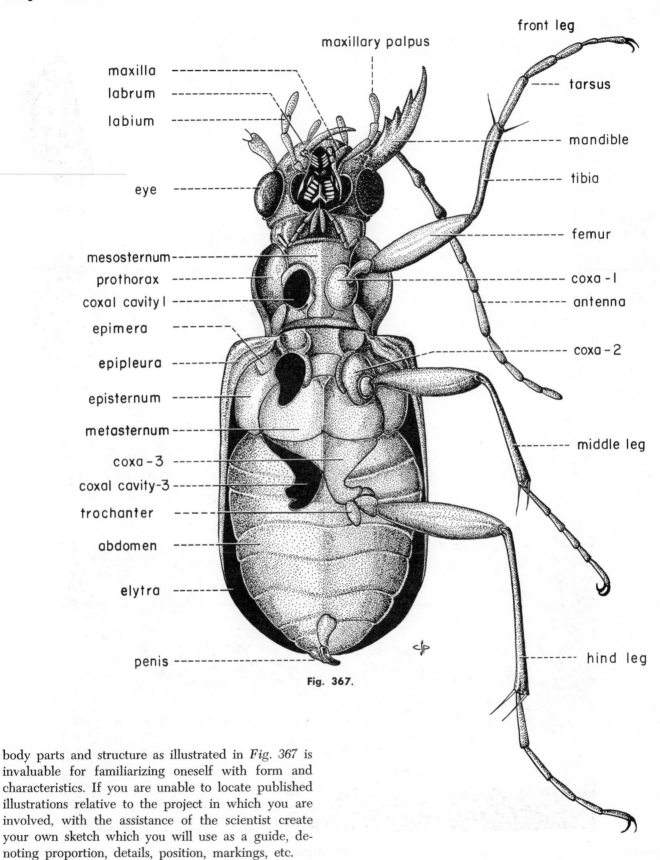

front leg

maxillary palpus

maxilla - - - - - - - - - - - - -

labrum - - - - - - - - - - - - - - -

labium - - - - - - - - - - - - - - -

tarsus - - - -

mandible - - - - - - -

eye - - - - - - - - - - - - -

tibia - - - - - - - - - -

femur - - - - - - - - - -

mesosternum - - - - - - - - - - -

prothorax - - - - - - - - - -

coxal cavity I - - - - - - - - - -

coxa - I - - - - - - - - -

antenna - - - - - - - - -

epimera - - - - - - - -

epipleura - - - - - - - -

coxa - 2 - - - - - - - - -

episternum - - - - - - -

metasternum - - - - - -

coxa -3 - - - - - - - -

middle leg - - - - - - - -

coxal cavity-3 - - - - -

trochanter - - - - - -

abdomen - - - - - - -

elytra - - - - - - - -

penis - - - - - - - - - - - - - - - -

hind leg - - - - - - - -

Fig. 367.

body parts and structure as illustrated in *Fig. 367* is invaluable for familiarizing oneself with form and characteristics. If you are unable to locate published illustrations relative to the project in which you are involved, with the assistance of the scientist create your own sketch which you will use as a guide, denoting proportion, details, position, markings, etc.

Accuracy cannot be overstressed. Your drawings will appeal to the young beetle collector (*Fig. 370*), as well as the renowned scientist. Whether your work be done as a simple coquille board drawing (*Figs. 362-365*) or the more complicated scratch board technique (*Fig. 366*), a demonstration chart of an insect (*Fig. 367; Fig. 368* and *369* — details in original size), or a detailed line drawing in specialized taxonomic structure (*Fig. 371*), strive for perfection, selecting the best possible technique for each drawing.

Entomological illustrations are generally done as line drawings. The various methods have been previously discussed and result in effective, accurate artwork. Color prints, because of the high cost of reproduction, are rarely used.

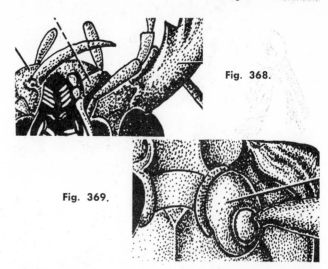

Fig. 368.

Fig. 369.

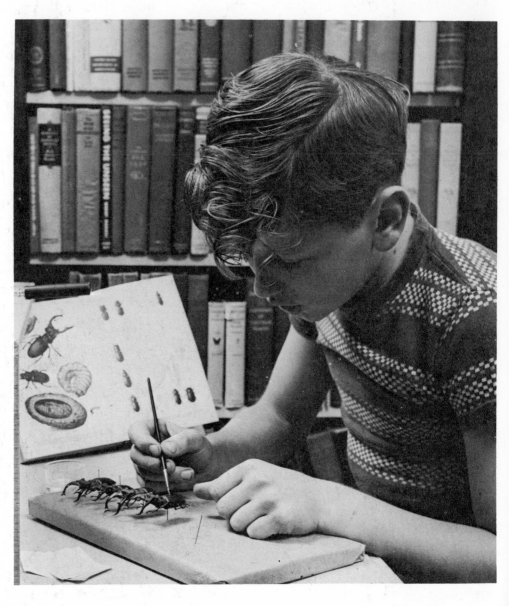

Fig. 370.

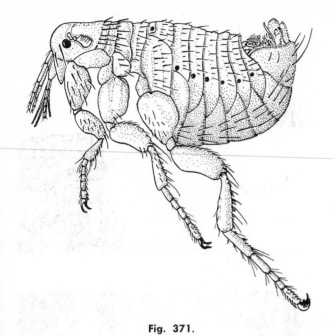

Fig. 371.

In making line drawings be certain that all individual lines are black (*Figs. 372-379*). This assures perfect reproduction. Select good quality illustration paper (*Figs. 372-375*) or scratch board (*Figs. 376-379*). Observe the techniques used: *Fig. 372* demonstrates even ink lines; *Fig. 373* has heavier shading lines on one side of the antenna; *Fig. 374* employs short strokes for shading; *Fig. 375* registers color differences by regulating the density of short lines; *Fig. 376* indicates by scratch board method that the antenna is covered with short hairs; *Fig. 377* shows by the same method that there is a separation of joints and that there are longer hairs present; *Fig. 378* illustrates additional short hairs and color distribution; and *Fig. 379* is simply a dark antenna showing the separation of joints, highlighted with a narrow white line. In these figures you have the components that are the basis of all line drawings.

The scratch board technique is superior to all others for drawing insects. The following examples are given as evidence of the quality of work that may be expected by using this technique.

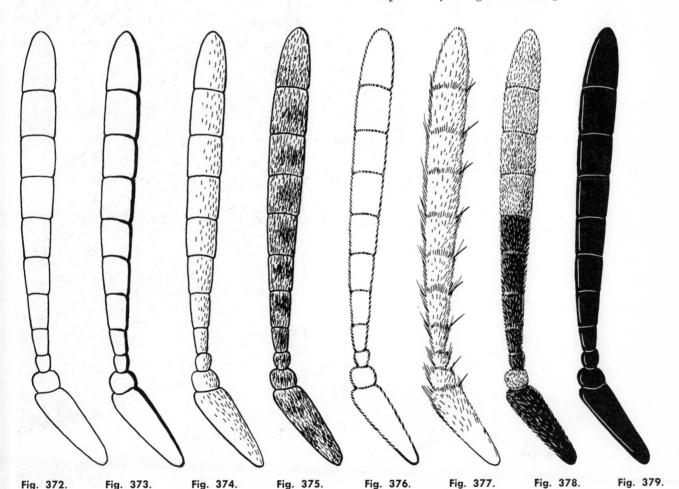

Fig. 372.   Fig. 373.   Fig. 374.   Fig. 375.   Fig. 376.   Fig. 377.   Fig. 378.   Fig. 379.

Figure 380: This is a relatively easy drawing of a sphinx-moth. First the pencil outline was drawn, marking margins of the predominant color pattern and the location of the abdominal joints. The outline was then inked with crowquill pen and India ink and the pencil lines erased.

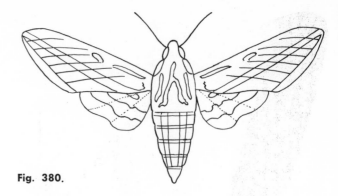

Fig. 380.

Fig. 381.

Figure 381: Determination was made for representing color tones. Using a fine brush (No. 00 or No. 0) and India ink the darker areas were covered. Faint thin lines on the light areas were drawn in with crowquill pen.

Figure 382: After the ink was well dried (about five to ten minutes) shading throughout the specimen was done. Note the fine hairs on the body and the rings on the abdomen. By breaking the antennae with both fine and dense lines, the antennal joints are represented. Very fine lines on the very edge of the wings achieve a realistic effect.

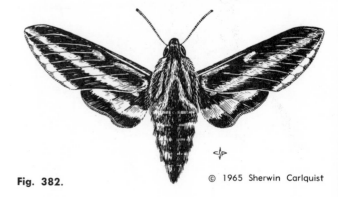

Fig. 382.   © 1965 Sherwin Carlquist

Figure 383: The structure of the wings on this specimen differ. The fore wing is smooth, the hind wing coarser and lined. Although it is generally recommended not to use both dots and lines within

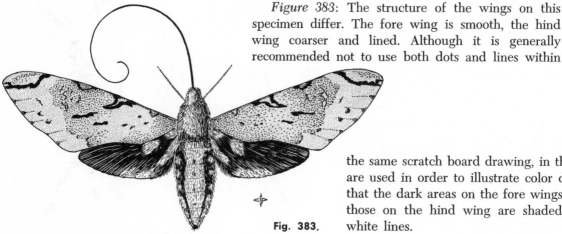

Fig. 383.

the same scratch board drawing, in this instance both are used in order to illustrate color differences. Note that the dark areas on the fore wings are solid, while those on the hind wing are shaded with very fine white lines.

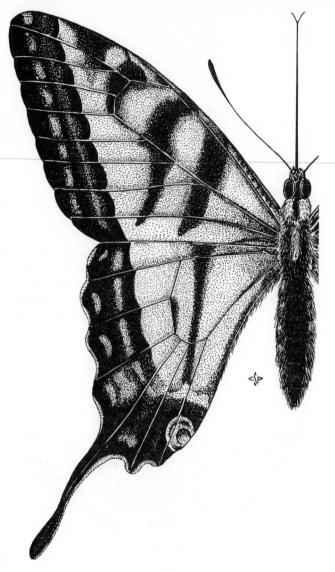

Fig. 384.

Many insects, including butterflies, are covered with scales. In most cases they are so minute, unless the specimen is large, they are difficult to see and the artist omits them. If individual scales are drawn, care should be taken that the artwork is not reduced to a degree where details are completely lost. To avoid drawing scales a series of fine lines and dots work out effectively.

Figure 384: This is the original size of the drawing. Scratch board was used, working out details on the body and the edges of the hind wing. Preliminary steps were the same as described earlier: outline in pencil, then inked. The dark areas were covered with India ink. Dots were made with a fine crowquill pen, starting at the edges next to the solid black areas and working toward the middle of the white portions. Dots in the black areas were done with a pointed scalpel. The body is composed of a series of strokes with a scalpel in the blackened surface as seen in *Figs. 382* and *383*. By regulating the density of dots on the shaded side of the elevated veins on the wings a 3-D effect was achieved. The eyes are black, faintly highlighted with a narrow white line. A few dots on the antennal club highlight the left side of the club.

Figure 385: In this drawing, the same technique was employed as in *Fig. 384* but with fewer details on the antennae and the body. Compare the two drawings, looking especially for differences in composition of the wings and abdomen. This is a 50 per cent reduction of the original.

Before starting a drawing know the dimensions of the allotted space in the publication. If you use the scratch board method, the original artwork should not be more than twice the size of the reproduction (printed) size.

Fig. 385.

If the artist is asked to draw numerous species within the same genus, it is suggested that considerable time be spent first in studying the specimens. Decide upon the technique best suited to that particular project. As an example, let us take a genus of bees comprised of exceedingly minute specimens. A preliminary study indicated that many of the species were bi-colorous: black and yellow, and that the most suitable technique of drawing them was the scratch board method. This assignment dealt with taxonomic details. The following figures demonstrate the procedure followed:

Figure 386: A pencil outline is inked in evenly and smoothly.

Figure 388: Incidental patterns in the eyes are added, with fine strokes the pubescence of the antennae. Note the triangular plate between the basal joints of the antennae. Shading this area brings out the 3-D effect. Highlighting the ocelli gives life. Details at the base of the antennae give a moderately concave appearance. Shading the mandibles and lip region, and finally, placing hairs with very fine lines around the edges, on the top of the head, mandibles, etc. Hair lines on the black areas are scraped with a scalpel. Hairs crossing the outline (as on the mandibles) should break the continuity of the outline. This is accomplished by scraping a thin line parallel to the hair line.

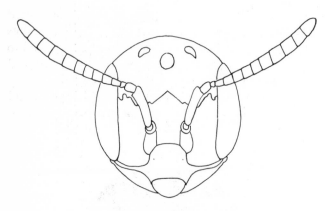

Fig. 386.

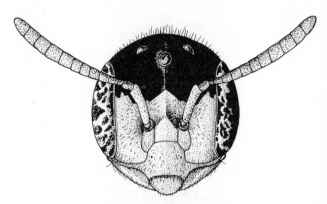

Fig. 388.

Figure 389: Pubescence on the antennae is illustrated by scraping very fine lines close together on the outline and on the lines separating the individual joints. To finish the eyes a prefabricated tone (see samples in *Fig. 1089*, etc.) was placed over the area and cut with a sharp razor blade with very light pressure, so as not to cut into the chalk coating of the paper.

Figure 387: Dark areas are covered with India ink, leaving highlights around the ocelli and the middle of the frons.

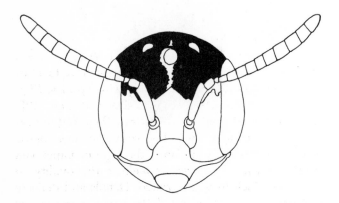

Fig. 387.

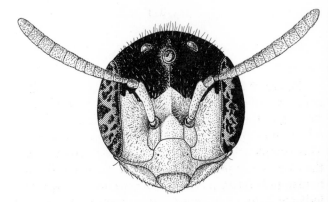

Fig. 389.

Figure 390: Another type of bee whose head is entirely black and covered with hairs. The preliminary steps are the same: outlined in pencil and inked.

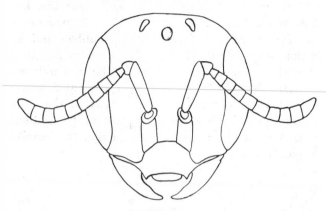

Fig. 390.

Figure 391: The entire head with the exception of the highlight areas is covered with India ink. Concavity around the origin of the antennae and the adjacent convex area are also left white. Let the ink dry thoroughly.

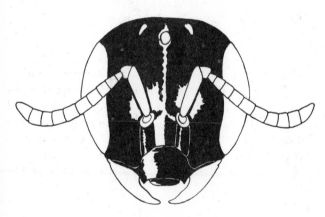

Fig. 391.

Figure 392: To blend dark and light areas stippling is added with India ink and crowquill pen, starting at the clypeal area, then working on the mandibles and around the antennal base toward the ocelli. This completed, the dark areas on the antennae and the eyes are applied with a brush. To make the antennae pubescent, place thin, short lines on them and indicate hairs on marginal areas, such as the top of the head, clypeus and mandibles (see also *Fig. 378*).

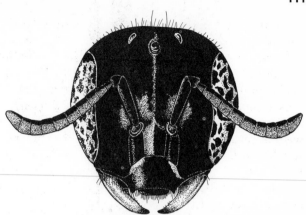

Fig. 392.

Figure 393: After the ink is thoroughly dried scratching with a scalpel commences. The white dots around the eyes and in the black areas are applied to decrease the contrast between the black and stippled portions and also to add additional highlights, giving a more pronounced 3-D effect. The last step is to add the tone to the eye. For different grades of prefabricated tones see *Figs. 1089*, etc.

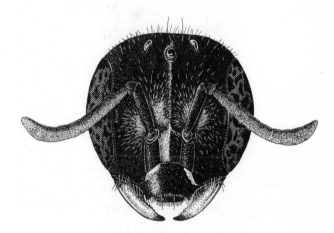

Fig. 393.

In taxonomic work the artist will be called upon to draw a head in a lateral view, as well as to illustrate both male and female of a specific species. *Figs. 394-396*, reproduced in original size, and *Figs. 397-399* in 60 per cent reduction illustrate these differences in size, pattern and view. How your drawings appear in print depends largely upon the type of paper you select for your drawings, as well as the quality of paper on which they are printed. Details and delicate characteristics may be lost if the paper is too coarse or too soft.

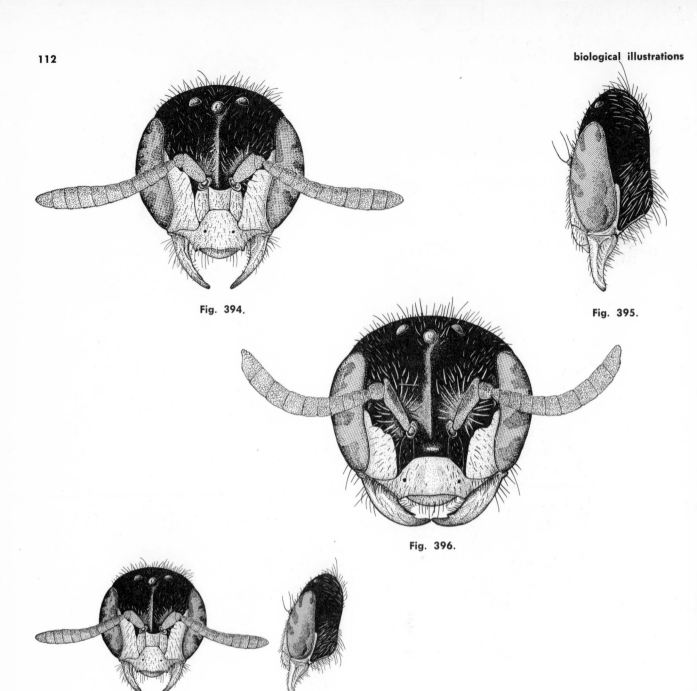

Fig. 394.

Fig. 395.

Fig. 396.

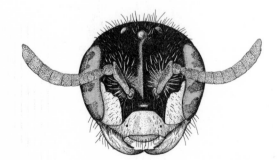

Fig. 397.

Fig. 398.

Fig. 399.

The preceding has been confined to the heads of insects. Drawing the entire insect is somewhat more complicated. Color patterns of wings are an important taxonomic feature. If the illustrator has to draw a large number of insects, he may use presurfaced paper. Coquille paper with a rough surface is recommended. Do the original about two to four times larger than the final reproduction.

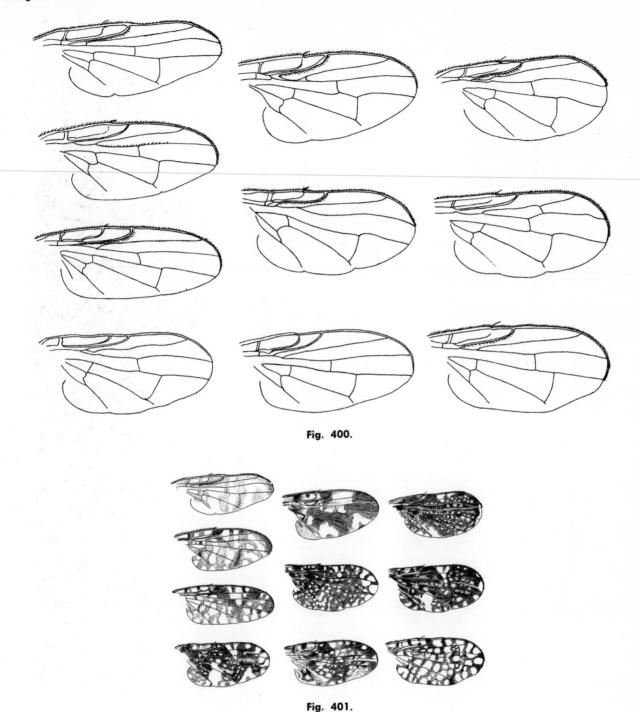

Fig. 400.

Fig. 401.

Step one is the outline and the veins, inked in carefully, then the pencil marks cleaned off (*Fig. 400*). With black wax pencil and light pressure add the pattern. By regulating the pressure on your pencil it is possible to denote variation in shading (*Fig. 402*). *Figs. 400* and *402* are 50 per cent reductions of the original, and *Fig. 401* is reduced to 25 per cent of the

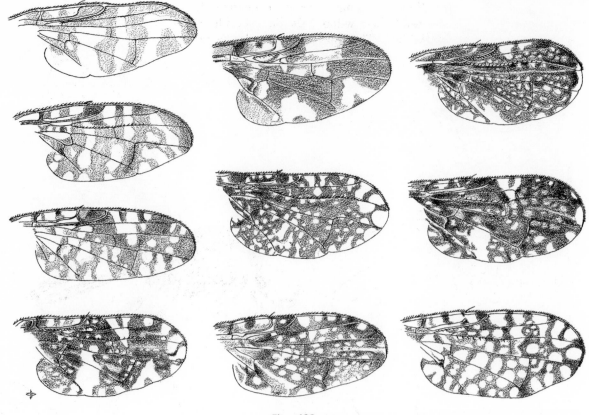

Fig. 402.

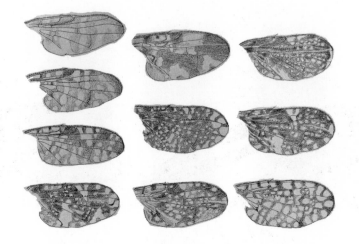

Fig. 403.

original size, showing detailed characteristics of ten different wing patterns and reproduced in line cut. *Fig. 403* is the same drawing reproduced in half-tone.

Often the wings have no coloration. However, if we draw them without shading, the illustration looks unfinished. The following examples were drawn on

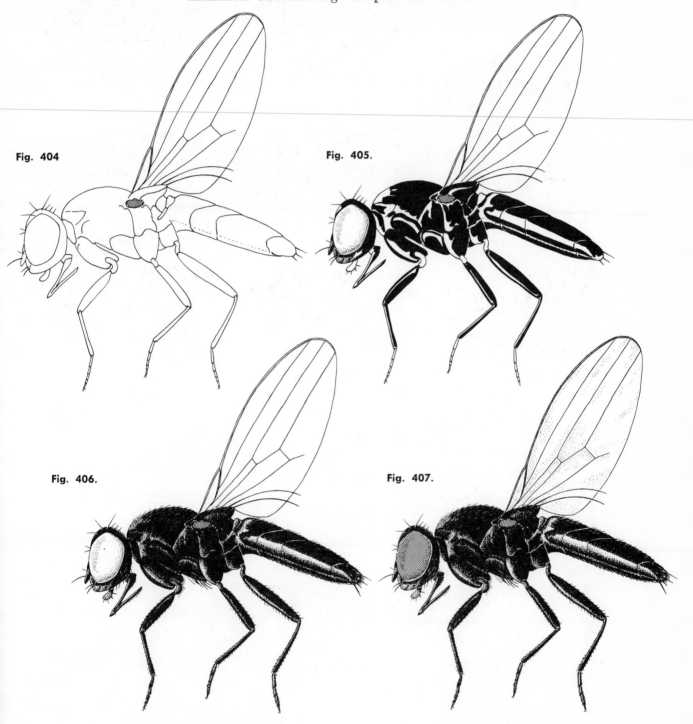

Fig. 404

Fig. 405.

Fig. 406.

Fig. 407.

scratch board. The final outline is inked (*Fig. 404*). The dark and shaded areas are covered with ink (*Fig. 405*). After the ink is thoroughly dry stippling begins. Hairs are added with crowquill pen. The outline is

softened with fine hair lines. Highlights are added with scalpel (*Fig. 406*). Stippling is added to the wing and similarly to the eye. The final step is covering the eye with prefabricated tone (*Fig. 407*).

2.0 mm

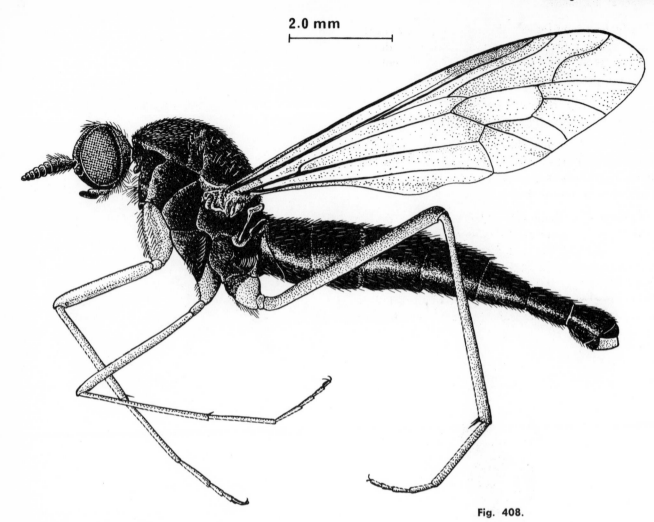

Fig. 408.

When an insect is drawn in a lateral view, usually one set of legs and one wing are omitted in order to insure clarity. Omitting one wing helps to portray the body parts more clearly, which otherwise would be covered by the wing.

Figure 408 is a scratch board drawing reproduced in the original size (reduced in *Fig. 409*). Observe the difference between these two figures. In the reduction the courseness of lines and the roughness in stippling disappear.

It is recommended that you put a scale on your illustration so that the reader can determine the size of the specimen. Make the scale clear, conspicuous, not too long or too short. Set the measurement so that it is easy to compare and multiply, such as 1.0 mm., 2.0 mm., etc. Do not use such figures as 1.37 mm. or 2.05 mm., making it needlessly difficult to use. Place your line parallel to the length of the insect or to the longest diameter (*Figs. 408* and *409*).

2.0 mm

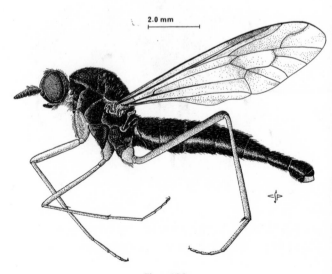

Fig. 409.

The following figures illustrate two species of flies, demonstrating the scratch board method of drawing the insects in lateral view, having two different types of pattern on their abdomens.

Figure 410 is the usual outline already inked. Note the outlines of the lighter markings on the abdomen.

Figure 411 shows the black coloring (done with India ink and brush), the dark area on the eyes, highlights on the thorax, as well as the white areas and highlights on the abdomen.

Figure 412: Shading is added to the eyes, dots are placed on the parts of the abdomen covered by the wings and highlights added. Marginal hairs are done with a scalpel in the dark areas. The wings are freed from the outline with a white line scraped into the background wherever they veil the abdomen. This immediately and automatically separates the wing from the abdomen.

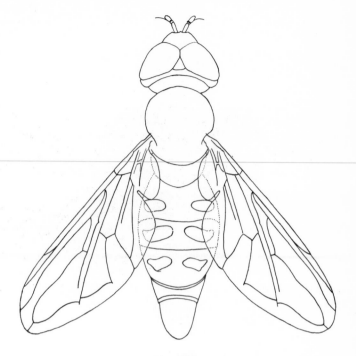

Fig. 410.

Fig. 411.

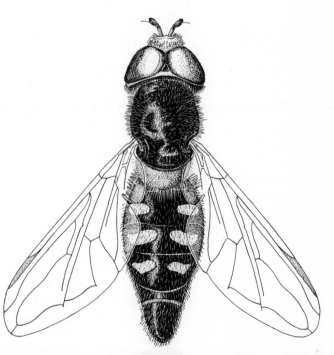

Fig. 412.

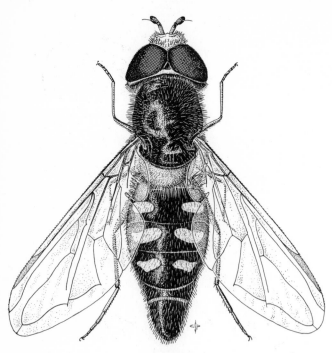

Fig. 413.

Fig. 414.

Figure 413: Fine dots (stippling) added to the wings with a crowquill pen signify slight differences in coloring of the membrane. The artwork is completed by applying prefabricated tone (*Fig. 1089*) to cover the eye. The same illustration is reproduced in about one-third the original size in *Fig. 414*.

Figures 415 and *416* illustrate the same technique on another species of insect where the pattern of the abdomen is different. Note the color differences represented on the thorax. Observe the black markings on the abdomen and the shading on those areas beneath the wing. Compare the construction and position of the legs in these figures and those in *Figs. 412* and *413*.

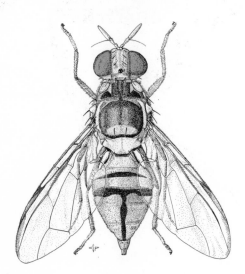

Fig. 415.

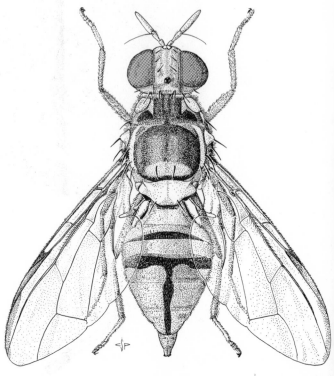

Fig. 416.

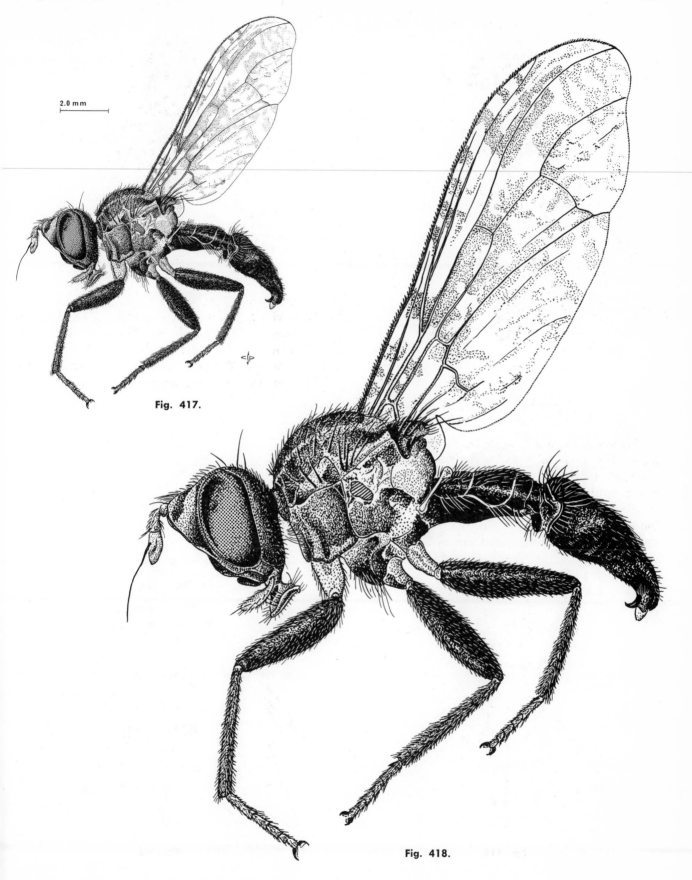

2.0 mm

Fig. 417.

Fig. 418.

Figures 417 and *418* illustrate insects with patterns on their wings. As pointed out (*Figs. 400-403*), maculation may be achieved in drawing wings by use of the stippling technique. This drawing is on scratch board. Seen in its original size (*Fig. 418*) prominent lines were used in black with pen and ink or in white with scraper. The dots composing the pattern on the wings are relatively fine. When the illustration is reproduced (*Fig. 417*) the wing has a smooth, delicate, membranous appearance in relation to the other parts of the insect.

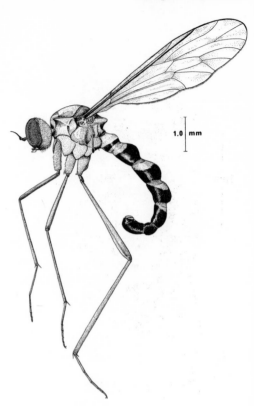

1.0 | mm

Fig. 420.

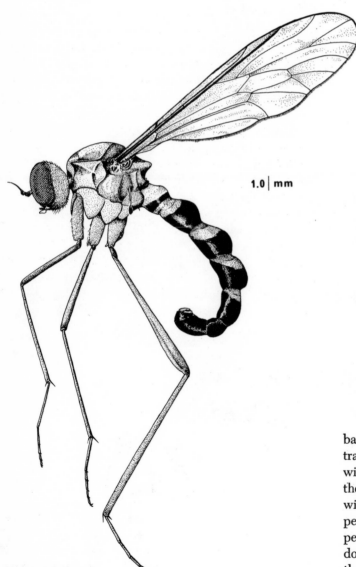

1.0 | mm

Fig. 419.

The right wing is illustrated. If the veins at the base of the wing are important and should be illustrated, or if it the wing is narrow enough so that it will not cover up any taxonomically vital parts of the thorax or the anterior end of the abdomen, the left wing may be drawn. For example, *Fig. 419* is a 75 per cent reduction of the original and *Fig. 420* is a 50 per cent reduction. You will note the colors on the abdomen in this lateral view, the fine series of lines on the edge of the wing, the dots on the wing to give it smoothness and transparency. Note also the fine lines along the edge of the wing.

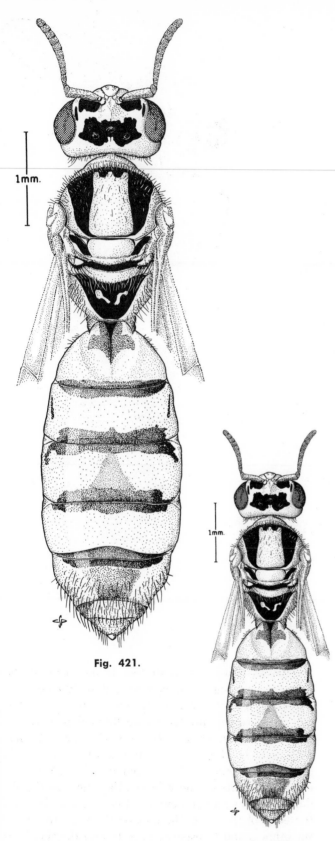

Fig. 421.

Fig. 422.

In order to show maximum features and color patterns of an insect's body and give minimum attention to the wings, which in many cases may not be of importance, it is acceptable to draw only the basal one-third or one-fourth of the wing with a fine dotted line. *Fig. 421* illustrates this technique, as well as showing differentiation of colors by regulating the density of dots. The markings on the head and thorax are solid black, while on the abdomen you will see tones of gray. The basic color is light, the 3-D effect is accomplished by stippling (darkening) the shaded (right) side of the entire body, and highlights, giving the body a shiny appearance, were achieved with less dense, smaller dots. Note the highlight on the darker surface. *Fig. 442* is the same artwork reduced to two-thirds of the original size.

If there are variations of color and pattern within the same species of an insect, a series of illustrations showing these differences may be drawn. For example, the heads illustrated in *Figs. 423, 424,* and *425* demonstrate coloring variations within the same species. Artificial color tones were used in *Figs. 423* (darker) and *424* (lighter), whereas *Fig. 425* (light) was left without added color tones. The identical color tone is used for the eyes in all three examples, but it differs from the tones used on the heads. The outlines for these drawings are very simple in design, the same outline being used for the three examples. The quick, easy way to do this type of illustrating is to draw the outline, photograph it, making as many prints as you may need. Then, add the pattern (color tones), and your assignment is finished. You have uniform, clear, precise drawings which define the differences found within a given species.

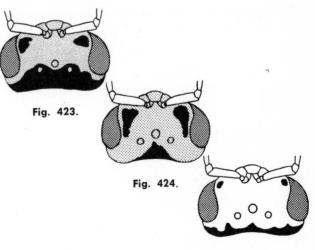

Fig. 423.

Fig. 424.

Fig. 425.

Scientific illustrations of insects are not frequently drawn in their natural habitat today as they were about 50 years ago (*Fig. 426*). That type of illustration is excellent for quick identification when there are clearly visible differences between species. However, if the species is small and closely resembles other members of the same species, scientists prefer to use detailed illustrations of body parts. A flea is used in *Figs. 427-431* to exemplify this procedure. *Fig. 427* shows the composition of the egg, *Fig. 428* is a gross figure of the larva, *Fig. 431* is a detailed enlargement of the mouth parts of the larva, *Fig. 430* is the adult, and *Fig. 429* illustrates only the adult head area. These are very simple drawings composed of solid ink lines and shaded by stippling. Examine the technique used to accent the setae, making them stand out from the body, the cross-segments and the outline. It is unnecessary to use a great deal of shading in drawings of this type. Use shading for an artistic effect.

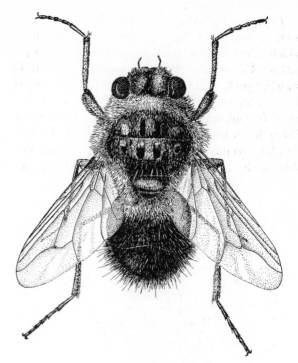

Fig. 426.

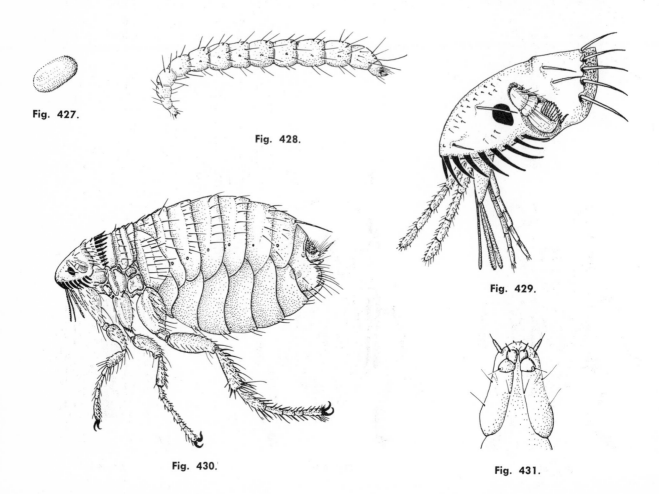

Fig. 427.

Fig. 428.

Fig. 429.

Fig. 430.

Fig. 431.

Figure 432 illustrates a mite with setae extending from a smooth body, the internal composition of which shows through a more or less transparent cuticle. Unless the smudging method is used for a drawing such as this (as illustrated in *Fig. 90*, etc.), the only alternative is stippling or, in the case of semi-scientific illustrations, presurfaced drawing paper. There is no substitute or time-saver for the tedious stippling technique for accentuating minute details. Start with the external outline of the body, mouth parts, legs, and all of the joints. Place the bristles (setae) with firm, distinct strokes, broad at the base and gradually diminishing to a fine, pointed end. Work out the remaining details with dots. You will note in *Fig. 432* that smaller dots were used for shading the legs than those used on the body. In this instance an old crowquill pen was used for shading the body and a new one was used for the legs. It is needless to be concerned with complicated or excessive artist's supplies. The importance lies in the quality of your work which is a reflection your knowledge of the subject, your ability as an artist, and your mastery of a technique.

Another effect may be achieved by using a combination of varied sizes and dots, and dots extended into lines, and lines as seen in *Figs. 433-435*. If the surface of an insect has a definite pattern or a structure of characteristic significance, these markings should be individually drawn. This is also applicable if the insect possesses a color pattern (*Fig. 434*), or a rough granular surface (*Fig. 435*). The anterior third of the elytra was drawn with the same technique that would be used to indicate color except that dots of irregular size and shape were used. Originals were drawn on Strathmore drawing paper with crowquill pen and Pelican India ink.

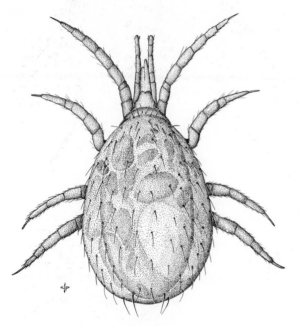

Fig. 432.

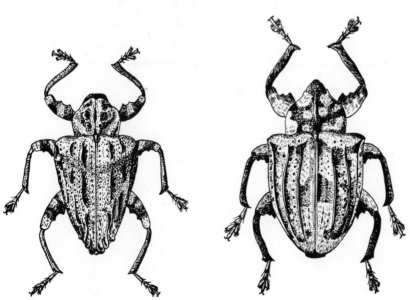
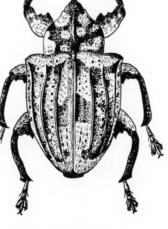
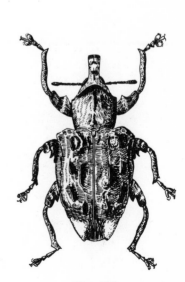

Fig. 433.

Fig. 434.

Fig. 435.

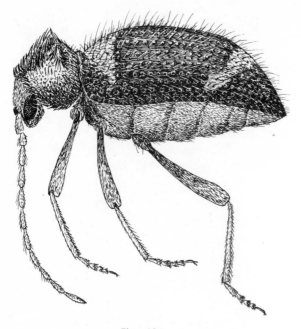

Fig. 436.

der and the pre-apical cross-band were left white and blended into the surface with short black lines. The white shadows of the individual hairs were added with diluted white cover ink and fine crowquill pen.

This drawing can be done very effectively and more easily on scratch board. *Fig. 440* employs the scratch board method, as does *Fig. 437*: the entire areas were darkened and then scraped with a scalpel. *Figs. 438a, 439* show elevated tubercles and longitudinal lines which, in these examples, were stippled. Mandibles are highlighted by leaving white areas in the dark background (*Fig. 438, b*). Drawings employing this technique are attractive and reproduced very well. *Fig. 440* is reduced to 80 per cent of the original. The legs have been omitted since they have little importance taxonomically.

Using the same material but another technique, *Fig. 436* is composed of lines. The longitudinal puncture lines on the elytra were penciled and inked. The white ring-like area around the individual punctures were left white, and the interspaces shaded with short, thin lines. Convexity of the elytra was achieved by placing the lines closer together near the margin of the elytra and gradually further and further apart toward the suture. The light source coming from the upper left, the apical portion of the elytra must be kept dark. Lighter shaded areas as seen on the shoul-

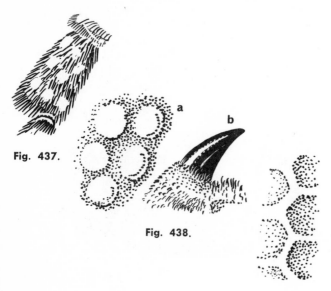

Fig. 437.

a

b

Fig. 438.

Fig. 439.

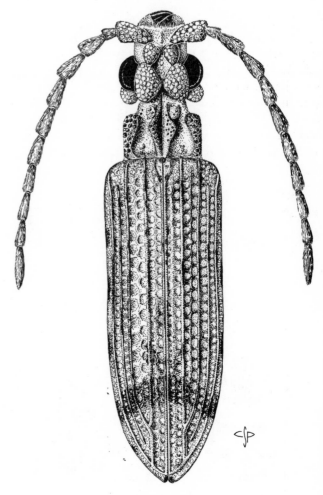

Fig. 440.

The following figures will illustrate a fast method of making ink and pencil drawings on presurfaced paper, in these cases either coquille or pebble boards.

At the beginning of this chapter, *Figs. 362-365* illustrating four lady beetles, were given as examples to show the sharp contrast between this easy drawing method and a more complicated one (*Fig. 366*), the scratch board technique.

A rough grade of pebble board was used for *Figs. 442* and *443*. The outlines are drawn first and inked. The next step is to fill in the color pattern with ink and brush, leaving the areas white where the light reflects. Shading is placed with wax pencil. Try first a species without a pattern as seen in *Fig. 362*, then go to one with a variable pattern (*Fig. 443*).

For practice try this technique on a form such as the lantern-fly in *Fig. 441*. This technique on rough-surfaced coquille board differs from the one you just did of the beetle. The pattern is composed of small dots, and you do not have to be concerned about symmetry.

If you are drawing a two-colored insect, start with the outline, as usual, and cover the dark areas with ink, leaving the highlight portions white. Mark the structural characteristics, such as longitudinal puncture lines as seen on the Necrobia in *Fig. 444*, and ink them in. Using white cover ink, do the same on the black areas. Place the shading, black on white and white on black, and the illustration is completed.

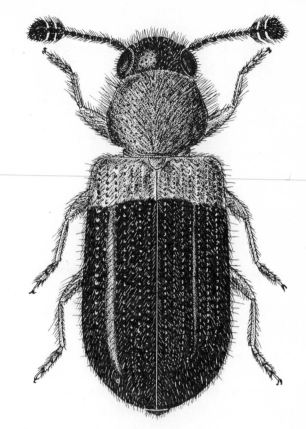

Fig. 444.

For insects with shiny surfaces, as the one in *Fig. 445*, the pebble board is preferred. The steps are the same: ink the outline, cover dark areas with brush and ink, add intermediate shades with wax pencil (*Fig. 446*). If the surface is grooved or punctured, work out the details with pen and shade the intermediate area (*Fig. 447*). Draw the antennae in detail and add shading with ink then place hairs (*Fig. 448*). If the highlights are correctly placed, your beetle will appear shiny. Compare *Figs. 445* and *452*.

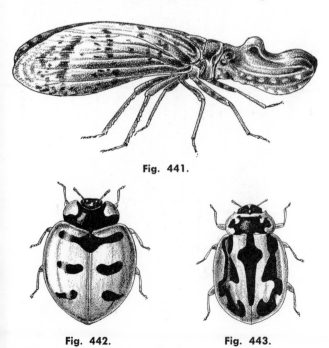

Fig. 441.

Fig. 442. **Fig. 443.**

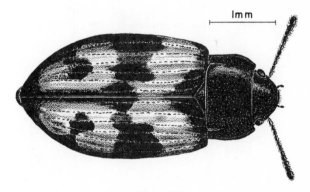

1mm

Fig. 445.

Fig. 446.

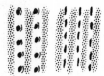

Fig. 447.

Fig. 448.

Sometimes markings are not sharp and distinct, as in *Fig. 441*. When this is true, wax pencil may be used for markings. At other times markings are sharp and contrasting, as seen in *Figs. 384* and *385* in the two-colored butterflies (Papilios).

Figure 449: Observe the hind wing; the outlines are present, darker areas are marked. On the fore wing dark areas are blackened with India ink and brush; veins are left white in the black area.

Figure 450: A few strokes with wax pencil are added to ink lines. Note the slightly darker shaded areas on one side of the veins.

Figure 451: Tone is added to the entire wing using prefabricated tones of irregular dots (the same as in *Figs. 1127-1131*), according to the requirement. If you do not want to use these tones, spray artwork after penciled shading. Do not spray if you do use tones. These samples were done on rough coquille board and reproduced in original size.

Fig. 450.

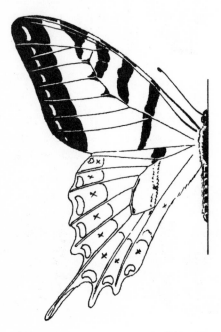

Fig. 449.

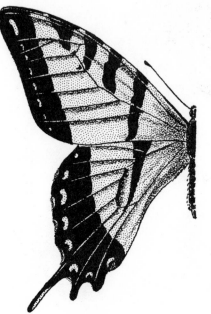

Fig. 451.

The very rough presurfaced paper, as the roughest coquille board, is useful in drawing such creatures as the Curculionidae seen in *Fig. 452.* The pencil-ink combination technique is used advantageously on that type of paper. Concern need not be exercised in drawing the surface structure of the elytra. The original should not be reduced extensively, as too much reduction will decrease the roughness of the lines, thus detracting from the effectiveness. *Fig. 452* is slightly reduced; it may be acceptable reduced to 75 per cent of the original size. This technique may be used for a true background drawing; however, authors seldom use them, preferring taxonomically important body parts, as seen in *Fig. 453,* the head and pro-thorax, or in *Fig. 454,* the tibia of the hind leg. With three such drawings, it is possible to introduce and describe new species.

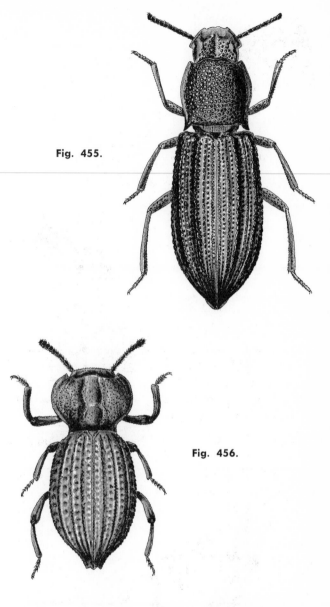

Fig. 455.

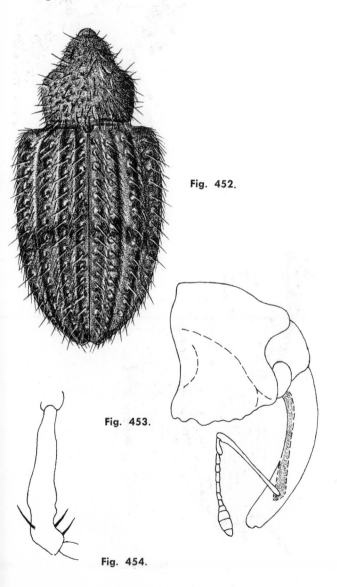

Fig. 452.

Fig. 453.

Fig. 454.

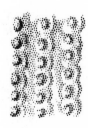

Fig. 456.

Contrary to the present trend, whole drawings can be of great value to a scientific paper. Such would give clarity and value to a manuscript. Observe the samples shown in *Figs. 455* and *456;* analyze the details present in *Figs. 457* and *458.*

Fig. 457.

Fig. 458.

There are many different techniques suitable for drawing larvae. There is the simple outline drawing, as seen in *Fig. 459;* and the more detailed habitat drawing in *Fig. 462.* Both are suitable but serve different purposes.

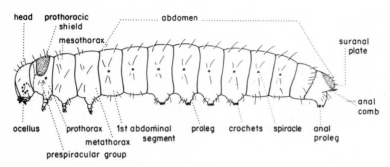

head · prothoracic shield · mesothorax · abdomen · suranal plate · anal comb

ocellus · prothorax · metathorax · prespiracular group · 1st abdominal segment · proleg · crochets · spiracle · anal proleg

Fig. 459.

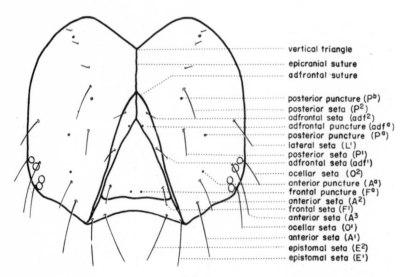

— vertical triangle
— epicranial suture
— adfrontal suture
— posterior puncture (P^b)
— posterior seta (P^2)
— adfrontal seta (adf^2)
— adfrontal puncture (adf^a)
— posterior puncture (P^a)
— lateral seta (L^1)
— posterior seta (P^1)
— adfrontal seta (adf^1)
— ocellar seta (O^2)
— anterior puncture (A^a)
— frontal puncture (F^a)
— anterior seta (A^2)
— frontal seta (F^1)
— anterior seta (A^3)
— ocellar seta (O^1)
— anterior seta (A^1)
— epistomal seta (E^2)
— epistomal seta (E^1)

Fig. 460.

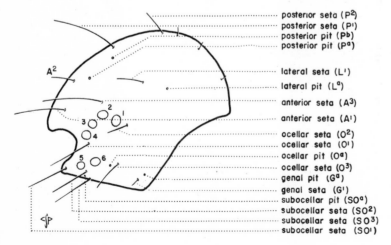

A^2

— posterior seta (P^2)
— posterior seta (P^1)
— posterior pit (P^b)
— posterior pit (P^a)
— lateral seta (L^1)
— lateral pit (L^a)
— anterior seta (A^3)
— anterior seta (A^1)
— ocellar seta (O^2)
— ocellar seta (O^1)
— ocellar pit (O^a)
— ocellar seta (O^3)
— genal pit (G^a)
— genal seta (G^1)
— subocellar pit (SO^a)
— subocellar seta (SO^2)
— subocellar seta (SO^3)
— subocellar seta (SO^1)

Fig. 461.

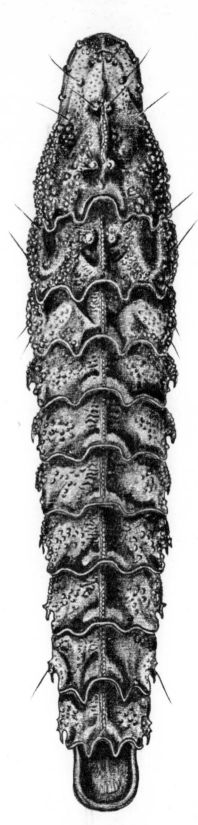

Fig. 462.

In describing a larva the author is required to define more body parts than in describing an adult insect; the most common of these are seen in *Fig. 459*, and additional parts of the head may be seen in *Figs. 460* and *461*. It is well if the artist is familiar with these definations, particularly if he cannot work cooperatively in contact with the author. Illustrating the head only, as in *Figs. 463-469*, presents the problem of frontal or lateral view and also the problem of arranging the specimen under the microscope at the precise angle and in the exact position required by the scientist. It is recommended that the artist draw a sketch first, place the eyes, ocelli, setae, etc., and have the scientist review it carefully before attempting the final artwork.

Illustrations of larvae, to be used strictly for identification purposes, for insertion in a key, or to be kept in groups, may be drawn in ink using the scratch board method. Line drawings reproduce neatly (*Figs. 463* and *466*). It is better if you do not add shading in such drawings, but if it is necessary to represent color differences or patterns of taxonomic importance, light stippling may be added, in addition to light and dark shadings (*Figs. 464* and *467*). You will rarely find a larva with more distinct colors; it will consist of intermediate tones. The lighter colors will be achieved by regulated densities of individual dots (*Figs. 465, 468, 469*). Pay attention to the exact location of the setae, their length in relation to the rest of the head, and the precise angle and curvature. If some

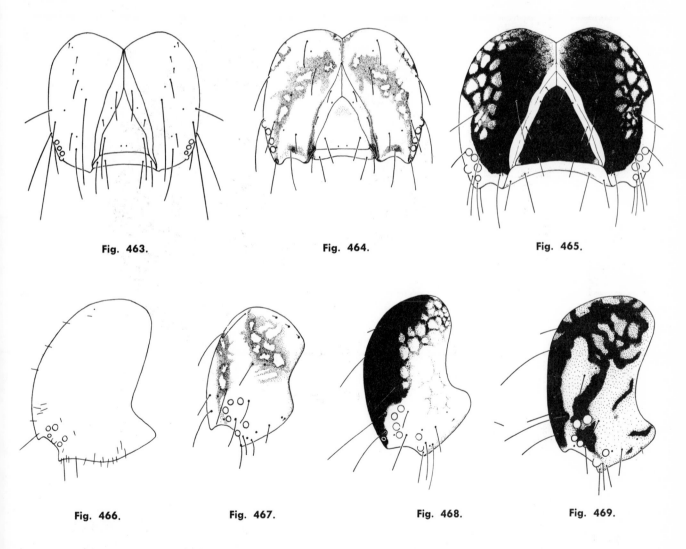

Fig. 463.   Fig. 464.   Fig. 465.

Fig. 466.   Fig. 467.   Fig. 468.   Fig. 469.

of the setae are broken off, check with the author or seek reference literature before risking an unscientific drawing.

Another important body part is the jaw. You may have to mount this with an insect pin on a hard paper point and place it under the microscope. Here again, proper angle is stressed. A preliminary sketch to be checked by the scientist is the safest procedure to follow to insure accuracy. Stippling is used to achieve the 3-D effect, as seen in *Figs. 470-476*. Use extreme care in drawing the mandibles correctly, their curvature and color (*Figs. 472, 475*); the variation in shading at the points (*Figs. 473, 476*), or making them with outline and tone (*Fig. 477*). If tubercles and spinules are present, try to illustrate them in 3-D fashion (*Fig. 478*); or if a single segment is required (*Fig. 479*), present it in detail. In addition to spines, setae and occasionally a pattern, crotchets are present and may have to be illustrated. The shape, length and curvature of these tiny hooks are of importance and must be represented in a 3-D manner (*Figs. 480-481*).

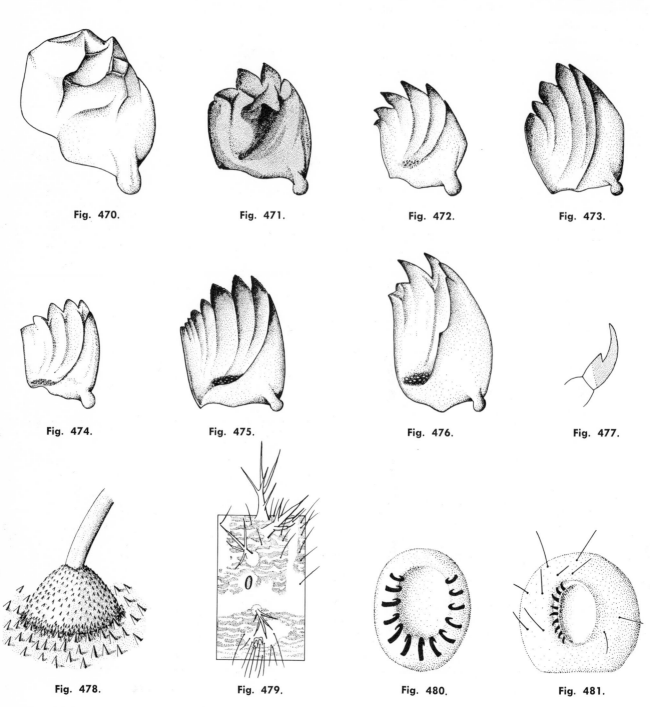

Fig. 470. Fig. 471. Fig. 472. Fig. 473.

Fig. 474. Fig. 475. Fig. 476. Fig. 477.

Fig. 478. Fig. 479. Fig. 480. Fig. 481.

Frequently an artist must illustrate the texture of larval skin. In this event keep the specimen in the fluid in which it is preserved, using a small dish for it while you are drawing. If you must leave the drawing board, cover the specimen to prevent the fluid from evaporating and possibly distorting your model. Stippling is the best method for drawing textures. *Figs. 482-488* are examples employing the same technique. *Fig. 484* is the original size; *Fig. 485* is reproduced in 75 per cent reduction; *Fig. 486* is reduced to 50 per cent of the original. If you will observe the reproductions, you will readily see the effect that reduction has on the original and how roughness is minimized.

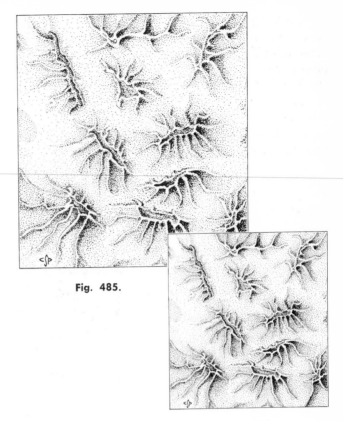

Fig. 485.

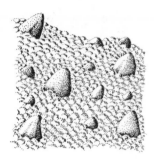

Fig. 482.

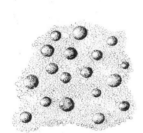

Fig. 483.

Fig. 486.

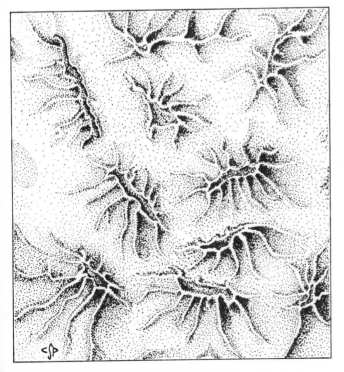

Fig. 484.

Fig. 487.

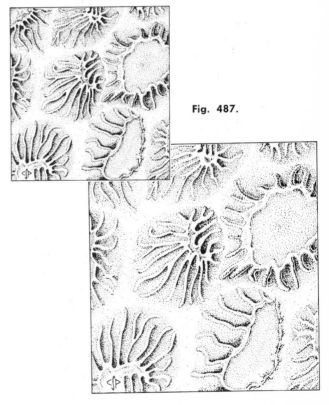

Fig. 488.

A wax pencil-India ink combination may be used effectively on presurfaced paper, preferably when minute details do not appear or if the artwork is to be used in a non-technical publication. *Fig. 489* is drawn on pebble board; outlined, shaded with India ink, and highlighted with wax pencil and white cover ink.

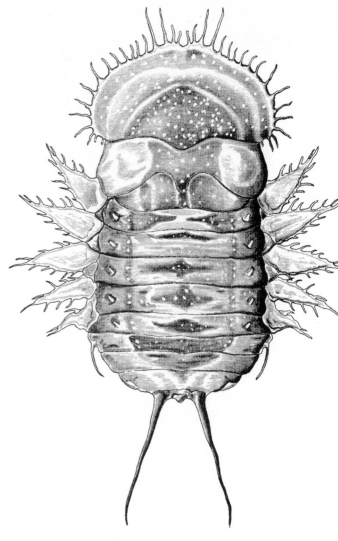

Fig. 490.

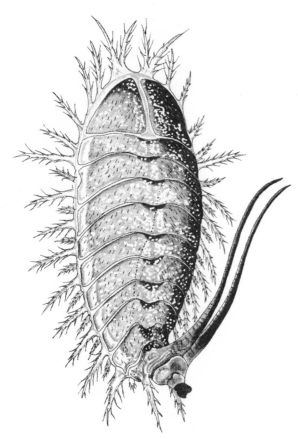

Fig. 489.

When drawing larvae and pupae of the same species in the same publication, use the same drawing materials. *Figs. 489* and *490* represent larvae and pupae, while *Figs. 491-494* stress individual areas of *Fig. 490*. This technique is acceptable for general purposes and clearly shows the structure and accurate dimensions (*Fig. 495*), omitting fine details. Although the drawings are attractive, they would not be considered real scientific illustrations.

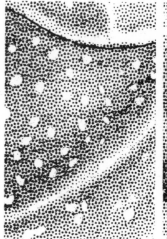

Fig. 491.   Fig. 492.

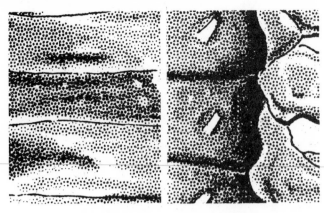

Fig. 493.   Fig. 494.

Fig. 495.

Fig. 497.

Illustrations of larvae can be effectively drawn by the smudging method. *Fig. 462* is an example of a uni-colorous (jet-black) larva, done with this technique. Many larvae, however, have at least two distinct colors. With smudging it is possible to represent colors and also to achieve a 3-D effect (*Figs. 496, 497*). Certain parts of those drawings are enlarged in *Figs. 498-501*, demonstrating details. Outlines were pen-ciled, graphite powder applied with a stump in vari-

ous degrees of darkness, hairs were drawn and accented with white cover ink applied to one side. Finished drawing was sprayed. This technique is re-producible in half-tone only.

Fig. 496.

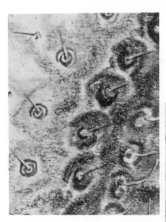

Fig. 498.

Fig. 499.

Fig. 500.

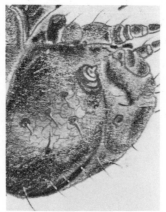

Fig. 501.

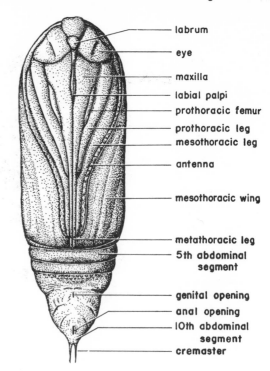

labrum
eye
maxilla
labial palpi
prothoracic femur
prothoracic leg
mesothoracic leg
antenna
mesothoracic wing
metathoracic leg
5th abdominal segment
genital opening
anal opening
10th abdominal segment
cremaster

Fig. 503.

The smudge method is suitable for drawings of pupae (*Fig. 502*), when there are a minimum of details. Illustrating pupae in more detail is accomplished by the line and stippling technique (*Fig. 503*). Segments of taxonomic importance may be individually drawn (*Figs. 504, 505*). This technique is effective for ventral (*Fig. 503*) or dorsal (*Fig. 506*) view and results in a truly scientific illustration.

7
8
9
10

Fig. 504.

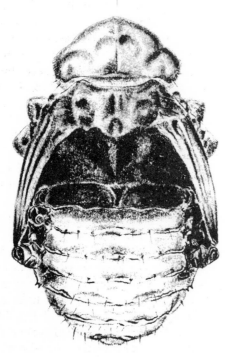

Fig. 502.

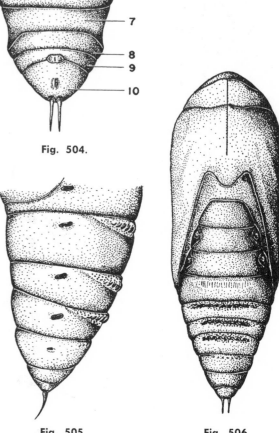

Fig. 505.   Fig. 506.

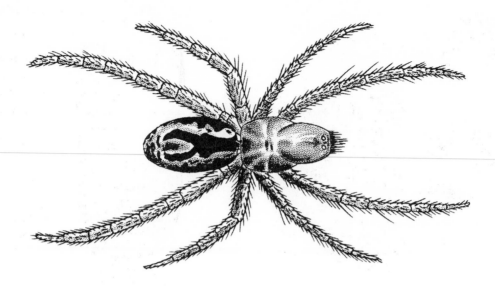

Fig. 507.

Fig. 508.

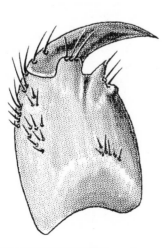

Fig. 509.

Spiders are seemingly difficult to illustrate until you have acquired some practical experience in drawing them. Of all the techniques discussed there is one that is especially applicable for drawing spiders: the ink and pencil combination on presurfaced illustration board, such as coquille board or pebble board. The 3-D effect is of great significance, as are the taxonomic characteristics and the hairy composition of the body. *Fig. 507* illustrates this technique; the outline is drawn, markings are outlined and shaded, hairs are added. The same materials and technique are used for individual body parts, as seen in *Fig. 508* of the palpus; the chelicera in *Fig. 509;* and the anal view of the abdomen in *Fig. 510.* These parts are only partially visible when the creature is in its habitat; taxonomic characteristics and body parts are distorted or completely hidden by component parts or by hairs. Shading and highlights were added with wax pencil, India ink and white cover color; solid light markings as seen in the upper center portion of *Fig. 510* were done with Snopake (a white correction fluid). At the completion of the artwork it was sprayed with Krylon spray.

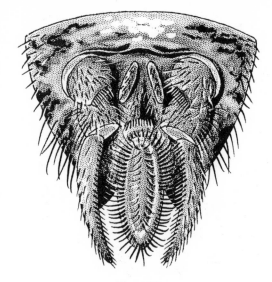

Fig. 510.

The spider illustrations presented here are reproduced in their original size to demonstrate the technique in detail. You may wish to view *Fig. 510* with a reducing glass. This will give you an idea of how it would reproduce in reduction. The originals do not have to be large. If reduced to 75 per cent of the original size you will have a very impressive illustration.

Fig. 513.

Fig. 511.

Fig. 512.

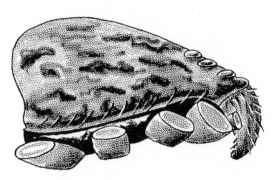

Fig. 514.

Figures 511 and *512* are simple line drawings without any shading. In instances where clarity is necessary in order to show shape, proportion and precise detail, do not burden your artwork with unnecessary detractions.

There may be instances when an artist will mix two illustrating techniques to represent taxonomic differences of species, genera, etc. *Figs. 513* and *514* show you how two examples of cephalothorax drawings of genus *A* and *B* may be drawn with the same technique and still represent differences. You are urged to keep your artwork uniform and not to use different techniques within the same drawing.

g. Illustrating Nematodes

Drawing nematodes (microscopic, colorless worm-like creatures) requires a trained eye and special equipment. A good compound microscope, sufficient light source with various filters, and most important, a good camera lucida are necessary items. Nematodes cannot be stained and consequently, many of the internal body parts are extremely obscure.

Figure 515 is a 3-D illustration of the cellular structure of a plant showing the shapes of nematode species in various stages of development feeding on plant cells. In this particular illustration the nematodes are superficially represented, while the plant structure is precisely detailed. Similar examples may be seen in *Figs. 558* and *559*.

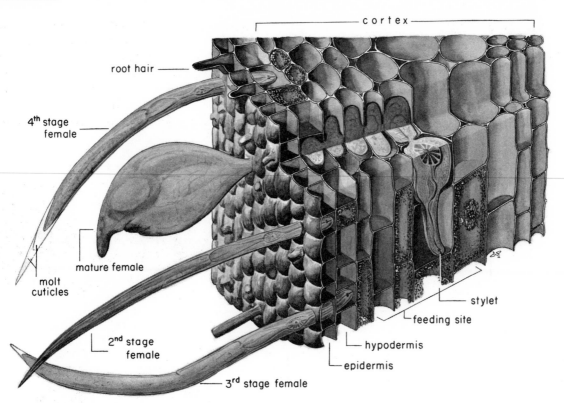

Fig. 515.

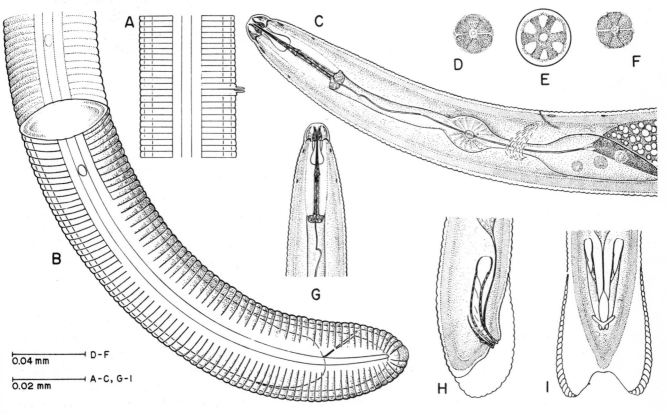

Fig. 516.

To record complete taxonomic features, perhaps the best technique to use for nematodes is line drawing, designing one plate for each species and emphasizing notable characteristics by drawing individual body parts. *Fig. 516* illustrates the face views, the anterior portions of the male and female, the male genitalia and the characteristic annulation of the species.

Whichever drawing technique you select, first make a complete pencil sketch through a camera lucida and have the scientist check it carefully before transferring it to the final drawing paper. If possible, examine many specimens of the same species before you attempt your drawing. In this way you will acquaint yourself with the peculiarities of the species and have a good mental picture of its composition.

Illustrating nematodes requires time and patience. The old practice is to use a broken-line outline, the only solid lines being the cuticle with its annulation (*Fig. 517*). These are acceptable if they are accurate in detail and proportion.

For a more artistic drawing solid lines may be used (*Fig. 518*). As you see, there is no 3-D effect in either of the examples used in *Figs. 517* and *518*.

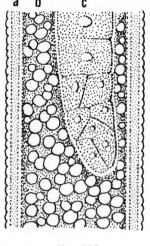

Fig. 519.

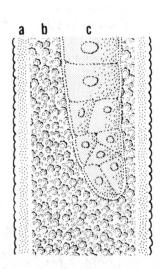

Fig. 520.

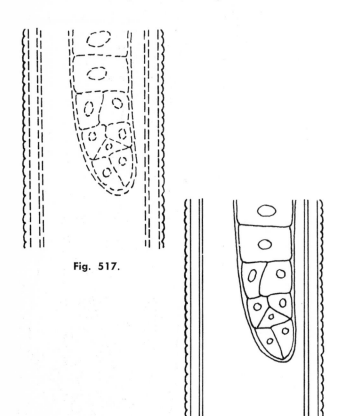

Fig. 517.

Fig. 518.

Figure 519 employs stippling and thus creates a more professional and detailed effect. Longitudinal body muscles (*a*) are represented by fine dots; the intestine (*b*) is composed of irregular circles (indicating food particles) and small dots; internal parts within the intestine (*c*) are outlined and shaded with stippling. If the artist has a large number of drawings of nematodes to prepare and time is of the essence, it is permissible to use prefabricated tone, as in *Figs. 1127, 1128*.

Figure 520 shows the annulation drawn with solid lines; longitudinal muscles (*a*) and the intestine (*b*) are of prefabricated tones (*Figs. 1127* and *1151*), and the internal parts within the intestine (*c*) are stippled. You will note the different effects achieved by comparing *Figs. 519* and *520*.

The four examples presented above may be mixed in the following way: *Figs. 517* and *518* or *Figs. 519* and *520;* never mix the techniques of *Figs. 517-518* with those of *519-520*. Use the same technique consistently throughout a drawing.

For best results in line drawings a heavy-duty, Ross-type of scratch board is recommended; changes and corrections are easily made on this material. The following procedure has proven satisfactory: transfer the original sketch made through a camera lucida to tracing paper, using a No. 3 or No. 5 pencil (*Fig. 521*). On the reverse side of the tracing paper shade the outline with a soft pencil. Turn the tracing paper over and place it on your Ross board, and with a No. 3 pencil trace the lines. The next step is to ink first the annulations. Heavy outline (*Figs. 522-523*) or light, thin outline (*Figs. 524-527*) is a matter of preference. Details were worked out on and around the spear and also the longitudinal body muscles. The medium bulb and nerve rings are represented in a way to give a 3-D effect. The longitudinal muscles and the spear-muscles employ two types of tone.

If you are doing plate drawings comprised of several detailed illustrations, follow the same technique throughout, including the density of the outline (*Figs. 522* and *533*).

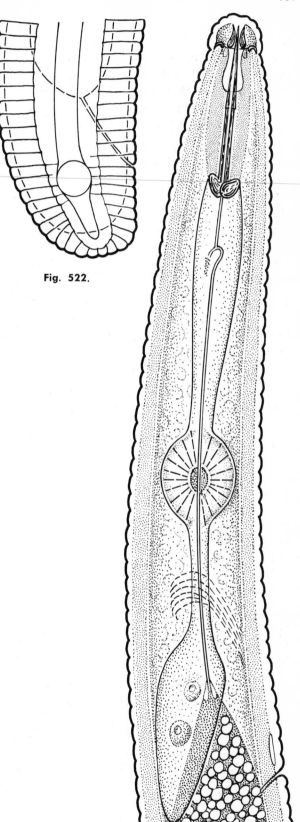

Fig. 522.

Fig. 521.

Fig. 523.

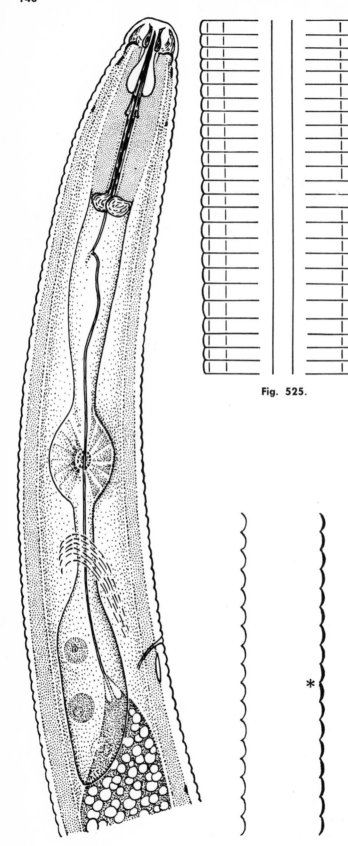

Fig. 524.

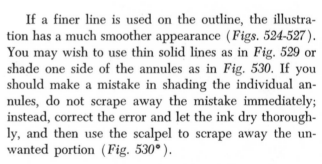

Fig. 525.

Fig. 526.

Fig. 527.

Fig. 528.

Fig. 529.

*

Fig. 530.

If a finer line is used on the outline, the illustration has a much smoother appearance (*Figs. 524-527*). You may wish to use thin solid lines as in *Fig. 529* or shade one side of the annules as in *Fig. 530*. If you should make a mistake in shading the individual annules, do not scrape away the mistake immediately; instead, correct the error and let the ink dry thoroughly, and then use the scalpel to scrape away the unwanted portion (*Fig. 530**).

The face view of a nematode is of taxonomic importance and may be represented in two sections; the upper portion (*Fig. 527*) and the lower portion (*Fig. 528*). Solid lines are not used within the structures seen in the above figures. Dots are used for shading to achieve the 3-D effect, as well as to signify the various component parts. It is difficult to correct drawings of this type. If the dots or density of shading are not exact, the final reproduction will appear unsightly. It is better to redraw the illustration than to have a flaw in your work. If you cannot cut an individual drawing out of the plate and replace it with another, Snopake over the entire area and redraw the view containing the error.

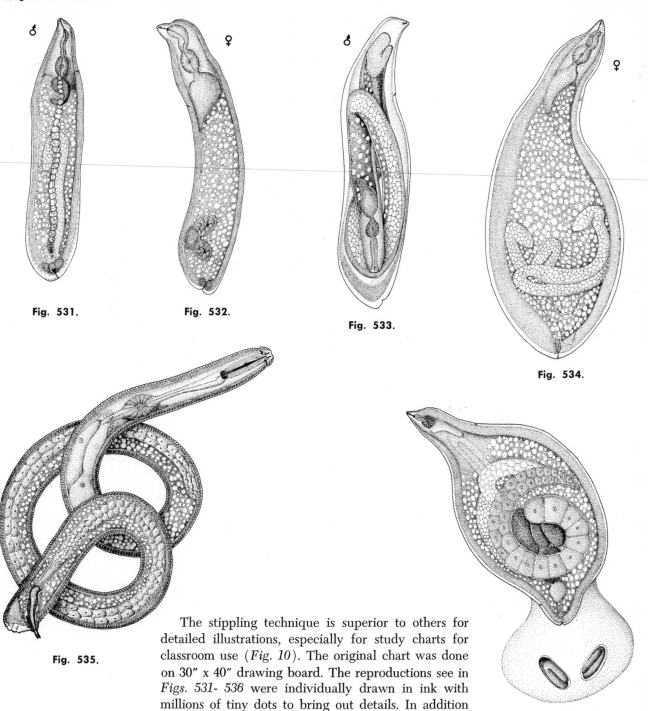

Fig. 531. Fig. 532. Fig. 533. Fig. 534. Fig. 535. Fig. 536.

The stippling technique is superior to others for detailed illustrations, especially for study charts for classroom use (*Fig. 10*). The original chart was done on 30″ x 40″ drawing board. The reproductions see in *Figs. 531- 536* were individually drawn in ink with millions of tiny dots to bring out details. In addition to the chart-size for classroom demonstrations, these originals were reduced to 8 1/2″ x 11″ for students' notebooks. You will note that the detailed sharpness is not lost in reproduction. The annules in *Fig. 535* are shaded with dots; observe the details with a magnifying glass. The entire chart with the exception of the sugar-beet, which is painted in full color, was drawn with the same crowquill pen on heavy-duty white illustration board.

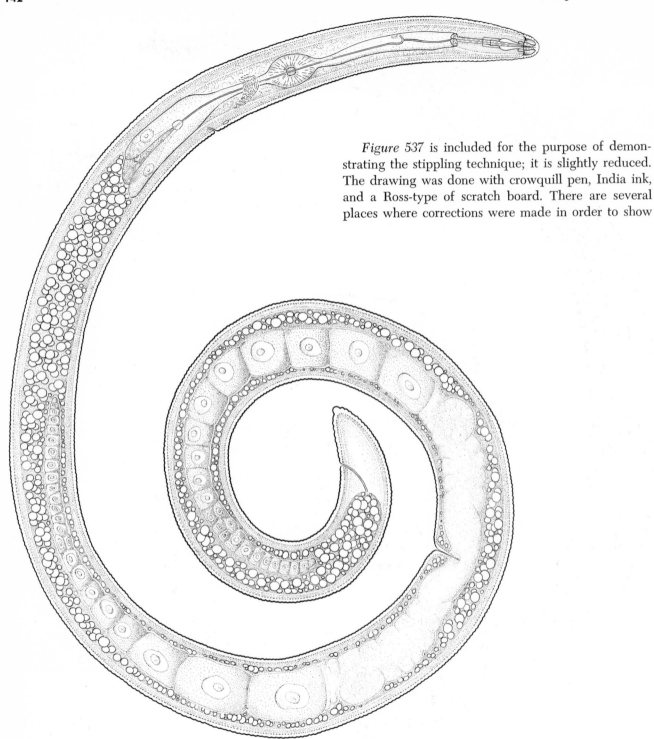

Figure 537 is included for the purpose of demonstrating the stippling technique; it is slightly reduced. The drawing was done with crowquill pen, India ink, and a Ross-type of scratch board. There are several places where corrections were made in order to show

Fig. 537.

the reader that necessary corrections may be made and will not show up in the finished product if they are done with extreme care and exactness. This technique is very time-consuming and painstaking, but truly scientific illustrations are the fruits of the artist's labor.

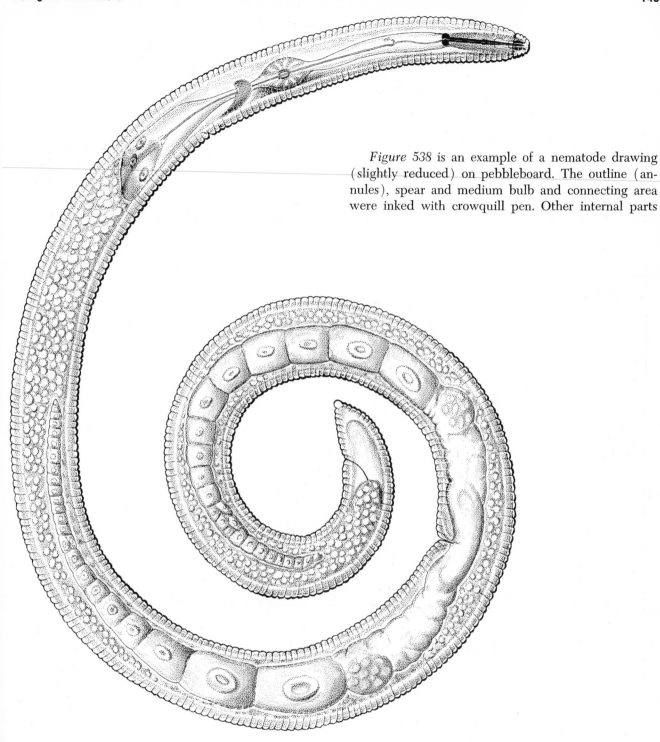

Figure 538 is an example of a nematode drawing (slightly reduced) on pebbleboard. The outline (annules), spear and medium bulb and connecting area were inked with crowquill pen. Other internal parts

Fig. 538.

were done with a wax pencil as was the shading. Note how the annules are shaded. This technique is satisfactory if minute details can be omitted and it is far less-time consuming than stippling.

Fig. 539.

Fig. 539 represents the smudging technique, which is another easy and fast way to illustrate nematodes. You may select your own personal smudging material. However, be consistent throughout a chart or related drawings. As far as possible, if you select pencil for outlines, remain with pencil. If, however, you wish to accentuate numerous details, you may outline the annulation with crowquill pen and India ink and outline the internal parts with pencil. *Fig.* 96 demonstrates this technique. The darker areas should be gently covered with soft pencil strokes (No. 1). Shading is accomplished with graphite powder and a stump. You may make your own graphite powder by rubbing the pencil on fine-grain sandpaper. Examples of suggested shading for various body parts are given in *Figs. 540-545*. If you wish to lighten certain small areas, use a sharp corner of an eraser, or the flat or rounded side for large areas, as shown in *Figs. 542* and *543*. When your drawing is completed, clean it thoroughly and spray it with Krylon clear protective spray.

Illustrations using this technique may be reproduced only by half-tone. These illustrations have a photographic appearance, particularly if reduced to half size or less. *Figs. 546* has been reduced 30 per cent of the original size. Background has been opaqued on the negative, making the surrounding area appear white (*Figs. 1298* and *1299*).

Fig. 546.

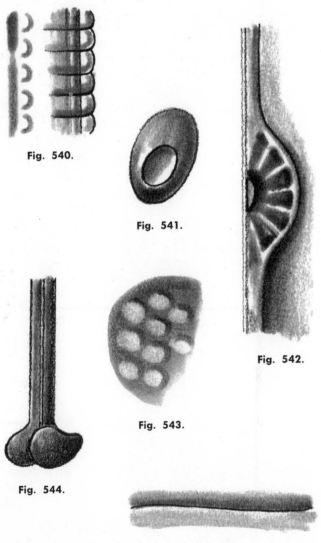

Fig. 540.

Fig. 541.

Fig. 542.

Fig. 543.

Fig. 544.

Fig. 545.

h. Illustrations for Histology and Parasitology

The scientist's knowledge and comprehension of nature's mysteries are heightened by the steady influx of precision instruments. With the help of the microscope we are able to search for minute organisms which are parasitic to animals and plants; the usefulness of optical instruments is unlimited. Many of the creatures too small to see with the naked eye may be photographed through a microscopic lens, but in most instances illustrations are preferred for scientific publications. There are various ways of fulfilling the requirements, and each technique, used artistically and expediently, surpasses all others under certain circumstances. For example, the line drawing (*Fig. 547*), the pencil drawing (*Fig. 567*), or the brush technique (*Fig. 558*) are completely satisfactory for specific purposes.

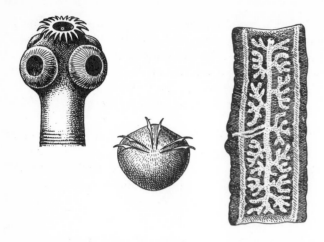

Fig. 547.

The scientist usually supplies the artist with specimens mounted on microslides, commonly called "slides." The artist is rarely involved in mounting specimens, but *Fig. 548* is a photograph of a technician (in this case, the author's wife) preparing slides. The procedure for preparation of specimens is shown in this photograph, and *Figs. 558* and *559* are illustrations drawn from these slides. After the specimen is treated, it is imbedded in parrafin and placed in the microtome for sectioning (*a*); this is followed by an evaporating process (*b*), then staining (*c*). Coverglass (*d*) is applied and the drying process begins. All slides must be labeled and stored in boxes (*e*) for future reference.

Fig. 548.

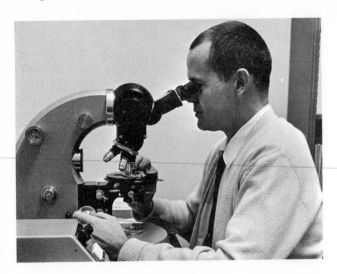

Fig. 549.

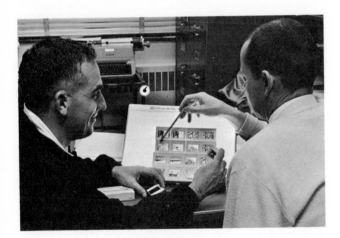

Fig. 550.

microslides, enabling him to view the object clearly and comfortably (*Fig. 551*). Another way to achieve this goal is with a bio-projector (*Fig. 575.*) The image may be projected directly on the drawing paper on the table, or, by moving the projection mirror (*e*) to a 90 degree angle of the setting as shown in *Fig. 575*, the image will be projected horizontally. It is strongly recommended that an artist drawing microscopic creatures have one or the other of these instruments in his studio — it will save a great deal of valuable time, as well as alleviate the fatigue and discomfort that are otherwise unavoidable.

After the slides are completed by the technician, the scientist critically examines them and selects those specimens from which illustrations will be made (*Fig. 549*). Often transparencies are made of a series of slides in order that two or more scientists may scrutinize the specimens simultaneously and determine which of the lot best manifests the true character of the species. (*Fig. 550*). At this point the illustrator may be brought into the discussion, and planning of the illustration commences. Transparencies will give the artist a general idea of the makeup of the specimen and sufficient preliminary information to proceed with the outline. For minute details he will have to revert to the microscope. To spare himself tedious eye strain and neck-tilting, it is imperative that the illustrator equip his microscope with a prism-set and adequate light source in order that he may project

Fig. 551.

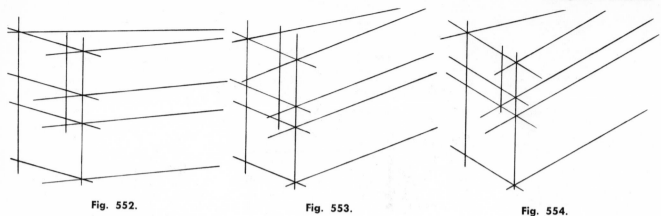

Fig. 552.   **Fig. 553.**   **Fig. 554.**

The procedures mentioned above constitute the sequence of events which precluded *Figs. 558* and *559*. In the examples used here it was important to achieve a 3-D effect by constructing an angular cutaway. This effect was discussed and demonstrated in detail earlier (*Fig. 46*). In order to determine the cor-

rect angle several sketches were made, as seen in *Figs. 552-554*. The following step was to place individual cells within the frame. Each had to be outlined to represent cell walls (*Figs. 555-557*), nuclei, etc. The parasite was then placed between the cells and details added to show that those cells have been damaged. The wash method was used; Pelican India ink diluted with water. Several degrees of color depth were prepared in advance and maintained until the drawing was completed.

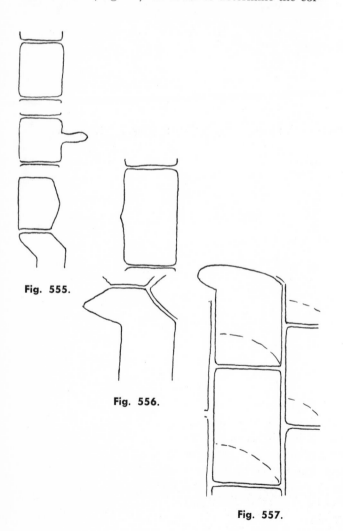

Fig. 555.

Fig. 556.

Fig. 557.

The original was drawn on heavy-duty illustration board. Pencil outlines were checked by the scientists and later inked with crowquill pen and India ink. Double lines were used to achieve sharp divisions between individual cells. The drawing was then cleaned of all pencil marks; brush work followed.

1. A light tone was applied to the entire illustration including the nematodes. If the drawing board is slightly tilted, excess fluid will run to the lower portion and can be removed with a squeezed-out brush, and this will prevent dark streaks occurring from an accumulation of fluid on the surface area of your drawing.

2. After the first application was completely dry, vertical surfaces were covered with a darker shade.

3. The third and darker tone was brushed on outer surfaces of the epidermis and allowed to dry thoroughly .

4. *Figure 560*: The external surface of the epidermis was applied first, leaving the cell wall lighter. Lighter tones were used in other portions (*Figs. 561-563*). Horizontal lines are represented with lighter tones; darker tones are used on vertical sides. After completion of the live cells, dark shading was applied to the dead cells to distinguish them from the others.

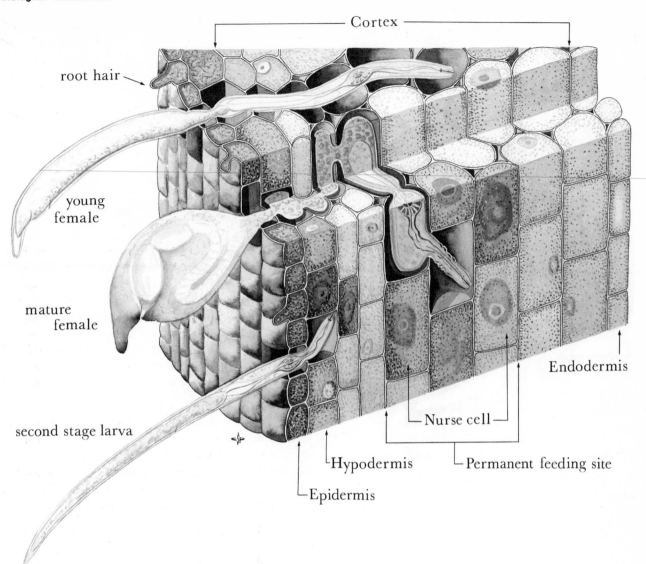

Fig. 558.

These may be black or very dark gray (*Fig. 558*). The
final step was to complete the parasites. Specific taxonomic details were not required in this instance. Correct body shapes and proportionate sizes were of
uppermost concern. An image was created of the most
vital internal parts which may be visible through the
cuticle. The illustration was labeled (*Fig. 558*) and
ready for release to the scientist.

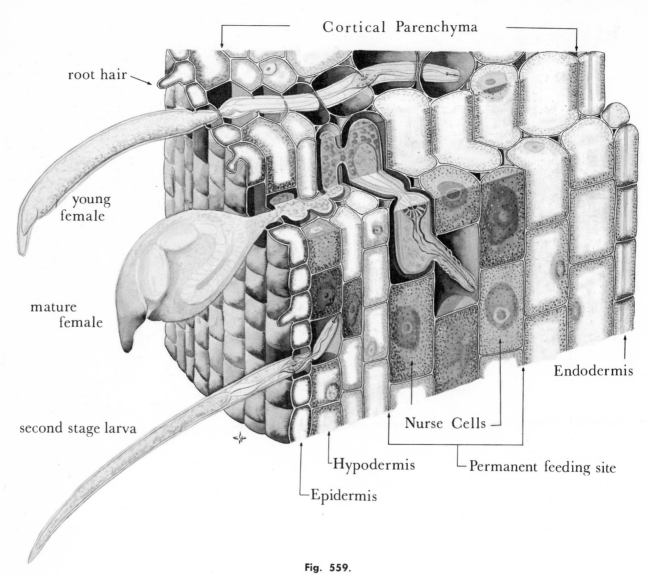

Fig. 559.

Cortical Parenchyma

root hair

young female

mature female

second stage larva

Endodermis

Nurse Cells

Hypodermis

Permanent feeding site

Epidermis

Figure 559 is included here to show how the same original (*Fig.* 558) may, by slight modification, achieve a distinguishable alteration. Some of the cells were lightened by using an electric eraser. By comparing *Figs.* 558 and 559 you will observe that removing some of the solid, flat vertical walls and opening the cells produces greater depth (*Fig.* 599).

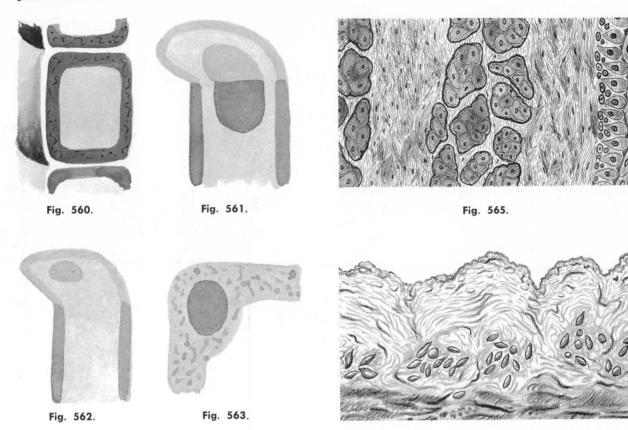

Fig. 560.   **Fig. 561.**

Fig. 562.   **Fig. 563.**

Fig. 565.

Fig. 566.

Histological illustrations may be effectively drawn by the pen and ink technique (*Fig. 564*). If your finished drawing, using this technique, appears too rough for satisfactory reproduction, you may apply a slight amount of shading with carbon or graphite powder to surfaces requiring slightly darker coloring. This type of drawing is reproduced in half-tone and will give a photographic appearance (*Fig. 565*).

Fig. 567.

A faster method for histological drawings is using presurfaced papers, either coquille boards of varying roughness or pebble boards with differing dotted patterns. The combination pencil-ink technique adapts well to these materials (*Fig. 566*) or pencil alone (*Fig. 567*) makes an attractive drawing. Both of these drawings were reproduced at 50 per cent of the original size. The use of these materials facilitates artwork and produces attractive results in a very limited time.

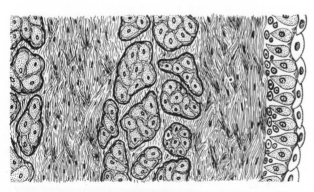

Fig. 564.

The most popular patterns of presurfaced paper are demonstrated in *Fig. 568* (*a* and *b* are pebble boards; *c* and *d* are coquille boards) in order to show the effects that may be achieved by shading. Each artist ultimately selects materials which appeal to his personal taste and which are most compatible with his ability and his choice of drawing technique. Illustrations drawn on presurfaced paper are reproducible as line cuts.

Fig. 569.

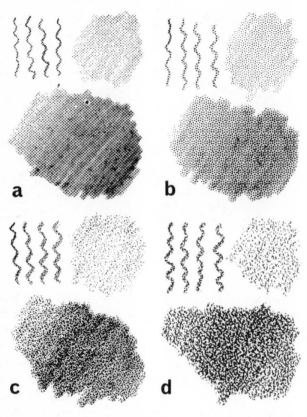

a   b

c   d

Fig. 568.

It has been mentioned previously that the addition of shading to an ink drawing imparts a photographic effect, and that this type of artwork will be reproduced in half-tone (*Fig. 565*). A similar effect will result by using pencil (No. 2) outline and shading with graphite powder from the same pencil (*Fig. 569*). Shading should be applied in accordance with the natural appearance of the specimen. If the cells are small, cover the entire area with shading. However, if they are not small, shade each individual cell separately. When intercellular spaces are present, after shading each cell individually, darken these spaces with a sharp-pointed pencil. The completed drawing should be sprayed with Krylon protective spray.

This technique is especially recommended to those who are unable to draw small, delicately detailed illustrations. It can be quite drastically reduced without becoming distorted or losing any of its definition. *Fig. 569* is reduced to 14 per cent of the original size (14″ x 24″). A decided advantage in drastic reduction is the visible transformation of a large, rough original to a delicate, smooth, attractive reproduction.

To illustrate this further *Fig. 570* shows a pair of similar objects; the one on the left is drawn with

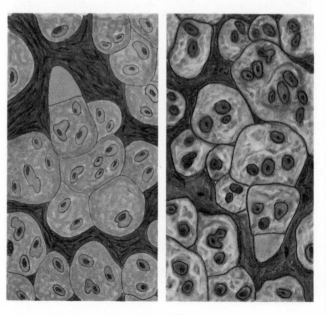

Fig. 570.

by hand   *by electric*

Fig. 571.

graphite pencil and powder on Strathmore drawing paper, the one on the right with carbon pencil (Wolffs) and powder on Beverly brilliant opaque pastel paper. The tone density is varied in both cases to denote texture and highlights. To reduce tones which are too dark, or to add pale spots (*Fig. 571*) an eraser was used. *Fig. 572* reproduced in its original size is presented for comparison purposes, showing how coarseness and unsightliness may be transformed

into a distinctive reduction of good quality. Working on details is far easier and much faster when the original is large.

Figure 573 illustrates two textures differing in composition. This figure in its original size was ten times larger than the reproduction, yet the details remain intact, and reduction, as mentioned above, has refined the appearance.

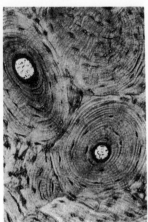

Fig. 573.

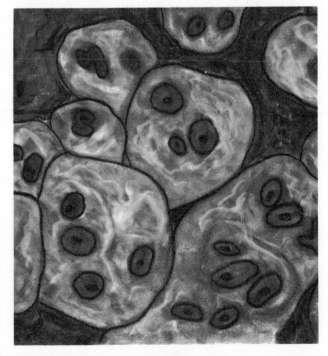

Fig. 572.

Figure 574 illustrates a tapeworm and introduces a reproduction technique not mentioned previously. You will note that the tapeworm is white and the background is black. This is the effect that the artist wants to achieve, since the coloring of the tapeworm is truly white. This particular drawing was done with carbon pencil and carbon powder shading in black and shades thereof on a white background. The original was four times the size of the reproduction seen in *Fig. 574*. A negative was made at a 25 per cent reduction from the original, after which a positive film was then made from the negative. It is the positive print that was used for insertion in this book. In this way the colors used in the original drawing were reversed; thus, the white tapeworm and the black background. You might like to try this technique yourself; try drawing a simple line drawing of a leaf, drawing the veins, etc., and follow the procedure discussed above.

The bio-projector was mentioned earlier in connection with microslides. This is a very useful and relatively inexpensive optical instrument which an artist will value highly. Another of the many uses of this equipment is to observe live protozoa, algae, etc.

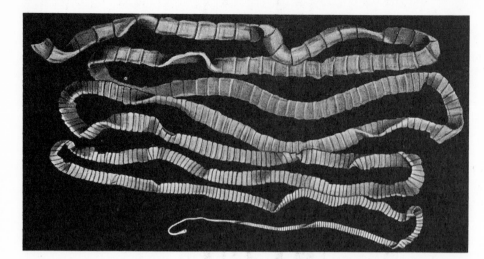

Fig. 574.

Fig. 575.

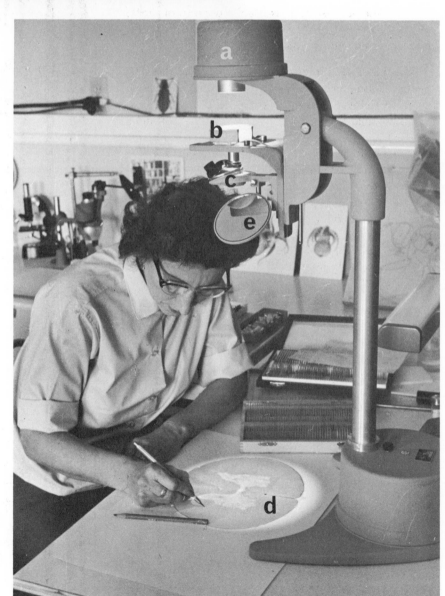

The light source (*Fig. 575, a*) radiates heat too intense for living organisms; therefore, it was found through trial and error that an empty slide glass glued to two narrow strips of woods (1 1/2″ high) and placed between the light source and the specimen (*b*) keep direct heat from the slide. The lenses are below the slide (*c*) and project the image onto the table. If the mirror (*e*) is turned to a 90 degree angle from its present position, the image may be projected on a screen. The fact that this instrument is invaluable to the scientific illustrator for drawing micro-organisms is worthy of repeated mention.

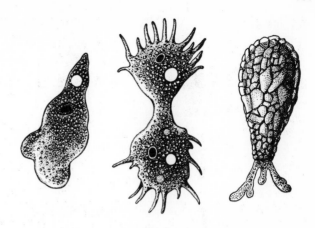

Fig. 576.

i. Illustrating Microorganisms

This type of illustrating is usually done from slides; seldom from live specimens. In addition to the bio-projector a compound microscope is essential.

The ink and pen technique is best for drawing microorganisms because there are obscure areas intermixed with well-defined morphological characters, and these may be recorded by using lines or dots. Solid ink lines were used for the outline and dots for the internal body parts and shading in *Figs. 576-583*. The specimen in *Fig. 577* had more detailed body parts; therefore, both the individual parts and the body were outlined and shading was done by stippling. As a rule, the artist will be advised to use either dots or lines within a drawing but not to use both. In *Fig. 577* it was necessary to differentiate between very distinct, well defined major portions of the specimen, and, therefore, contrary to this rule which is stressed time and again, line shading was used to accentuate this distinction. Materials used for these drawings were a crowquill pen, Pelican India ink and Strathmore three-ply drawing paper.

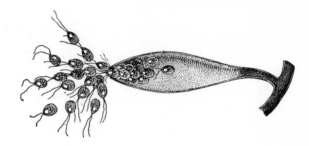

Fig. 577.

These same materials may be used advantageously in a number of different ways. For specimens containing cilia there will be less shading but more fine lines (*Fig. 583*). The primary requirements for a drawing such as this are a fine pen and a steady hand. If you are not able to draw longitudinal lines evenly, make your original large (as much as ten times larger than the required size of the reproduction) and use curv-rules or French curves when drawing the lines.

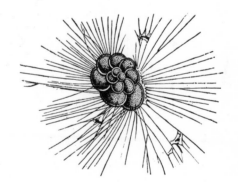

Fig. 578.

The scratch board technique is excellent for drawing microorganisms, as seen in *Fig. 578*. Shading in this instance was done with a round-tipped scalpel to give a definite division between the lobes. *Fig. 579* is a specimen of more simple construction with addi-

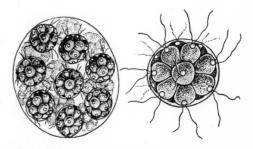

Fig. 579.

tional inner detail. The dots in this drawing were made by drawing very thin solid lines which were then broken by short, closely spaced strokes with a sharp pointed scalpel.

Another technique which lends itself effectively to drawing of microorganisms is the combination of ink and pencil on presurfaced paper. With this technique you will not get the fine sharp lines as shown in *Fig. 583*, but by drawing the original 50 per cent larger than the printed-size specifications, using a fine crowquill pen, the reproduction should be very satisfactory. *Fig. 580* is on pebble board, shaded with India ink; *Fig. 581* is on rough-surfaced coquille board; *Fig. 582* is on fine-screened pebble board — all are reduced to 57 per cent of the original size. For comparison of surfaces and the different effects achieved refer to *Fig. 568, a-d*. Species illustrated on *Fig. 578* may be done with the wash technique as demonstrated on *Fig. 584*, the body with brush, ciliae fine crowquill pen and India ink.

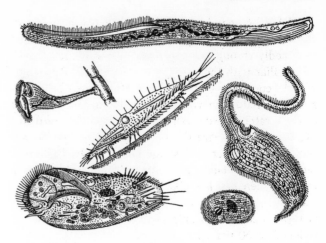

Fig. 583.

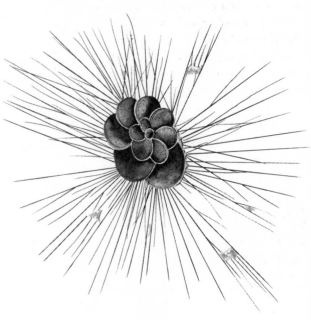

Fig. 584.

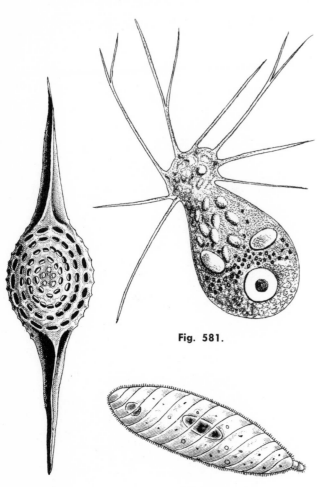

Fig. 581.

Fig. 580.   Fig. 582.

j. Illustrating Bones

This is a challenging and interesting assignment with no limitations insofar as techniques are concerned.

Figure 585 demonstrates the ink outline with stippling (darker areas more densely shaded); *Fig. 587* shows a dotted outline with very fine, dense shading. The former could be reduced to one-third and the latter to one-half of the original size if the same proportions are used as in these examples which are reproduced in their original size. *Fig. 588* presents them in 50 per cent reduction.

Fig. 586 employs the scratch board method, shaded with lines. This technique has been discussed repeatedly throughout the book, so the reader should be familiar with the various steps involved. By changing the curvature of the lines, surfaces may be represented as flat, concave or convex. In earlier discussion of the scratch board method, white drawing board and black India ink were the materials suggested. To get the opposite effect reverse the colors of the basic materials (using black drawing board and white cover ink), as seen in *Figs. 606* and *607*. The procedure is exactly the same as previously mentioned. *Fig. 586* is reproduced in its original size; *Fig. 588* shows it reduced to 50 per cent.

All artwork will begin with an outline. Therefore, when determining the size of the original and the degree to which it will be reduced for printing, it is vitally important that dimensions are accurate. Determine the angles on a specimen (*Figs. 589, 590*) and, if necessary, use a gird (*Fig. 591*) to insure proper size and proportion. Study the object from all

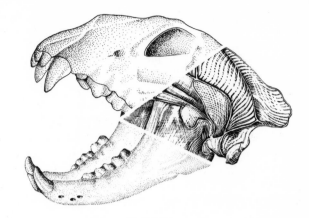

Fig. 588.

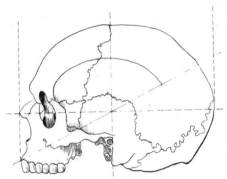

Fig. 589.

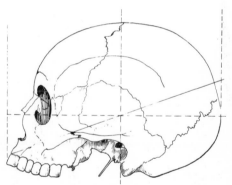

Fig. 590.

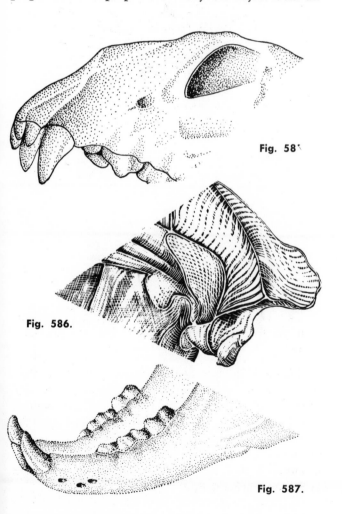

Fig. 58⁷

Fig. 586.

Fig. 587.

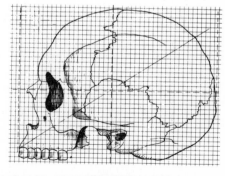

Fig. 591.

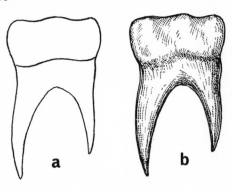 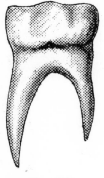 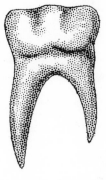 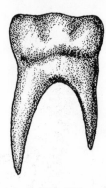

Fig. 592.   Fig. 593.   Fig. 594.   Fig. 595.

angles, determine the most appropriate angle from which the light source should come, and, most important, detect minor details. These are the factors upon which the quality, the authenticity, and the scientific value of your artwork are dependent.

Certain requirements will be met by simple outline drawing as in *Figs. 589, 590 and 592, a.* Others may need the addition of shading (*Fig. 592, b*).

If it is necessary to draw a number of illustrations of certain bones in a relatively short period of time,

the ink and pencil combination technique on pre-surfaced paper is recommended. *Fig. 593* illustrates a tooth drawn on fine-screen pebble board; *Fig. 594* is on a coarser pebble board; coquille boards are used in different textures — fine in *Fig. 595;* medium rough in *Fig. 596;* rough in *Fig. 597.* Those drawings have been reproduced in their original size to demonstrate the effects achieved by using the various presurfaced drawing boards. For further comparison of techniques and materials, *Fig. 598* illustrates the smudging technique and *Fig. 599,* the wash method.

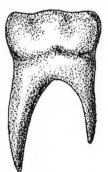

Fig. 596.

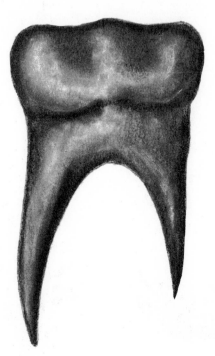 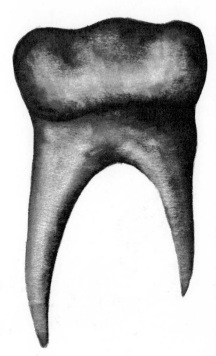

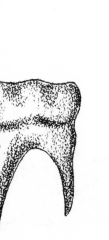

Fig. 597.   Fig. 598.   Fig. 599.

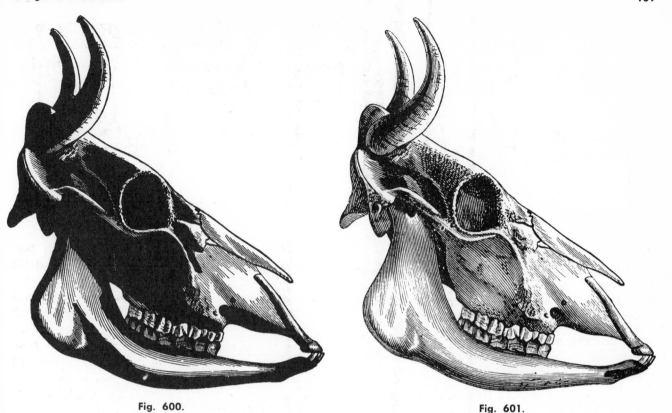

Fig. 600.   Fig. 601.

A cow's skull is selected to demonstrate the scratch board technique in *Figs. 600* and *601*. After the outline has been drawn and the inner surface covered with ink, surface characteristics, contour lines and shading are worked out, using a scalpel. Continuous shading throughout the entire skull is worked out (*Fig. 601*), and the same technique is applied to the lower jaw section drawing in *Fig. 602*. These four drawings were reproduced in their original size. If you examine *Figs. 601* and *603* with a reducing lens, you will see that drawings of this size and made with this technique may very effectively be reduced as much as 25 per cent of the original size.

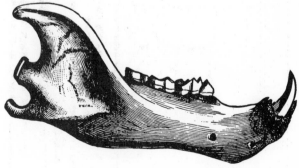

Fig. 602.   Fig. 603.

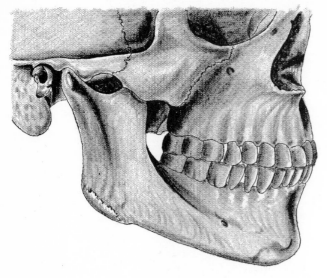

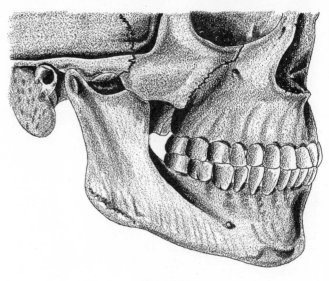

Fig. 604.

Fig. 605.

In all types of drawing neatness and uniformity are stressed. If you are unable to draw lines smoothly and evenly free-hand, use French curves as demonstrated in *Figs. 606* and *607*.

A much faster and easier way of drawing skulls than the scratch board technique is the combination ink and pencil method on presurfaced paper. Ink the outline as well as the sutures and the teeth. The remainder will be done with wax pencil. *Fig. 604* is done on rough pebble board, *Fig. 605* on rough coquille board. Both are reduced 50 per cent of the original size. Note the shading effects and how by changing the pressure on the wax pencil the 3-D effect is accomplished; particularly, observe the area of the zygomaticum in *Fig. 604*.

Figures 608 and *609* (illustrating the thigh bone) are also done on presurfaced drawing boards — the fine-screen surface (*Fig. 609*) has a very sensitive surface and requires regulated pressure of the wax pencil. A rougher surface (*Fig. 608*) does not require the controlled pressure to such a degree and is less sensitive to the touch.

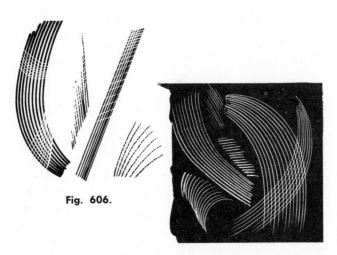

Fig. 606.

Fig. 607.

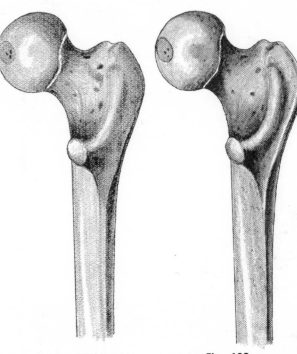

Fig. 608.   Fig. 609.

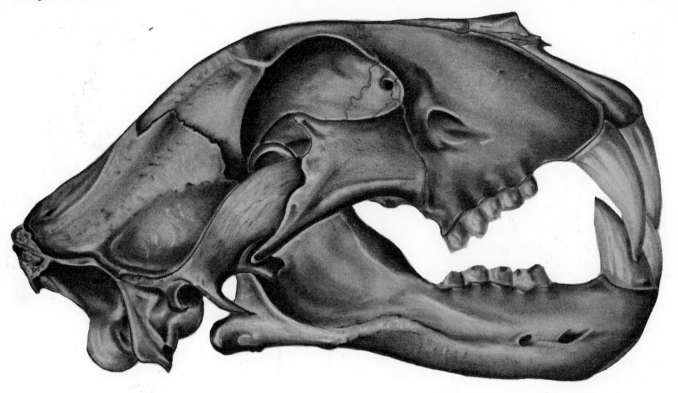

Fig. 610.

The smudging method is very good for drawing of bones; it is less time-consuming than the wash method and still produces an attractive, photograph-like illustration. This is the technique used in *Figs. 610* and *611* (details describing this method and examples may be found in *Figs. 90-96*). Originals may be four times larger than the required size of the prints. Fig. *610* is a 50 per cent reduction; *Fig. 611* is reduced 25 per cent of the size of the original. The backgrounds on both reproductions were blocked out on the negative (see *Figs. 1298* and *1299*). Illustrations made with this technique are reproducible in half-tone.

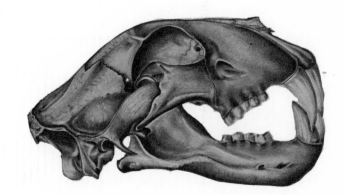

Fig. 611.

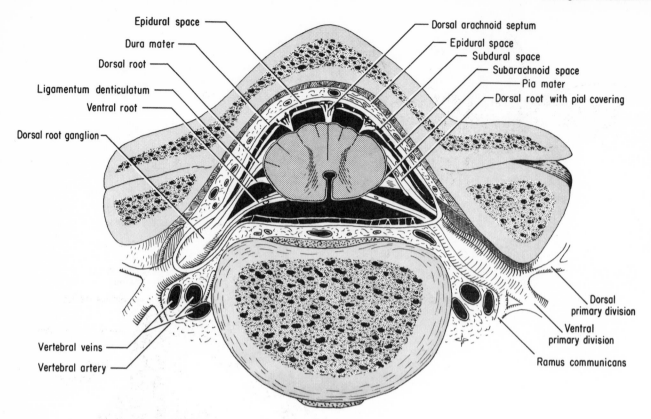

Epidural space
Dura mater
Dorsal root
Ligamentum denticulatum
Ventral root
Dorsal root ganglion

Dorsal arachnoid septum
Epidural space
Subdural space
Subarachnoid space
Pia mater
Dorsal root with pial covering

Dorsal primary division
Ventral primary division
Ramus communicans

Vertebral veins
Vertebral artery

Fig. 612.

Bone drawings for classroom use or to be published in an anatomy textbook require the most accurate, precise and detailed presentation. *Fig. 612* illustrates the minute details and labeling required for such assignments. Strathmore three-ply drawing paper was used, details were carried out in ink, and two types of artificial tones (No. 11 as shown in *Fig. 1094*) on the upper area, (*No. 2* as seen in *Fig. 1090*) on the lower area were used. Details may be worked out in various ways (*Fig. 613*).

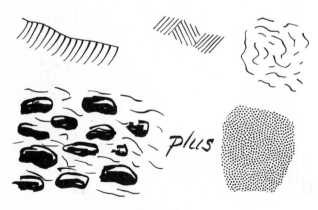

plus

Fig. 613.

We cannot omit the mention of muscles, since they, too, are vitally important. While there are a great number of books on the subject of human anatomy and suggestions for illustrating them, it is worth suggesting that an easy and fast method for drawing muscular structure is the pencil and ink combination method on presurfaced paper. *Fig. 614* was done on the fine-screen pebble board; the body outline was inked and the individual muscles done partially with ink. The shading and directional flow of the individual muscles were done with wax pencil. The underarm areas and the background of the neck muscles were heavily shaded to give a 3-D effect. The skull was only slightly shaded.

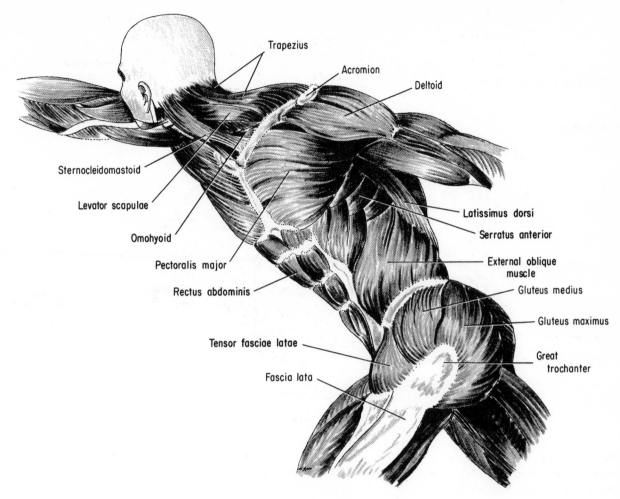

Trapezius

Acromion

Deltoid

Sternocleidomastoid

Levator scapulae

Omohyoid

Pectoralis major

Rectus abdominis

Tensor fasciae latae

Fascia lata

Latissimus dorsi

Serratus anterior

External oblique muscle

Gluteus medius

Gluteus maximus

Great trochanter

Fig. 614.

Overlay illustrations of muscles are effectively and attractively done in full color, using the colors to differentiate between certain muscles, groups of muscles, origin of muscles, or their insertion. An example, done by this author, of acetate overlay sheets on the basic illustration may be found in G. B. Pearson's book "Anatomy and Kinesiology." The easiest way to do overlays is to use an air-brush, setting the density of spray at the required degree (*Figs. 615-617*) and spraying over a cut-out of stencil. Each acetate sheet will be designed to represent a particular detail, and each will be printed in a different color. When these acetate sheets overlay the basic drawing which is in black and white, the spectator immediately identifies the individual details by their representative color.

The printer uses the overlay to make his negative and will make prints in the desired color. This type of illustration is excellent for demonstration purposes and is less expensive than full-color prints.

Fig. 615.   **Fig. 616.**   **Fig. 617.**

B. BOTANICAL ILLUSTRATIONS

If your profession or hobby is botany, you are aware of the fact that the majority of scientific books on this subject are conspicuously lacking in illustrations. This is partially due to insufficient funds to enable the author to employ a scientific illustrator to fulfill his needs. An additional problem confronting the botanist is the very meager number of well trained botanical illustrators qualified to specialize in this field. To produce highest quality illustrations field sketches are a necessity (*Fig. 618*). An illustrator who specializes in this field should definitely have his own herbarium (*Fig. 619*), as well as a personal library devoted to the species of his chosen profession. Aside from the initial investment in these resources, a tremendous amount of time for study and close scrutiny is required.

Fig. 618.

Fig. 619. New plants are added to the author's herbarium.

Fig. 620.

The preliminary step in drawing plants is to learn how to draw leaves; first in their simplest form, singly and in groups. With pencil or ink, draw a series of flat leaves, curved leaves, and groups of leaves on a stem, as shown in *Fig. 620*. Then try odd shaped leaves

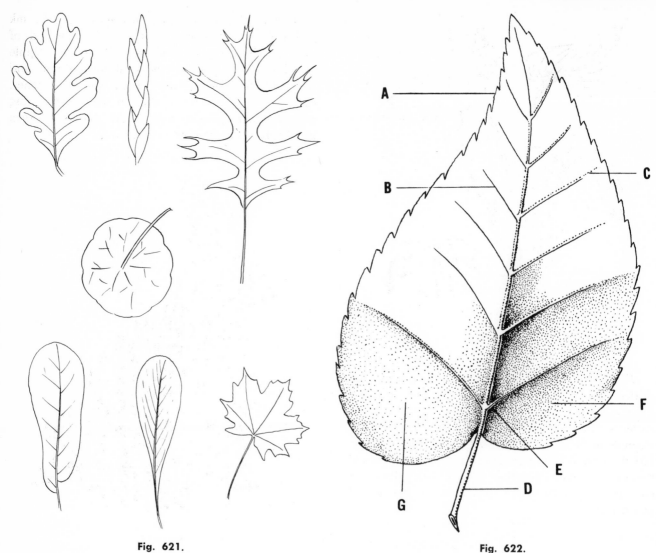

Fig. 621.

Fig. 622.

(*Fig. 621*). Now invest some time in analyzing a leaf and draw it, adding stippling with a fine pen to produce shading (*Fig. 622*). This is done by drawing the outline (*A*) and the veins (*B*), add the dots (*C*) to elevate the vein from the flat surface, shade the darker areas (*E*) toward the lighter area (*F*), leaving the well lighted areas white or add just a few dots (*G*). These are the basic steps; when you have mastered these and are able to compose a leaf which has a 3-D effect, you will be ready for the more complex compositions. *Fig. 623* illustrates a complicated network of veins and detail, while *Fig. 624* is a relatively simple structure. *Fig. 625* is a smooth- leaved plant in its natural state, having very little shading. This type of shading, created with a few lines (also *Fig. 622, D*) is impressive but should not be used to excess, especially if your artwork is to be considerably reduced.

Fig. 623.

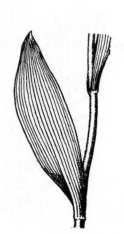

Fig. 624.

Fig. 625.

Fig. 626 illustrates a pine branch; it appears more difficult to draw than it really is. By first analyzing the plant and drawing individual features, it is much easier to attempt the final drawing. The leaves in this example are relatively short and broad, placed at different angles (some crossing others), and shaded with two or three horizontal lines to give depth. Pine species are very attractively illustrated by the scratch board technique.

Fig. 626.

Figure 627 is done on presurfaced paper with ink and pencil combination. This is a fast method of drawing; the materials used were fine screen stipple board, crowquill pen and India ink for outlining and wax pencil for shading. Note the shading on the cones, especially the larger one at the top. The leaves, being narrower in relation to their length than those seen in *Fig. 627*, require very little shading.

Fig. 627.

Some species of pines have much longer leaves, as seen in *Fig. 628;* slight shading was used on the cones, but no shading was applied to the leaves. Compare *Figs. 626, 627* and *628* for shading and outlining, particularly where leaves cross one another. *Figs. 629* and *630* are details added to the main drawing (*Fig. 628*), using the same technique. It is very important not to change technique within a group of illustrations to be published as one figure.

A collection of his own sketches of various trees is a great aid to an illustrator who specializes in drawing trees. Drawing from live specimens in their natural habitat is the ideal way of making sketches and guarantees the ultimate in accuracy. Marking pencils with either nylon or bamboo tip and a convenient sized sketch pad are the best materials for carrying on field trips. Such sketches, as seen in *Figs. 631-637*, are examples of a few specimens which might be included in such a collection.

For those who prefer broader, heavier lines, a stump and carbon powder may be used for sketches, particularly if contour and silhouette are of primary interest. *Figs. 638-645* illustrate this technique, demonstrating shape instead of detail.

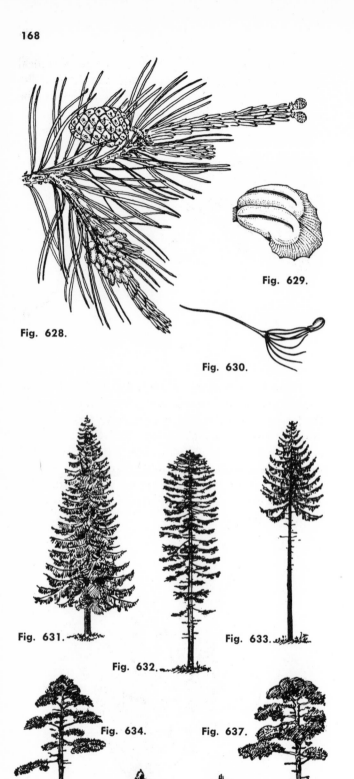

Fig. 628.

Fig. 629.

Fig. 630.

Fig. 631.

Fig. 632.

Fig. 633.

Fig. 634.

Fig. 635.

Fig. 636.

Fig. 637.

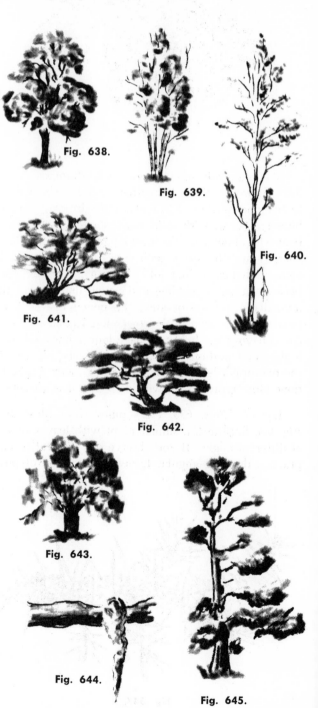

Fig. 638.

Fig. 639.

Fig. 640.

Fig. 641.

Fig. 642.

Fig. 643.

Fig. 644.

Fig. 645.

Fig. 646.

Fig. 648.

tions, it will be most helpful in numerous botanical specimens. A single line in the center of each leaf denotes not only shading but also characterizes the single vein in each leaf.

Shading with minute dots was discussed (*Fig. 622*); however, there is another method which is effective and quicker (*Fig. 646*). After drawing the outlines and veins with solid lines, shade the twig and fruit with slightly lighter lines longitudinally and horizontally and the leaves with very fine lines. Add side veins with pencil (not ink), leaving a narrow space between inked-in shading and pencil line so that the immediate area surrounding the pencil line will appear white, as seen in the lower left leaf in *Fig. 646*. Areas having less light will have longer lines, whereas highlighted portions will be the opposite, as seen in the two upper leaves. This method of shading may be done more rapidly than with dots, and it is attractive.

Earlier (*Figs. 626*, etc.) pines were illustrated. *Fig. 647* illustrates a similar plant with leaves placed at different angles. If you observe this illustration and practice drawing angular leaves in a variety of posi-

There is no shading on the leaves in *Fig. 648*; the stem is shaded on one side and a white line separates the joints. This technique was demonstrated earlier in drawing insect antennae (*Fig. 379*). The outline is clearly and evenly drawn (see arrow) and then shaded areas darkened. Plants of this type are not difficult to draw but time must be spent in drawing each individual leaf, if an illustration of high quality is to be obtained.

Fig. 647.

Fig. 649.

Ink and pencil combination on presurfaced paper is an effective and quick way of drawing plant illustrations. This technique was discussed in detail (*Figs. 70, 71*) and will be mentioned again in regard to cactus plants (*Fig. 778*, etc.). To accustom yourself to this technique for illustrating plants, take a piece of rough coquille board and create a simple leaf or combination of leaves, inking the pencilled outline. Select the shaded side and with a wax pencil add the shading, starting from the darker areas and working to the lighter ones. A few strokes artistically placed and your illustration is completed (*Fig. 649*).

Fig. 651.

Figure 652 illustrates an entirely different species; thus, the flowers and leaves are shaded in an entirely different manner. This illustration shows what can be accomplished with an ink outline and a few strokes with a wax pencil on presurfaced paper.

It is recommended that you learn this technique; it is very adaptable to rapid field trip sketching, especially for depicting shape, composition and general habitat (refer to *Figs. 701-706*).

Fig. 650.

For a second exercise try a group of leaves of different shape than previously used; place side veins with gradually lightened strokes. In this manner shaded tones are achieved at the same time you are placing the veins (*Fig. 650*).

If leaves are proportionately smaller and in clusters or groups (*Fig. 651*), very little shading is required; some are left entirely unshaded. Flowers of simple structure may be represented with only a few lines and just enough shading to give a 3-D effect; this is true of stems also, and very narrow ones are left white.

Fig. 652.

Another technique which is effective for plant illustrations and for half-tone reproduction is the wash technique; explained and illustrated in *Figs. 72-74.* This method of illustrating is not used extensively because it takes considerably more time and also because half-tone reproduction is more expensive than line cut. It is well worth learning, however, and the more you practice it the more proficient you will become. Start with a very simple, flat, smooth leaf with practically no visible veins, such as in *Fig. 653.* Make a pencil outline and use either black water color or thinned black India ink. Place a background tone on

Fig. 653.

Fig. 654.

each leaf, then returning to the first leaf cover each with water and then add the shading as desired. Add the veins last. The finished product resembles a photograph.

Using these basic steps try a more complicated leaf grouping and add a flower to your drawing (*Fig. 654*). Plan the location of the leaves at different levels on the stem; grade the shading according to the light source and highlight properly to bring out a 3-D effect. If you have a live specimen to work from, less is left to the imagination. Use *Fig. 654* for an example the first time and copy the technique illustrated here.

Fig. 655.

The wash method of illustrating may be used to create both attractive and scientifically detailed drawings. *Fig. 655* is a reproduction in its original size;

each leaf was studied and drawn individually. The light source was at the upper left; consequently, the lower right areas were shaded. Heavier veins were done with brush (No. 00, 0 and 1), and fine ones, with crowquill pen. Various mixtures of India ink and water constituted the different depths of color.

Attention is now called to the numerous ways of illustrating flowers. To bring out taxonomic details, line drawings (with pen and ink) are recommended. These are composed in two ways:

1. Solid outline drawings without shading (*Figs. 656-661*); the outlines were first done in pencil, then inked with a fine crowquill pen and India ink. Such illustrations are simply constructed and easy to draw, but are descriptive.

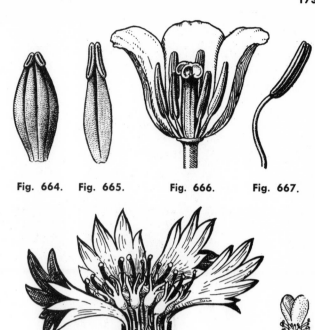

Fig. 664.   Fig. 665.   Fig. 666.   Fig. 667.

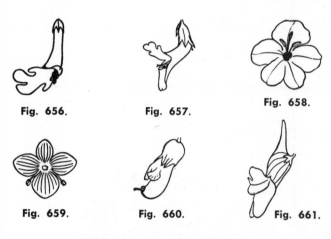

Fig. 656.   Fig. 657.   Fig. 658.

Fig. 659.   Fig. 660.   Fig. 661.

2. Solid outline drawings with shading (*Figs. 662-671*). Illustrations of this type require additional time and drawing skill; they represent details of taxonomic importance and are excellent for scientific journals. Often, in addition to the complete flower (*Fig. 662*) a longitudinal section is included (*Fig. 663*), where a minimum of shading is used. When several elements of a flower are of importance, they are drawn individually as in *Figs. 664 665* and *667*, and together in *Fig. 666*.

In greater detail and using a more complex species the same technique is used in a similar series of drawings; *Fig. 669* of the entire flower, and *Figs. 670* and *671* of the individual parts. *Fig. 668* represents the seed.

Fig. 668.   Fig. 669.   Fig. 670.   Fig. 671.

For scientific journals and textbooks the popular preference is the cross-section illustration; composition and structure are clearly defined in this method. Fresh, live material is invaluable to the illustrator; however, in many instances he must work from a photograph or sketch: in case of minute specimens or parts, he usually works from microscopic slides prepared by the scientist. The procedure is same in all cases: pencil outline is filled in with India ink, using a fine brush (*Figs. 672, 673*). If details are sharp and small in size, make the outline with pen and ink and then cover the enclosed area with a very fine brush (center of *Fig. 673*).

Fig. 662.   Fig. 663.

Fig. 672.   Fig. 673.

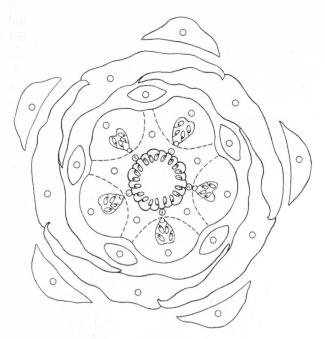

Fig. 674.

Illustrations showing numerous characteristics and parts, such as those used for demonstration purposes are outlined first in pencil and then inked (*Fig. 674*). If parts are to be labeled, that is the next step; dotted or solid lines may be used to target the parts, whichever is preferred. In *Fig. 675* the final step was to cover the corresponding parts with similar prefabricated tones. If you do not use prefabricated tones, you may make your original any size you wish; however, when using tones, do not make the original more than twice the size of the finished or reproduced size.

In *Figs. 676-678* you will note the step-by-step method of drawing a cross-section of fruit, using the wash technique. *Fig. 676* shows the outline with pencil; the entire inner surface is covered with a light gray color. The external and internal details of the fruit are worked out with various depths of grays and black. Note that (1) certain parts inside the fruit were left white (seeds), and (2) the pencil outline of the internal details are visible.

In *Fig. 677* starting *with* the lighter areas and working toward the darker ones additional shading was added in tones of gray.

Highlights (white areas) were added in the fleshy, juicy surface and finishing touches were added to the details and shawing. This drawing is reproduced in its original size; it may be reduced to one-third if printed on good quality paper. Reproduction is by half-tone only (*Fig. 678*).

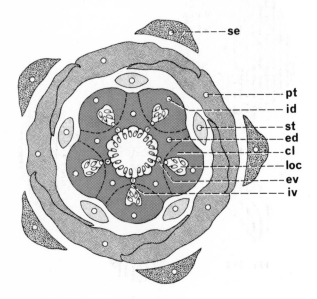

se
pt
id
st
ed
cl
loc
ev
iv

Fig. 675.

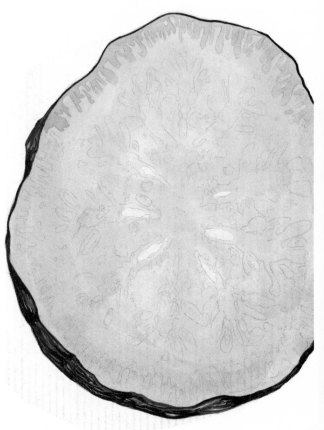

Fig. 676.

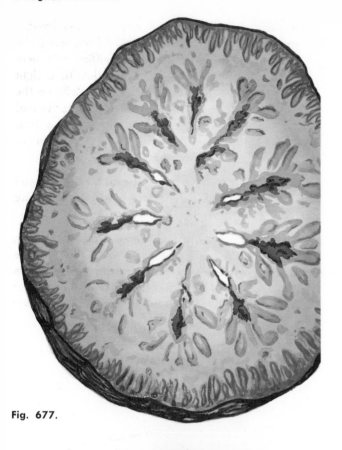

Fig. 677.

Seed pods are interesting subjects to illustrate and may be attractively drawn in a number of different ways. The most commonly used technique is the line drawing, as shown in *Figs. 679* and *680*. Materials used were India ink, a crowquill pen and three-ply strathmore drawing paper. The solid outlines are shaded with fine lines of different length; note the crossed lines on the outer surface and the technique used to represent the ribs in *Fig. 679*. Line drawings for seeds are recommended because it is possible to represent taxonomic details, the morphology of certain parts of the seed or cones and differentiate be-

Fig. 679.   **Fig. 680.**

tween the various speices. Observe *Figs. 681-685;* the differences in species are clearly visible, as are the structure, contour and composition. Taxonomists often prefer describing plants in an orderly sequence; one

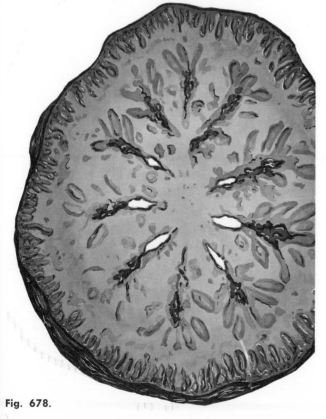

Fig. 678.

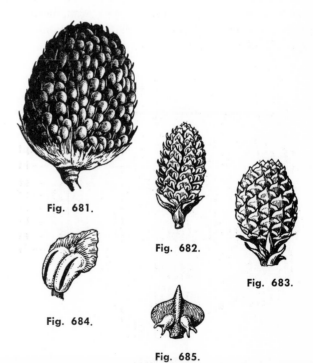

Fig. 681.

Fig. 682.

Fig. 683.

Fig. 684.

Fig. 685.

detail at a time, such as the leaves in *Fig. 686;* then the young cones in *Figs. 688* and *689;* the full grown cone in *Fig. 687;* and the individual seed, as seen in *Fig. 690.* These are simple drawings on Strathmore drawing paper, drawn with crowquill pen and Pelikan India ink. *Figs. 679-690* are reproduced in their original sizes.

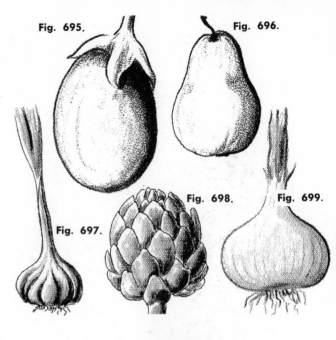

Fig. 695.   Fig. 696.

Fig. 698.   Fig. 699.

Fig. 697.

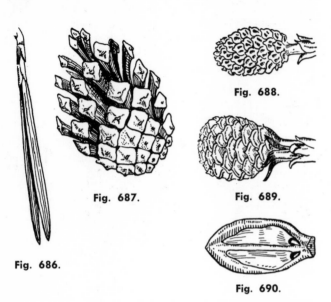

Fig. 688.

Fig. 687.

Fig. 689.

Fig. 686.

Fig. 690.

Presurfaced drawing papers are very useful and drawing time is greatly minimized if exacting detail and taxonomy are unimportant. The following examples are ink outlines, shaded with wax pencil on rough coquille board (*Figs. 691-693*); without ink outline (*Figs. 694-696*). Pebble board is used in the next series of figures; with ink outlines and shaded with wax pencil (*Figs. 697-698*); and wax pencil outline and shading (*Fig. 699*). Artwork done with this technique must be protected by clear spray.

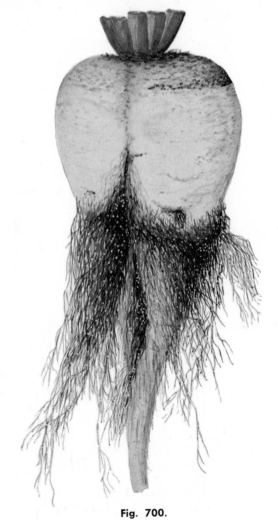

Fig. 700.

Fig. 691.   Fig. 692.

Fig. 693.   Fig. 694.

Printing costs prohibit the reproduction of color illustrations in this book. *Fig. 700*, although reproduced in black and white, is a color illustration in green, yellow and brown. Color slides in conjunction with a talk or teaching are very effective. Original illustrations in full color may be reproduced either in black and white or in color.

The importance of a plant collection (herbarium) by the illustrator has been mentioned (*Fig. 619*). Such specimens are excellent reference material when details are needed. If a plant is too big to be placed on a normal herbarium sheet, a sketch of the plant in its natural surroundings is valuable as reference material. Field drawings may be done in a variety of ways; simple silhouettes (*Figs. 800, 805*, etc.); simple illustrations with more detail (*Figs. 701-706*). In the latter, the illustrator will find his work much less complicated when he is asked to draw that particular species; and if he has preserved specimens, as well, the artwork will have characteristic natural qualities.

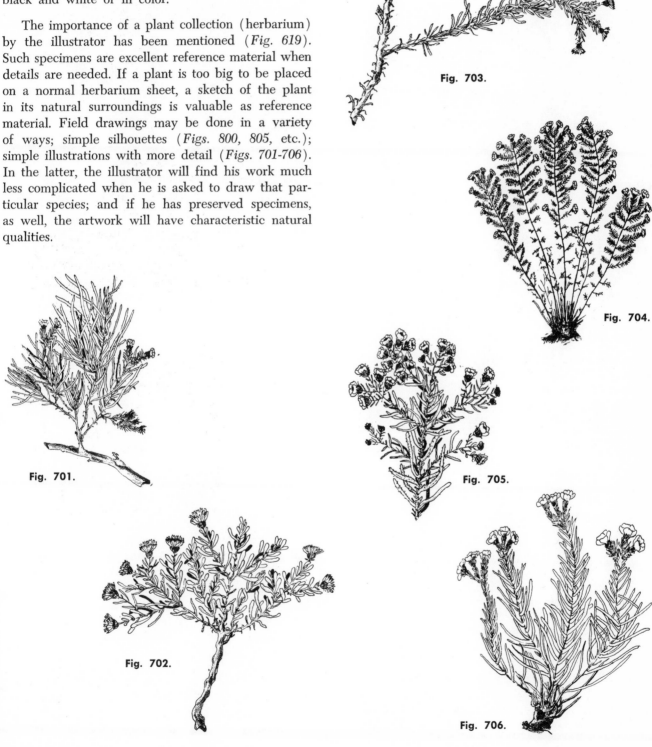

Fig. 703.

Fig. 704.

Fig. 701.

Fig. 705.

Fig. 702.

Fig. 706.

Fig. 707.

Fig. 708.

One of the favorite drawing techinques for botani-cal illustrations and similar to this is simple line draw-ings with India ink and pen. We will cover this tech-nique more thoroughly and accompany it will illus-trations. Three- or five-ply semi-smooth Strathmore drawing paper, crowquill pen and Pelikan India ink are the necessary materials. The original should not be too large — not more than twice the size of the pub-lished size.

Figures 709-720 are various species of grasses; if you will observe them carefully you will see that a definite uniformity exists throughout the various spe-cies. There is an indescribable order within each of these grasses. If you study live specimens of grasses, you will discover a definite growth pattern among each variety.

Regardless of what you attempt to draw, first study the object from all angles, observe the charac-teristic grouping, the size, shape, proportions, and then with pencil draw the outline. Start with the least complicated type and after mastering that one, such

Field drawings are best done on presurfaced draw-ing paper (either pebble boards or coquille boards), preferably with a fountain pen and shadings with wax pencil. The final drawings may be of another tech-nique, such as the solid line drawing seen of a Linan-thus in *Fig. 707*. *Fig. 708* is the same illustration re-duced to approximately 60 per cent of the original.

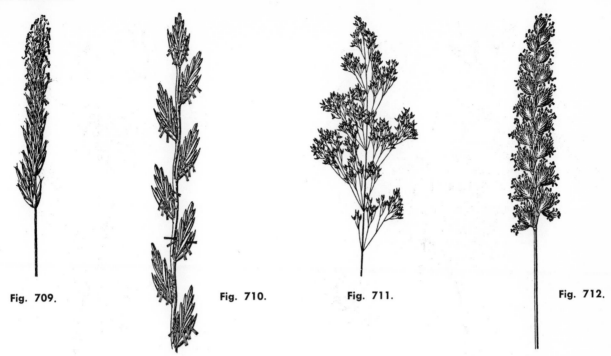

Fig. 709. Fig. 710. Fig. 711. Fig. 712.

as *Fig. 709,* go to a more detailed variety, as seen in *Fig. 710.* You will find that, as the easier species are learned, many of the same characters exist in the more ornamental ones, as in *Fig. 711.* *Fig. 712* is a little bit different in composition but is a combination of the characteristics of the preceding species.

Wheat-heads are interesting to draw. Do the individual seeds first and then add the spikes (*Figs. 713-715*). A minimum of shading is required; a few lines accomplish this, as seen in *Fig. 715.* In some grass species the seeds are not externally visible but are hidden among the dense and relatively fine spikes. In such instances the seeds are not drawn. Study the arrangement of the spikes and the general contour; see how the head broadens in *Fig. 716,* is narrower in *Fig. 717,* and loosely arranged and disorderly in *Fig. 718.* These are very simple drawings, yet they represent the life-like quality of the plant.

Fig. 713. Fig. 714. Fig. 715.

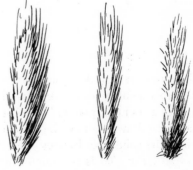

Fig. 716. Fig. 717. Fig. 718.

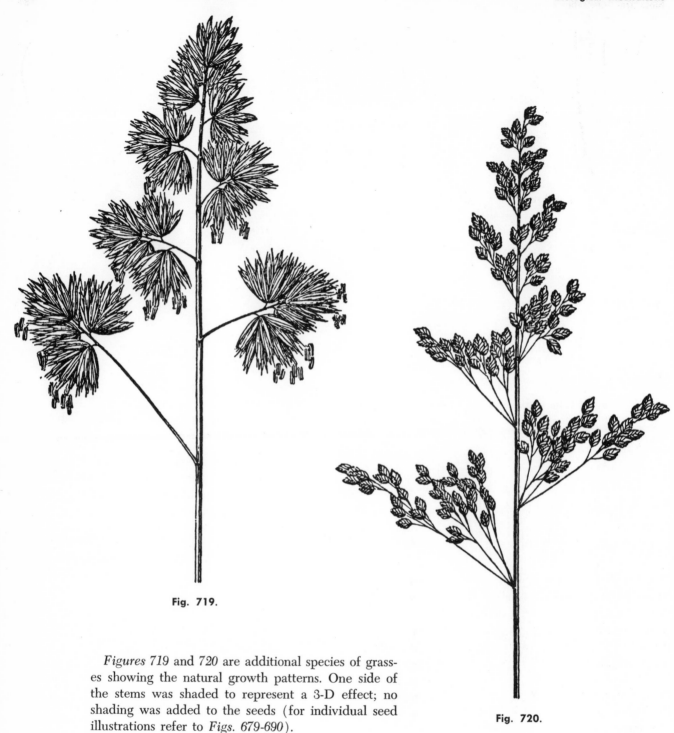

Fig. 719.

Fig. 720.

Figures 719 and 720 are additional species of grass-es showing the natural growth patterns. One side of the stems was shaded to represent a 3-D effect; no shading was added to the seeds (for individual seed illustrations refer to *Figs. 679-690*).

The basic beginner's technique for illustrating leaves was given previously (*Figs. 620-622*). If an illustrator is engaged in detailed work with a botani-cal taxonomist, he must learn some of the most com-mon technical expression pertaining to leaf shapes.

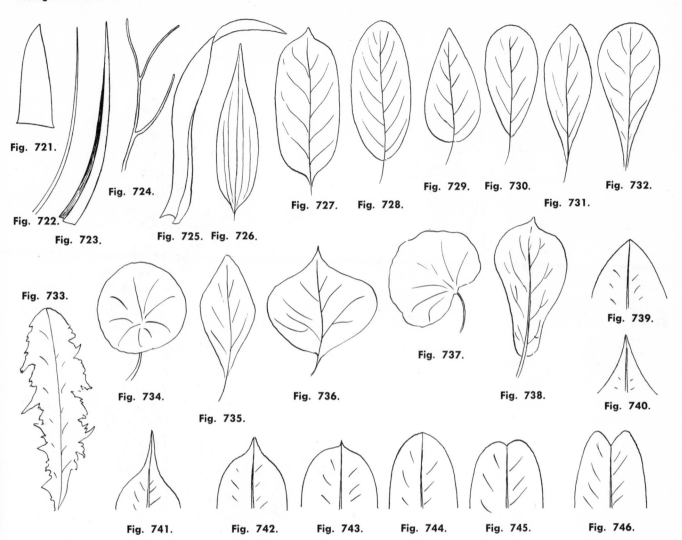

Fig. 721.
Fig. 722.
Fig. 723.
Fig. 724.
Fig. 725. Fig. 726.
Fig. 727. Fig. 728.
Fig. 729. Fig. 730.
Fig. 731.
Fig. 732.
Fig. 733.
Fig. 734.
Fig. 735.
Fig. 736.
Fig. 737.
Fig. 738.
Fig. 739.
Fig. 740.
Fig. 741. Fig. 742. Fig. 743. Fig. 744. Fig. 745. Fig. 746.

These are the "terms of vegetative structures" as defined by L. H. Bailey (Manual of Cultivated Plants. The Macmillan Co., New York, 1949.); it is highly recommended that the would-be illustrator learn these words and use them frequently in conversing or corresponding with the scientist. Knowing these terms will assure the illustrator that he fully understands his assignment and that he can communicate intelligently with the scientist. The following figures demonstrate the most commonly used terms:

721. subulate
722. acicular
723. linear
724. filiform
725. eorate
726. lanceolate
727. oblong
728. elliptic
729. ovate
730. obovate
731. oblanceolate
732. spatulate
733. runcinate
734. orbiculate
735. rhomboidal
736. deltoid
737. reniform
738. pandurate
739. acute
740. acuminate
741. aristate
742. cuspidate
743. mucronate
744. obtuse
745. retuse
746. emarginate

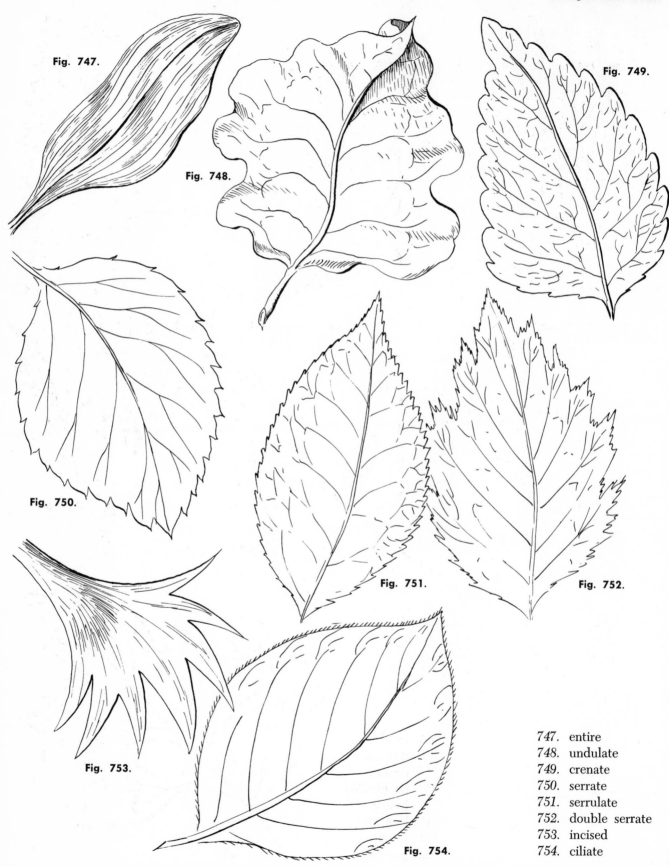

Fig. 747.

Fig. 748.

Fig. 749.

Fig. 750.

Fig. 751.

Fig. 752.

Fig. 753.

Fig. 754.

747. entire
748. undulate
749. crenate
750. serrate
751. serrulate
752. double serrate
753. incised
754. ciliate

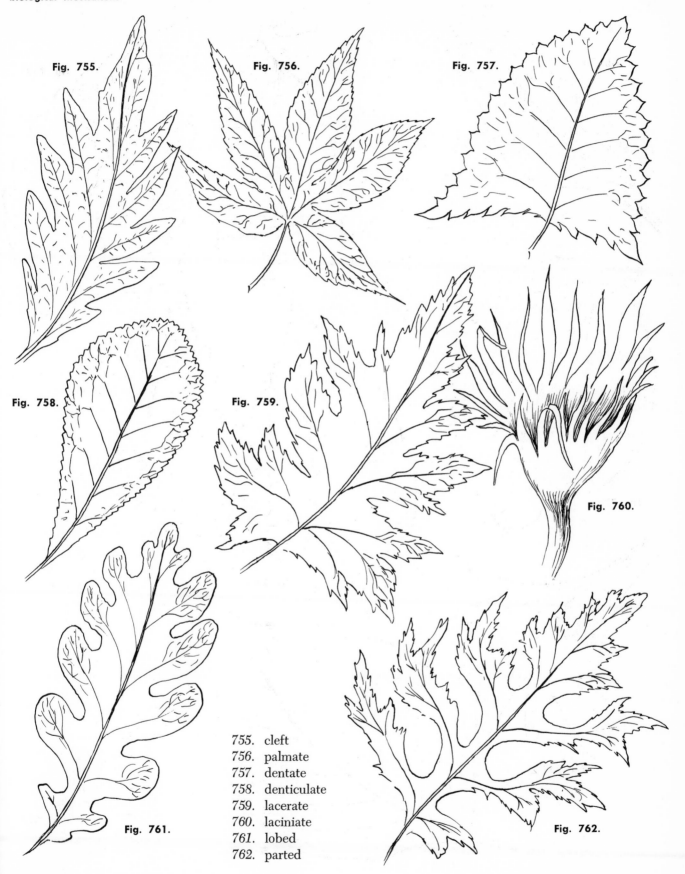

Fig. 755.

Fig. 756.

Fig. 757.

Fig. 758.

Fig. 759.

Fig. 760.

Fig. 761.

Fig. 762.

755. cleft
756. palmate
757. dentate
758. denticulate
759. lacerate
760. laciniate
761. lobed
762. parted

Fig. 763.

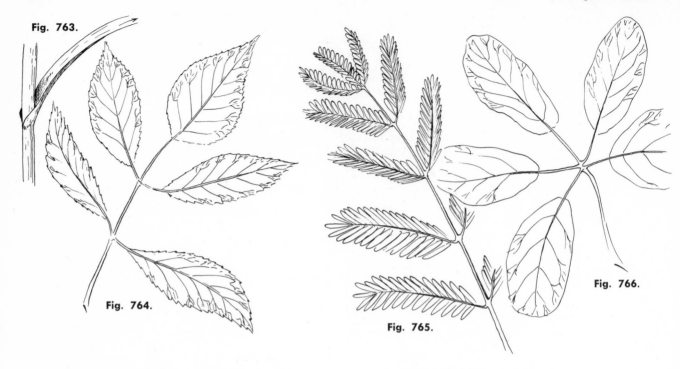

Fig. 764.

Fig. 765.

Fig. 766.

763. leaf sessile, parallel venation
764. leaf compound, odd-pinnate
765. leaf compound, even pinnate
766. leaf compound, palmate

The following terms apply to the base of leaves and are illustrated in *Fig.* 767:

a. attenuate   e. cordate
b. oblique   f. peltate
c. truncate   g. perfoliate
d. sagittate   h. connate perfoliate

In *Fig.* 768 some of the terms used to describe root formations are shown:

a. corm with membranous tunic
b. rhizome
c. bulb
d. tuber
e. as *a* with fibrous tunic.

Figure 769 demonstrates some casual field sketches of four formations. These are appropriate for "notes" but not sufficiently detailed for publication.

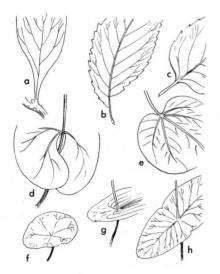

Fig. 767.

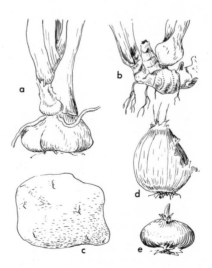

Fig. 768.

Fig. 769.

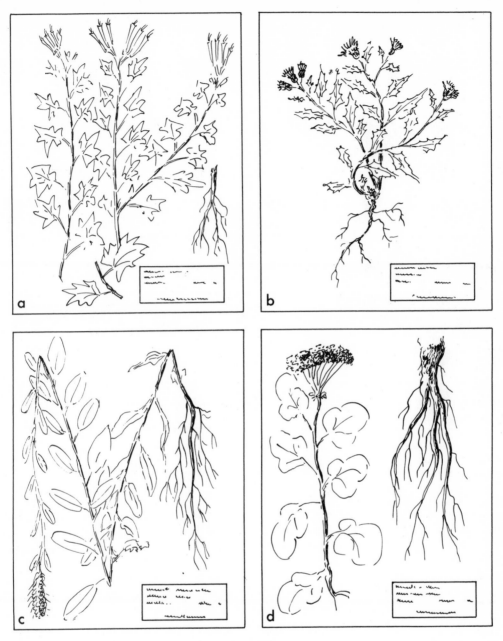

Fig. 770.

The importance of having a specimen to complete an illustration has been mentioned several times in this book. As is commonly known, many amateurs or novice plant collectors forget about collecting the root portion of the plant. It will be dirty, especially if you pull it out of muddy sand, but it can be washed off and preserved for future reference. If the plants are short, they may be placed in one piece on the herbarium sheet. (*Fig. 770, b*); or if they are long and thin, it is easy to fold and keep the entire plant (*Fig. 770, c*); or if the plant is brittle and cannot be folded, it may be broken into two or three pieces, keeping all parts and placing them in order on your collection sheet (*Fig. 770,a*). It may be that the plant is too large to keep all the pieces; in this case use the parts you think will be most helpful; definitely keep the roots (*Fig. 770, d*). Take care of your herbarium, checking occasionally for insects which feed on dry plant material. It is advisable to keep paradichloro-benzene granules in each of the storage boxes of the cabinet.

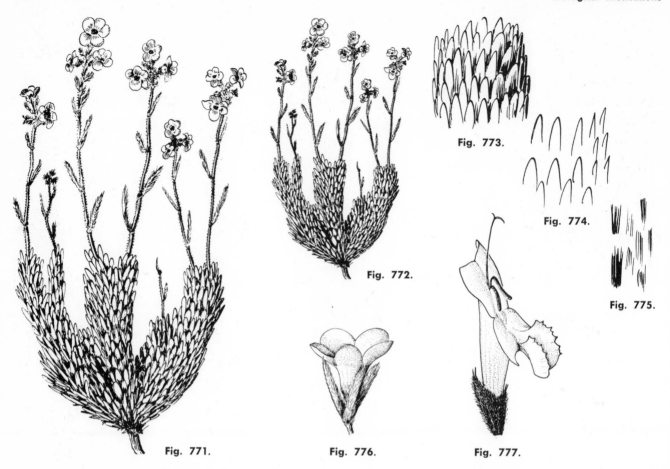

Fig. 773.

Fig. 774.

Fig. 775.

Fig. 772.

Fig. 771.

Fig. 776.

Fig. 777.

It was previously mentioned that with a few simple lines it is possible to create actual forms which may be readily identifiable for quick reference (*Figs. 716-718*). These sketches were done with pen and ink. To demonstrate how easy it is for the beginner to compose a very attractive illustration of a plant by applying single forms, refer to *Figs. 773-775*. Elements presented in these figures are grouped in *Fig. 771;* reduced to 75 per cent of the original size. *Fig. 772* is the same original reduced to 45 per cent.

Cacti are interesting plants to illustrate. Some prefer the smudging technique, which is acceptable if the original is to be used for decoration (framing) and not for publication. It is painstaking to work out the spines on a smudged background and the end result may be that the spines are not clearly visible in the reproduction. A much easier technique and one that produces very effective results is to use presurfaced paper (for example No. 12 pebble board). This technique was used by the author for a book on the *World's Opuntias* (Van Gundy and Papp, not yet completed).

Regardless of the form and shape of the species, the basic problem is to present the characteristic spines properly and with accuracy, as well as maintain the surface structure of the plant. In *Fig. 778* observe how the joints are globular, areolae fairly large, and the spints flat, papery and cross-ribbed; sometimes darker in color, as in *Fig. 778*, or lighter, as in *Fig. 779*. The outlines are done with India ink and crowquill pen; the individual tubercles are not outlined. Areolae are formed with short strokes; curved lines indicate the margin of the areole. Shading is added with a wax pencil. Note the origin of the flat, papery spines in *Fig. 780*. Some specimens have very few or no spines, which is indicative of the age of the joint (*Fig. 783*). You will note the difference in the areolae in this figure also. *Fig. 782* illustrates the fruit of this type of cactus; it is almost smooth and covered with large tubercles in alternating rows.

Some species of cactus are nearly smooth, with nearly unidentifiable tubercles on the young joints; tubercles are completely lacking on older joints (*Fig.

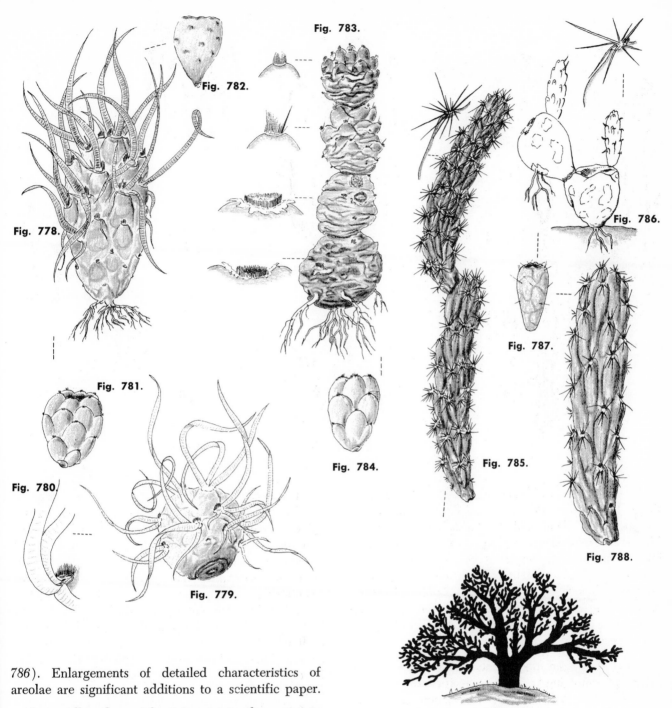

Fig. 783.

Fig. 782.

Fig. 778.

Fig. 786.

Fig. 781.

Fig. 787.

Fig. 780.

Fig. 784.

Fig. 785.

Fig. 779.

Fig. 788.

Fig. 789.

786). Enlargements of detailed characteristics of areolae are significant additions to a scientific paper.

It is well to draw at least two joints of a cactus to show its composition and proportion. *Fig. 785* is a species with rounded joints. The outline is done with India ink and crowquil pen; the location of the areoles and the spines are also linked with the same pen. The shading is added and characteristic longitudinal tubercles registered. The finished drawing will bear the features of the species. For additional taxonomic significance an enlarged portion of spines may

be inserted. *Fig. 788* illustrates the same plant specimen with joints of different proportions; *Fig. 789* is a silhouette illustration of another specimen; notice the joints are all solid black. Due to the relatively small size of the species, which is characteristic, individual spines are not easily visible.

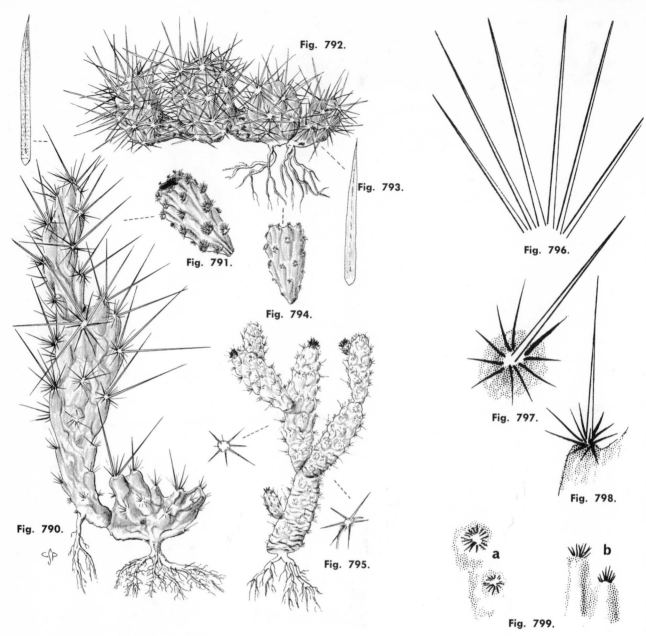

Fig. 792.

Fig. 793.

Fig. 796.

Fig. 791.

Fig. 794.

Fig. 797.

Fig. 798.

Fig. 790.

Fig. 795.

a

b

Fig. 799.

Figures 790 and 793 illustrate other types of spines, which may be drawn as separate drawings to show their structure in detail, and also as complete specimen drawings (*Figs.* 790 and 792). Long spines may be drawn with a ruler, placing individual spines correctly and at the proper angle (*Fig.* 796). If there are short spines surrounding the main ones, show them with solid black lines (*Fig.* 797), keeping the center of the areole white. The same technique is used for a side view (*Fig.* 798). Areolae with extreme short spines may be illustrated from top view, as seen in *Fig.* 799, *a* or from the side, as in 799, *b*.

Shading is worked out after all the ink work is done. Tubercles and characteristic markings on the surface are added after completion of the outline and spine placement. You will recall that it was mentioned previously that the form, size and shape of the areolae are different on the older joints than on the young ones. It is wise to present additional enlargements of details which are of taxonomic importance to a plant. Illustrating cactus fruit is done with the same technique and by following the same procedure just mentioned. It is advisable to illustrate from fresh samples whenever possible.

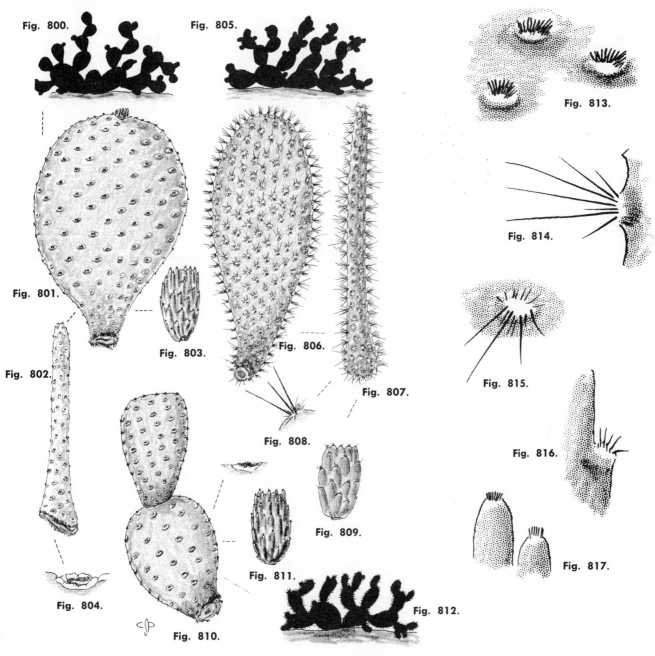

Fig. 800. Fig. 805. Fig. 813. Fig. 801. Fig. 803. Fig. 806. Fig. 814. Fig. 807. Fig. 802. Fig. 808. Fig. 815. Fig. 816. Fig. 809. Fig. 811. Fig. 804. Fig. 817. Fig. 810. Fig. 812.

Flat jointed cactus is easier to illustrate than cylindrical varities. *Fig. 801* shows a specimen which is spineless. In this example the outline was drawn and the small areolae located. After these were inked, the shaded areas were added with wax pencil. You will note that the areolae are represented by elliptical outlines immediately surrounded with areas left white to give a 3-D effect. The overall shading for a flat surface such as this is more subdued than in the cylindrical-joined species as seen in *Fig. 785*. You will note that a very narrow white area was left between the inked outline and the wax-pencil shading in *Figs. 801* and *806* in order to give an impression of flatness. *Figs. 802* and *807* are side views of the species shown in *801* and *806*. The spines in *Figs. 806* and *807* were drawn before the background shading was added. Characteristic details are enlarged in order to represent taxonomic features: areolae in *Figs. 804* and *808;* cactus fruit in *Figs. 803, 809, 811*. Often a silhouette drawing of the complete plant is required for descriptive purposes, as in *Figs. 800, 805* and *812*. Additional close-up details of areolae and spines for these species are represented in *Figs. 813-817*.

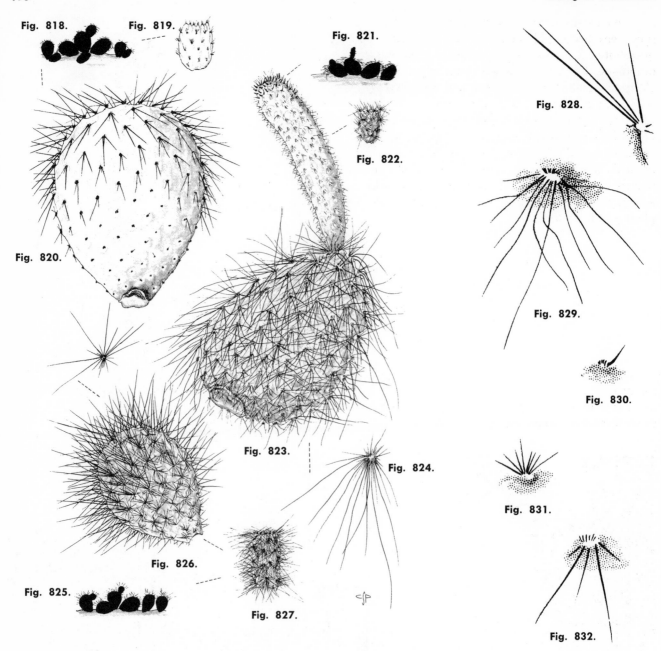

Fig. 818.
Fig. 819.
Fig. 821.
Fig. 828.
Fig. 820.
Fig. 822.
Fig. 829.
Fig. 823.
Fig. 824.
Fig. 830.
Fig. 826.
Fig. 831.
Fig. 825.
Fig. 827.
Fig. 832.

Some species of cactus are flat jointed and have unusually long, hair-like spines. Note how the spines in *Fig. 820* are distributed; they are longer and more dense toward the tip of the joint and absent on the posterior area. Straight, black lines represent the spines which barely change in elevation on the surface; the anterior portion being smooth, and the posterior slightly uneven. The species in *Fig. 826* has longer spines; these also are represented with solid black lines but are longer and denser. *Fig. 823* illustrates a species that has extremely long, hair-like spines which are placed in a definite order. Very little

shading is required — just a slight touch of wax pencil on the shaded side of the plant. *Figs. 828-832* are enlarged sections, showing placement of areolae and spines of these different species. The fruit of these cacti differ greatly and are shown in *Figs. 819* (a relatively smooth exterior with short spines) and *822* (granular surface covered with finer spines). *Fig. 827* is an almost parallel-sided variety of fruit with a dense covering of long, fine spines.

The most accurate illustrations are drawn from live specimens. Species of cactus are not very suitable for preservation in a herbarium collection; the moisture evaporates, leaving a wrinkled distorted surface (*Fig. 835*), the fruit becomes dried and shapeless (*Fig. 833*), and the areolae and spines droop unnaturally (*Fig. 834*). Plants growing in their natural habitat (*Fig. 836*) supply the utmost in characteristics that are taxonomically important. If your illustration must be made from a cutting, preserve it in a cool place or replant it; make a sketch as soon as possible, placing as many details and features as are visible while the plant is still fresh.

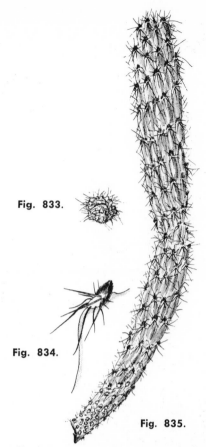

Fig. 833.

Fig. 834.

Fig. 835.

Fig. 836.
Sketching in the Joshua Tree National Monument, in southern California.

Fig. 836.

As previously pointed out, illustrations are limited to black and white reproduction for the most part. An illustrator must choose the technique that best fulfills the requirement of the assignment and is most adaptable to the method of reproduction used by the printer or publisher. Line cuts are the most reasonable and therefore the most popular; one of the most applicable techniques for such reproductions is ink outline and pencil shading on presurfaced paper (either coquille board or pebble board). This technique produces attractive results and is much less time-consuming than working out detailed surface patterns with ink and pen on smooth drawing paper. The sample seen in *Fig. 837* at the left was outlined in ink and shaded with wax pencil; this is a line reproduction. *Fig. 837* (right) is a half-tone reproduction. Always place some form of vegetation in your drawing unless the root system is also included.

Fig. 838.

Fig. 839.

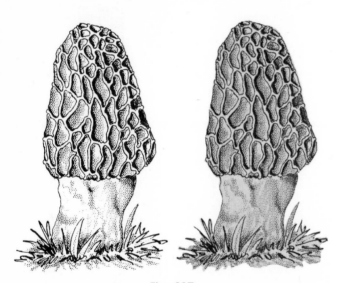

Fig. 837.

Fig. 840.

Illustrations in full color, naturally, reproduce best in color. Frequently authors specify that illustrations be done in color, but when the material is published, it is reproduced in black and white half-tone. In the original of *Fig. 838,* the colors clearly distinguished each detail; here, reproduced in half-tone the white color predominates, the pastel background is completely missing, and the surface shading appears rough. In *Fig. 839* the background color is lost, and the shades of brown in the mushrooms are distorted and unsightly. The original colors of red and white which predominate in *Fig. 840* have lost their depth and shading effects in this reproduction. These examples were shown in order to point out what is sacrificed in reproducing color illustrations in black and white. If accurate shading and precise detail in reproduction is to be obtained, do your originals in black and white for black and white reproduction. Whenever possible, use color in your originals only when they will be reproduced in color.

Fig. 841.

"On location" sketching is usually a thrilling experience for a botanical illustrator. Whether or not you specialize in a particular group of plants, there are always interesting and challenging specimens in the field. Mushrooms are fascinating subjects: they grow in numerous shapes, having unusual coloring, and live in various environments. *Fig. 841* is a carbon sketch randomly drawn on a field trip as the various varieties appeared in a period of several days. This is a 50 per cent reduction of the original, which was purchased by the Carnegie Institute of Technology, Pittsburgh, Pennsylvania, for their Collection of Botanical Illustrations. A 25 per cent reduction is seen in *Fig. 618.* Visualize the effectiveness of this sketch if it had been done in full color and thus reproduced.

Since the time of Anton van Leeuwenhoek (1632-1723), the great Dutch microscopist from Delft, who designed and built his own microscopes (*Fig. 842*) and first viewed plant cells (*Fig. 843*), mankind has learned a great deal about the secrets of life. Microscopy lead to the discovery that plants, like animals, consist of millions of tiny cells formed in a great variety of shapes and sizes, as well as to an ever increasing interest in the adventurous, challenging unknowns of nature which were not visible to the naked eye. It was soon learned that individual cells were connected and formed organized patterns; contemporary scientists made this fact known to the early artists and before long the first three-dimensional illustrations were created (*Fig. 844*). Soon the func-

Fig. 842.

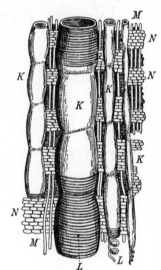

Fig. 844.

tions of the various cell groups were analyzed and slightly less than a century after Leeuwenhoek's death, man embarked upon the threshhold of a vast reservoir of new ideas, theories and techniques which ultimately led to professional specialization. Wide-spread versions of cell composition were published; printed from wood carvings or metal etchings, or the better known lithographic process in black and white or in color. Another century was not required to advance to an accumulation of accurate knowledge and to attain broader scientific boundaries; along with this development illustrations also became more meaningful and scientific and are still accepted by modern-day scientists (*Fig. 845*).

As the microscope was improved and new knowledge unfolded, the artist's techniques changed; his task was to illustrate in the best way possible the limitless facts which emanated from each evolutionary development.

Fig. 843.

Fig. 845.

Microphotography was a great advancement. Photographic evidence is an invaluable aid in discussions and in collecting scientific data. To go one step further in presenting clear-cut, defined and descriptive visual aids the scientist relies on the scientific illustrator to accomplish what no other medium of communication has succeeded in conveying.

Figure 846 is a very simple line drawing. Make your initial microscopic illustrations simple and attractive and after your introductory experience and practice in this new field proceed to a more complicated specimen. Before attempting an illustration designed to demonstrate the functioning of a cell or group of cells it will be necessary for you to consult with the scientist and get a complete and accurate description of the assignment. If possible, have the scientist make a sketch and formulate a rough image of what he desires. Examine a series of slides depict-

ing the structure and details to be included in the illustration. After these preliminary steps you are ready to create your first sketch. There are likely to be many changes and additions; therefore, use scratch board, India ink and crowquill pen. Changes and corrections are made easily when using these ma-

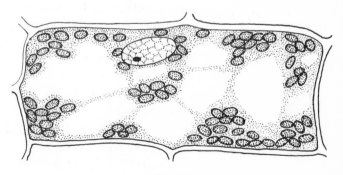

Fig. 846.

terials. The more critical the scientist, the more changes, and at the same time, the better your chances are for a truly scientific, flawless illustration.

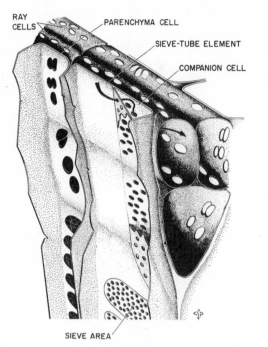

Fig. 847.

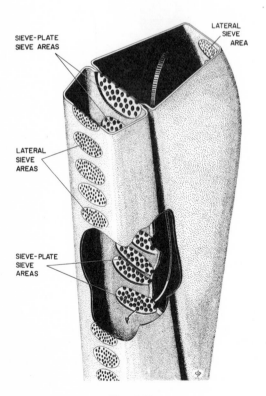

Fig. 848.

Labeling may be done in a variety of ways. The Leroy Lettering Equipment (*Fig. 847* and *848*) is satisfactory. It is recommended to first cover the area to be lettered with Snopake. Leroy pens work better and more smoothly on scratch board if it is first Snopaked. Or with Letraset instant lettering, which is available today in a variety of sizes at art-supply stores. Attractive and very practical for exclusive use by a scientific illustrator is the Varityper. Whichever type of lettering, be cautious to select the same size in a series of illustrations to be used in the same publication and also plan the illustrations to be uniform and in proportionate dimensions. Neatness and accuracy are the keys to successful artwork.

For the scientist whose field demands microphotographs for inclusion in books and journals and who has no access to an illustrator for defined explanatory insertions, it is suggested that you create simple line drawings with India ink on Strathmore drawing paper to be published parallel to the photographs, as seen in *Figs. 849-854.* If there are areas in your line draw-

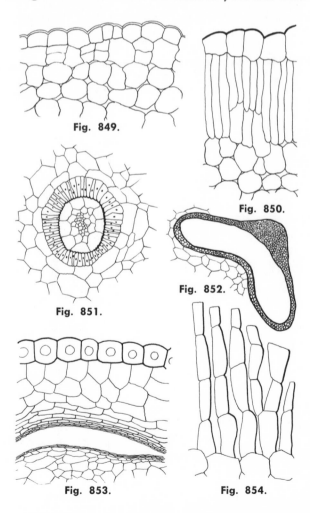

Fig. 849.

Fig. 850.

Fig. 851.

Fig. 852.

Fig. 853.

Fig. 854.

ings which you want to stand out in order to call attention to particular points of interest, these areas may be covered with prefabricated tones. *Figs. 855-860* show how *Figs. 849-854* were transformed with these tones to accomplish the desired results. Prefabricated tones are available in a wide selection of patterns; they are acetate sheets with adhesive backing (samples are shown in *Figs. 1089-1156*).

For superior workmanship, although tedious and time-consuming, adopt the inked outline technique with stippled shading. Examine *Figs. 847* and *848* with a magnifying glass; you will observe the thousands of individually placed dots which were placed on scratch board with crowquill pen. Two- or three-ply Strathmore illustration paper may be used for this type of illustration if changes and numerous corrections are not likely to be necessary. First draw an ac-

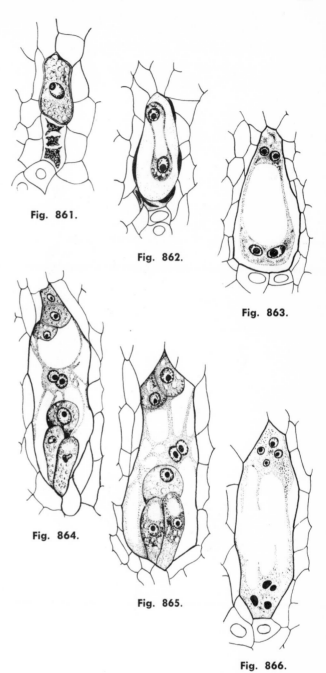

Fig. 861.

Fig. 862.

Fig. 863.

Fig. 864.

Fig. 865.

Fig. 866.

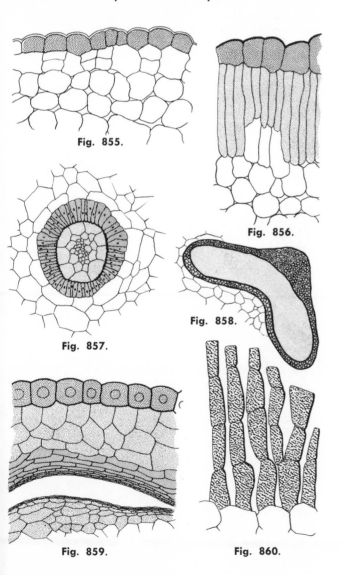

Fig. 855.

Fig. 856.

Fig. 857.

Fig. 858.

Fig. 859.

Fig. 860.

curate outline with pencil, working out the large cells and representing cell walls with a solid, thin ink line; heavier lines for thicker walls. Place a few inked dots in the areas which will be shaded; later, after the outline and details are complete, fill in the dotted areas with sharp, clear disorderly stippling. *Figs. 861-866*, illustrated with this technique, show a series of changes within a specific cell; seen in greater detail in *Figs. 867-872* in their original size. *Figs. 861-866* are reproduced at 54 per cent of the original size.

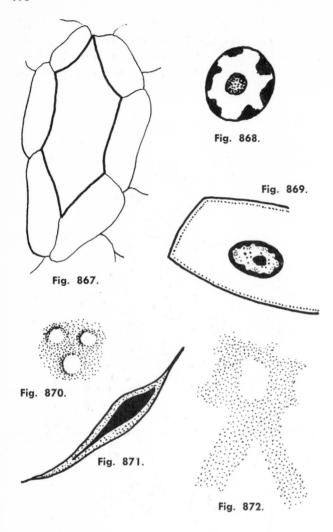

Fig. 868.

Fig. 869.

Fig. 867.

Fig. 870.

Fig. 871.

Fig. 872.

reason for their inclusion is twofold: although the greatest majority of a scientific illustrator's assignments are of a technical and exacting nature, occasionally he may have a request to create something simply eye-pleasing; secondly, we all know the adage "all work and no play makes Jack a dull boy" — this applies to scientific illustrating also. Moreover, it is quite possible that an imaginative, creative artist may alter a given technique in such a way as to increase its usefulness and artistic potential.

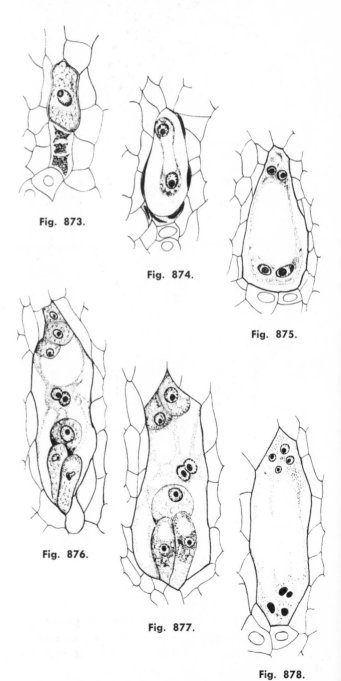

Fig. 873.

Fig. 874.

Fig. 875.

Fig. 876.

Fig. 877.

Fig. 878.

Illustrations made with this technique are seldom reproduced in half-tone. The half-tone process for reproduction of line drawings is inferior to line cut unless the illustration has visible uniformity in the outline or stippling; in this case half-tone reproduction distorts the sharpness of details sufficiently to conceal flaws. *Figs.* 873-878 demonstrate this process; avoid it if possible.

The smudging or carbon powder technique is seldom used in botanical illustrations; it is a messy material to work with and produces an inferior illustration for taxonomic value. There are instances when it may be used in conjunction with this method which poses; book covers, on botanical meeting notices or programs, etc. There are "tricks of the trade" which may be used in conjunction with this method which are fun and a welcome diversion for the scientific illustrator. Although the following techniques and illustrations deviate from the strictly scientific, the

Figure 880: An example of another paper material, rough-surface coquille board was used for this illustration, which is slightly enlarged to show details. It also may be reduced to one-fifth of the present size.

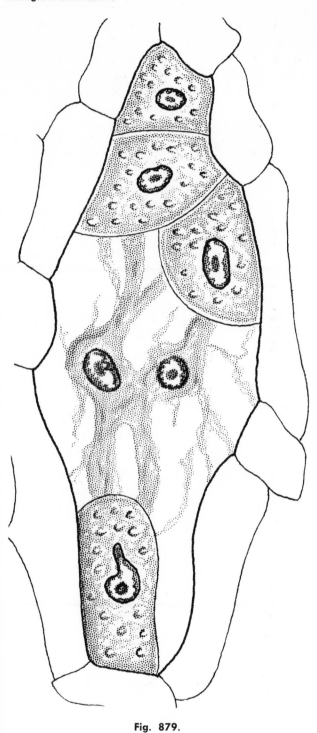

Fig. 879.

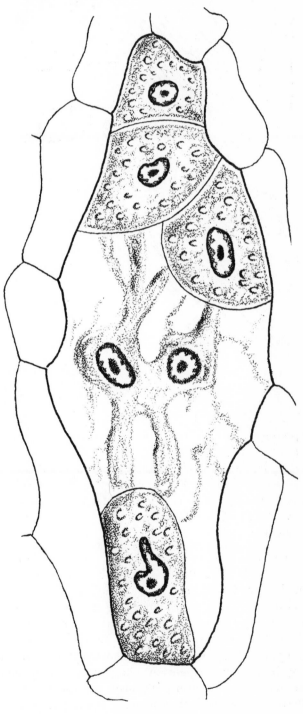

Figure 879: India ink outline and wax pencil applied to medium-rough pebble-board. To demonstrate details the original is slightly enlarged. It may be reduced to one-fifth of the present size.

Fig. 880.

Fig. 881.

Fig. 883.

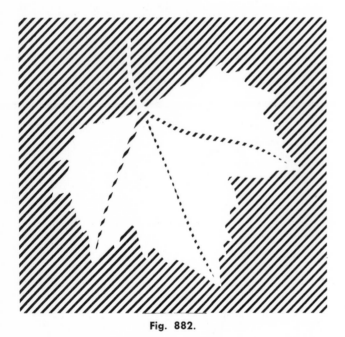

Fig. 882.

Fig. 884.

Figure 881: On an area make the desired outline with pencil and cut around the outline (the striped area has been cut out). Strathmore paper, acetate sheet or common tracing paper are satisfactory materials to use for this technique. This cut-out serves as the "negative" of your drawing.

Figure 882: The piece cut from the original, or the "positive" may be saved. If you want to show veins in the leaf, cut strips out as seen in this figure (in this instance the striped material is used as a background).

Figure 883: Place the "negative" on a sheet of drawing paper. Fasten securely with masking tape on two opposite sides to prevent it from moving. Apply carbon powder, smearing with chamois skin evenly and with different degrees of pressure for the shading effect desired. Caution must be taken to prevent fingerprints and smearing, as shown by arrows.

Figure 884: Place the "positive" over the smudged area and with a soft eraser remove the carbon from the veins and stem. The final step, after removing the "positive" is to add slightly darker shading.

Practice this technique with various objects, following the same general procedure as given for the leaf. An electric eraser may be effectively used with this smudging method. Try lines, dots and designs, as seen in *Fig. 885. Fig. 886* was done with an electric eraser and shaded with a deeper tone of loose carbon powder to accentuate the veins.

Upon completion of an illustration done with the smudging method, clean well with an eraser and spray with a protective spray. Drawings of this type may be reproduced only by half-tone.

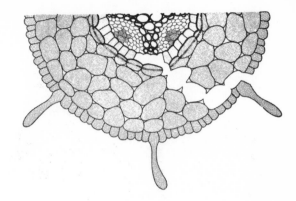

Fig. 887.

Fig. 885.

Fig. 886.

on each sheet; diseased areas are conveyed from individual slides in precisely the condition in which they appear under the microscope, leaving no margin of error or chance for misinterpretation of old records. *Figs. 887, 889, 890* and *891* show different types of damage and how they may be registered on the "map." The technique employed was ink outline and prefabricated tone. Note the loss of tone quality in the greater reductions as compared to the 25 per cent of the original in *Fig. 887.*

Scientists must keep records and collect data, regardless of their field of endeavor. The scientific illustrator may prepare worksheets which will greatly aid the scientist in maintaining accurate, progressive, detailed accounts of his research. As an example, a cross-section of a plant part is used in *Figs. 887-891.* The artist prepares a drawing of a healthy specimen (*Fig. 888*); from this drawing a number of prints may be made, the exact number will depend upon the scientist's need. (If his project is a long-term one, he would need a greater number of copies than for one of a short duration). For this particular example the research involved preparation of microscopic slides to determine the type, location and extent of damage inflicted on a plant by a certain disease. The investigator kept his data on a series of sheets upon which a perfect specimen was printed, and in addition to the required written notes he marked on the illustration the location and extent of damage observed on each slide. The drawing in each case acts as a map, so to speak. The perfect specimen is present

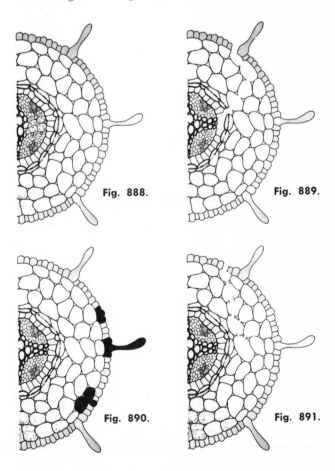

Fig. 888.   **Fig. 889.**

Fig. 890.   **Fig. 891.**

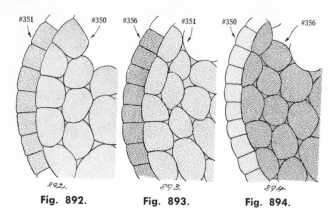

Fig. 892.   **Fig. 893.**   **Fig. 894.**

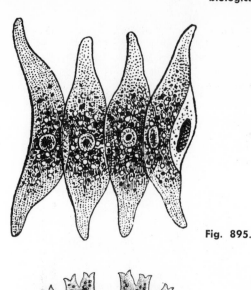

Fig. 895.

To further demonstrate tone coverage and the effect reduction has observe *Figs. 892-894* (the numbers indicate the tones which were used in each instance). These three figures are 50 per cent reductions of the original size. Be very careful to select the proper size for your original artwork in order that it will reproduce in a reduced size without losing any significant detail. Fine tones are especially prone to disappear in reduction, as seen in *Figs. 888-891.*

Accurate and appealing illustrations of microorganisms of plant origin are an interesting challenge to an illustrator. It helps considerably if he knows the subject; if not, it is advisable that he spend time with the scientist, viewing microscopic material and learning what to look for and which details are of importance. These may be easily overlooked by an illustrator, whereas, the scientist may regard them as significant disclosures in his particular field of research.

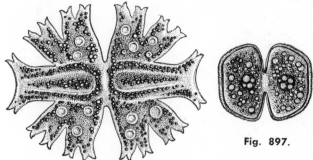

Fig. 896.   **Fig. 897**

The illustrating technique is determined by the amount of detail that is required; maximum taxonomic detail is best presented by line drawing. *Figs. 895* are examples, produced in their original size. Materials used in these figures were India ink, crowquill pen and three-ply Strathmore paper; inner details were worked out with dots, as was shading. Heavier lines denote the nucleus and/or nucleolus, seen in *Figs. 895-897.* A slightly different effect is seen in *Fig. 898*; instead of differentiating between body parts with the use of dots, a series of heavy lines achieved the desired results. You will note there is very little 3-D effect in these figures; they are taxonimically accurate and convey characteristics of importance but appear flat and without depth. This is partly due to the nature of the object and partly dependent upon the assignment; if taxonomy is of utmost importance, an illustration kept as simple as possible is preferred. In *Fig. 899*, using the same technique, you will note that

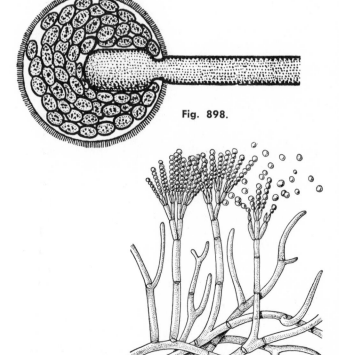

Fig. 898.

Fig. 899.

a 3-D effect is gained by regulating the density and size of the dots in the interior shaded areas.

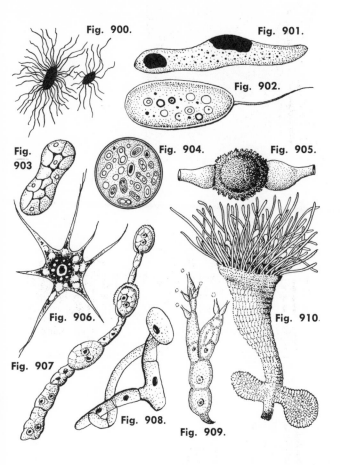

Fig. 900.   Fig. 901.

Fig. 902.

Fig. 903

Fig. 904.   Fig. 905.

Fig. 906.

Fig. 907

Fig. 908.

Fig. 909.

Fig. 910

Earlier, in discussing how to illustrate cacti, silhouette drawing was mentioned. This technique applies also to certain forms of microorganisms, such as Azotobacter where the outstanding feature is the flagella and the uppermost requirement is that they be demonstrated accurately in accordance with size, shape, placement and number (*Fig. 900*): a simple drawing such as this one is often sufficient for the purpose for which it is intended. *Fig. 901*, also simple in design but representing a 3-D effect, is a species of Clostridium; sulfur granules of the same species are shown in *Fig. 902*. The same technique is used in *Fig. 903*, showing zoospores, and in *Fig. 904* you will note a zoogloeal mass of cocci. *Fig. 905* demonstrates a Mucor having a mature zygospore; this area is heavily shaded and covered with prefabricated tone (No. 351 in this instance). Accentuate areas by using dark shading, as seen in *Fig. 906* of a polyphagous cell. It is preferable to obtain a 3-D effect, as in the aecial chain in *Fig. 907* or as demonstrated in *Fig. 908* unless the scientist specifies a preference for a simple flat draw-

ing, such as seen in *Fig. 909*. *Fig. 910* is a further example of this technique, having greater detail.

The smudging method may be used in illustrating microorganisms; *Fig. 911* shows the distribution of funguses in a liquid within a test tube. *Figs. 912* and *913* show characteristic shapes of colonies of fungi in a petri dish; another manner of illustrating the growth of a colony is seen in *Fig. 914, A-D*. An advantage in this technique is the ease with which corrections may be made — with an eraser changes are made quickly and unnoticeably in the finished product. An air brush may be used, but being a wet process it is more difficult to alter. This technique was discussed earlier (*Figs. 881-884*). An outline was made and cut out; this was used as a "negative" and fastened securely to the drawing paper. Areas may be shaded with carbon powder or the entire inner area uniformly darkened and the objects drawn into the background tone with an electric eraser; darker tones added last to bring out depth and surface characteristics. Completed artwork must be cleaned of fingerprints and sprayed with a protective spray.

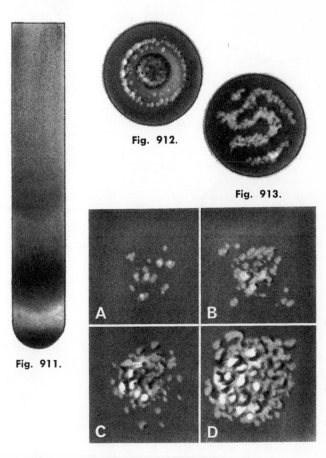

Fig. 912.

Fig. 913.

Fig. 911.

A   B

C   D

Fig. 914.

The technique is the same for enlarged details as in *Figs. 915-920*. Small units within an object may be outlined in pencil and shaded inwardly to bring out characteristics (*Fig. 915*). When using the "negative" method, start with simple shapes, as seen in *Figs. 918* and *919*; proceed to something more complicated, as in *Fig. 920*. Illustrations using this technique are reproduced by half-tones. The samples in *Figs. 915-920* are reduced to 66 per cent of the original size. Those in *Figs. 911-914* are reduced to 75 per cent.

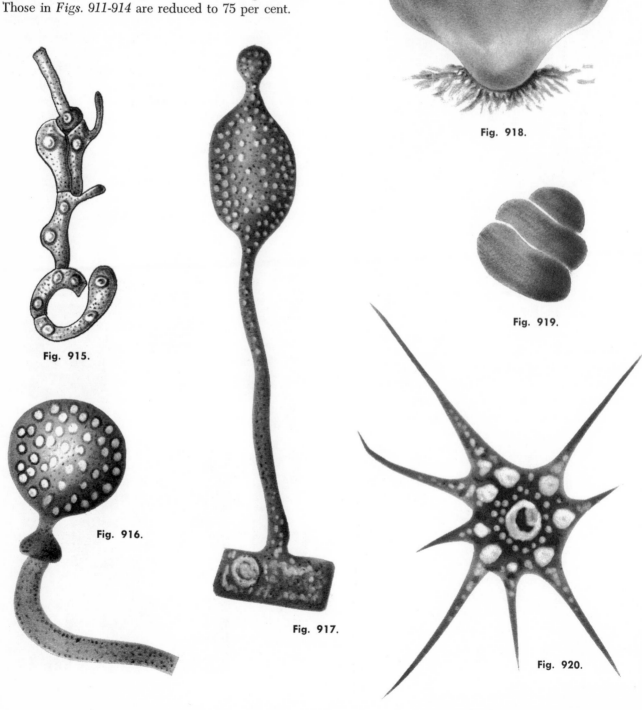

Fig. 918.

Fig. 919.

Fig. 915.

Fig. 916.

Fig. 917.

Fig. 920.

see how the shaded areas (dotted) show up through the prefabricated tone. *Fig. 922* (Distyoneurum sp.) pictures two leaves; the top one shows the outlined flow of details, while the leaf behind has some of the details worked out in India ink. Individual features, together with intermediate spaces, are shaded. *Fig. 923* is a smooth-leafed plant, the Alaria. Note how some areas are solid black in order to contrast with others which are covered with minute dots. Shading was applied in a manner to accentuate the waviness of the leaves. Irregular markings on the surface, shadings between these markings, and the flow of the ribs are characteristic of a Costaria and are illustrated in *Fig. 924*. An Iridae sp. (*Fig. 925*) has a distinct

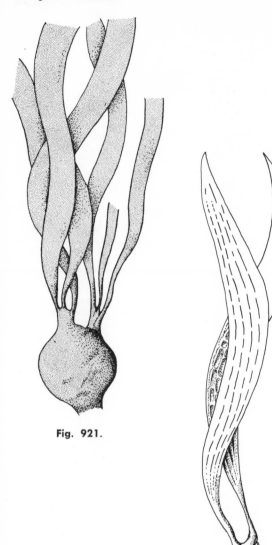

Fig. 921.

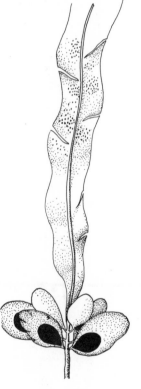

Fig. 922.

Fig. 923.

Fig. 924.

Marine plants are interesting, uncomplicated subjects to illustrate. For the most part they are smooth, quite large and the long "leaves" may be presented in an attractive manner. Here again, the technique depends upon the scientist's requirements, the extent of detail and the type of reproduction. To fulfill the threefold requirement of simplicity, accuracy and detail the best technique is line drawing with India ink; *Figs. 921-930* demonstrate this method. In *Fig. 921* (Nereocystis sp.) the surface is covered with prefabricated tone (No. 351) to obtain a grayish effect. The outlines and shading were done with crowquill pen and India ink. If you examine this figure, you will outline and shading gives "motion" to the leaves. A similar effect is achieved in *Fig. 926;* in this instance presurfaced paper (either pebble board or coquille board may be used) with India ink outlines and wax pencil shadings were used to create a Botryoglossum. Whenever use is made of wax pencil in an illustration, the finished artwork must be sprayed with clear plastic spray for protection against smearing. All of the figures in this series are reproduced in line cuts.

For comparison, half-tone reproductions (*Figs. 927-930*) are shown of *Figs. 923-926*. It is very important that backgrounds be opaqued on the negative before reproducing line drawings by half-tone process.

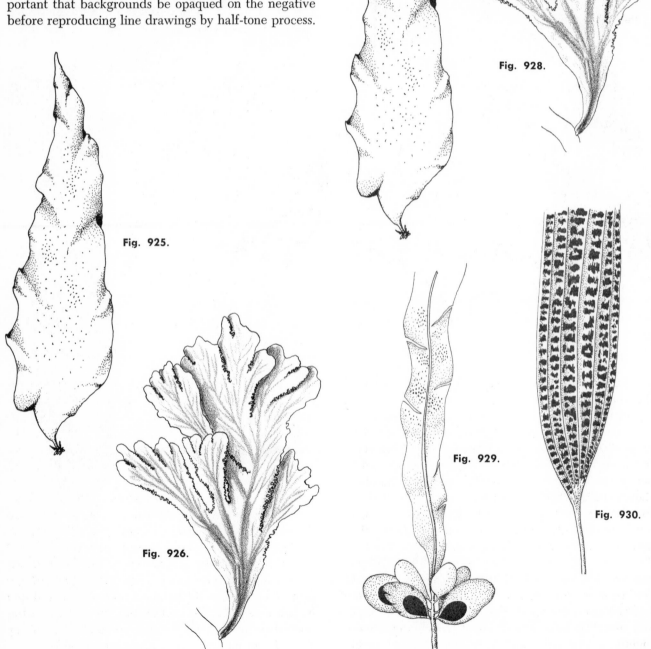

Fig. 927.

Fig. 928.

Fig. 925.

Fig. 926.

Fig. 929.

Fig. 930.

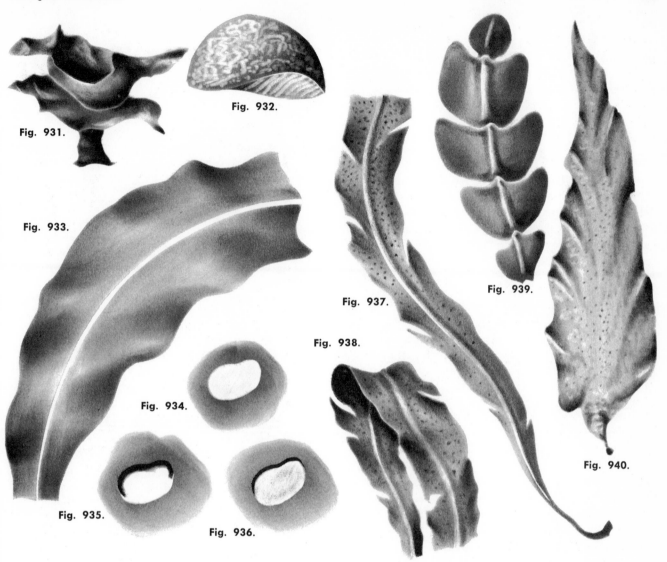

Fig. 931.

Fig. 932.

Fig. 933.

Fig. 934.

Fig. 935.

Fig. 936.

Fig. 937.

Fig. 938.

Fig. 939.

Fig. 940.

Marine plants may be attractively illustrated with the smudging technique (carbon powder and stump), especially those species having interesting shapes and large leaves. The steps have been mentioned previously in *Figs. 881, 911. Fig. 931* was drawn from three "negatives" to achieve the contrasting shades and to define the individual sections. A simpler example is shown in *Fig. 932.* Large wavy leaves are fun to draw; *Fig. 933* was left unfinished to show how the basic tones are applied and to demonstrate the smooth flow of contrasting densities. This effect was created on Strathmore two-ply medium-rough drawing paper; chamois skin was used for smearing the carbon powder. To show holes in the leaf place a cut-out on the leaf and erase the area (*Fig. 934*). To acquire depth and give the hole a 3-D effect, move the cut-out slightly to one side and add heavy carbon to the shaded side of the hole (*Fig. 935*). Now, move the cut-out back to the original position and erase the open portion once again (*Fig. 936*); clean excess carbon with an electric eraser. You will get a sharper outline if you use an electric eraser; the darkened area represents the thickness of the leaf and must be uniform and clearly defined. For half-tone reproduction the holes must be opaqued; observe the difference between *Figs. 934* and *936*, which were opaqued, and *Fig. 935* which was not opaqued. *Figs. 937-940* are further examples of this technique and may be used for practice material. Always spray the finished artwork with protective spray. *Figs. 931-940* are 67 per cent reductions of the originals and are reproduced in half-tone with the background opaqued. Illustrations done with this technique are reducible to any desired size and present a photographic effect.

Illustrations for Paleontology

You are now aware that no matter which field an illustrator specializes in, his work will offer an interesting and challenging career. There is scarcely an area in the illustrating profession that is more fascinating and stimulating than specimens of a paleontological nature. Quite frequently, as in drawing a brontosaurus of the Triassic Period, one has to extract from his imagination ideas for creating an artistic background, such as landscaping, vegetation and other small details. On the contrary, when illustrating fossils which he can hold in his hands or examine through a lens, he must decipher and record each minor detail in order to accurately and artistically present the ingredients which make up a paleontological specimen.

Fortunately, in most instances for this type of artwork there are specimens from which to draw; however, because of breakage or disintegration of some sort perhaps it is necessary to examine dozens of specimens to create one in its entirety. If sufficient specimens are not available, it must be drawn as it is.

As repeatedly mentioned, the technique depends upon the publisher's requirements, the scientist's choice, and/or the adaptability of a technique to a specific specimen.

One of the most preferred techniques for such illustrations is the use of presurfaced paper; either pebble board or coquille board. Simple drawings, as seen in *Figs. 942* and *943* and more detailed (*Fig. 944*) alike, are attractively drawn on this type of material using a combination of ink applied with a crowquill pen and wax pencil for shading effects.

Figure 941 employs the same technique and presents a specimen with a ringed surface. The outlines and internal dotted areas in *Figs. 942* and *943* were drawn with a crowquill pen on medium rough coquille board; these appear in their original size in *Figs. 945* and *946*. With a light touch of wax pencil the 3-D effect is achieved. *Figs. 942* and *943* are 50 per cent reductions of the originals and were reproduced in line cut; *Figs. 947* and *948* are also 50 per cent reductions but are reproduced in half-tone with background blocked out (opaqued).

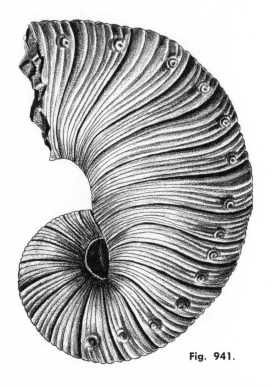

Fig. 941.

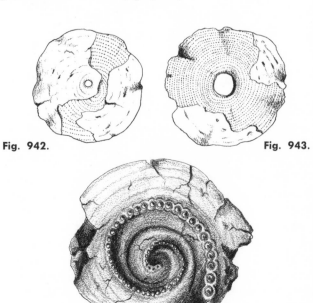

Fig. 942.

Fig. 943.

Fig. 944.

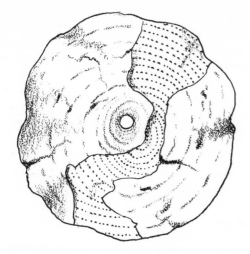

Fig. 945.

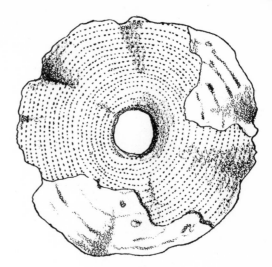

Fig. 946.

Fig. 947.

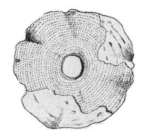

Fig. 948.

If you will examine *Fig. 949* you will see a very rough illustration in its original size. The outlines, the cracks on the surface and the pearl-like circles spiraling toward the center were drawn with ink and crowquill pen. The shading and 3-D effect were achieved by the use of a wax pencil. This illustration, reduced 50 per cent, may be seen in *Fig. 944* reproduced from a line negative, and in *Fig. 950* reproduced from a half-tone negative with the background opaqued; this picture has a photographic effect.

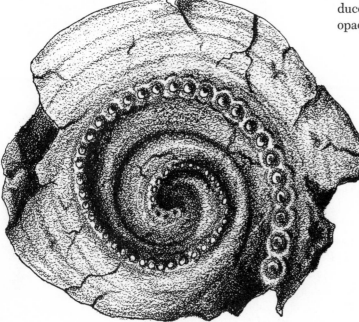

Fig. 949.

Fig. 950.

Fig. 952.

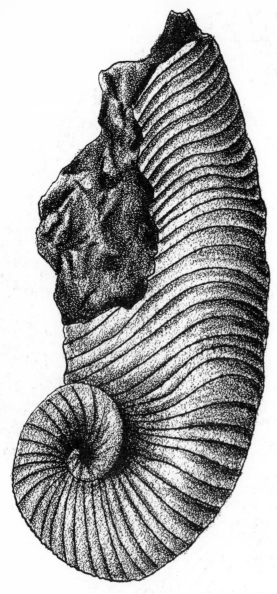

Fig. 951.   Fig. 953.

Turning to another example of the same technique
and materials, *Fig. 951* is, in its original size, a rough
drawing; the rings appear rugged and sharp. You can
see what a half-tone negative can do when you turn
to *Fig. 952*. This is a 50 per cent reduction; the roughness has disappeared and the illustration looks more
professional. You will get a smoother original if there
is a sharper contrast in shading, as seen in *Fig. 954*
in its original size. This drawing is reduced to 50 per
cent and reproduced from a line negative in *Fig. 941;*
Fig. 955 shows the same reduction and is printed from
a half-tone negative.

Fig. 954.

Fig. 955.

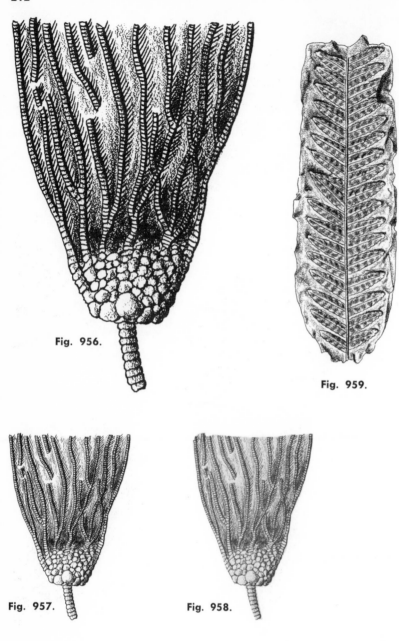

Fig. 956.

Fig. 957.

Fig. 958.

Fig. 959.

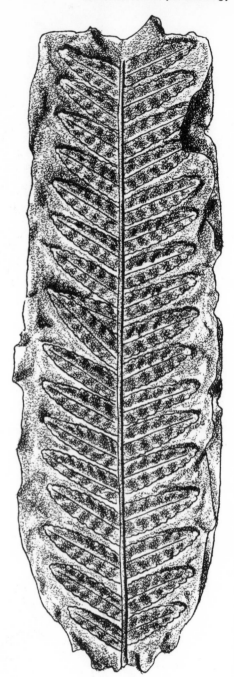

Fig. 960.

Figure 953 is an illustration, using the same technique, of a fossil fern, reduced to 50 per cent of the original (*Fig. 960*) and reproduced from a line negative. Compare the same original reduced proportionately and reproduced from a half-tone negative (*Fig. 959*). These reproductions will give you an idea of what may be expected in the two types of reproduction methods of a wax pencil illustration with ink outlines done on presurfaced coquille board. This type of material is extremely useful in illustrating paleontological specimens, especially if the specimen is imbedded, as in the case of this fern.

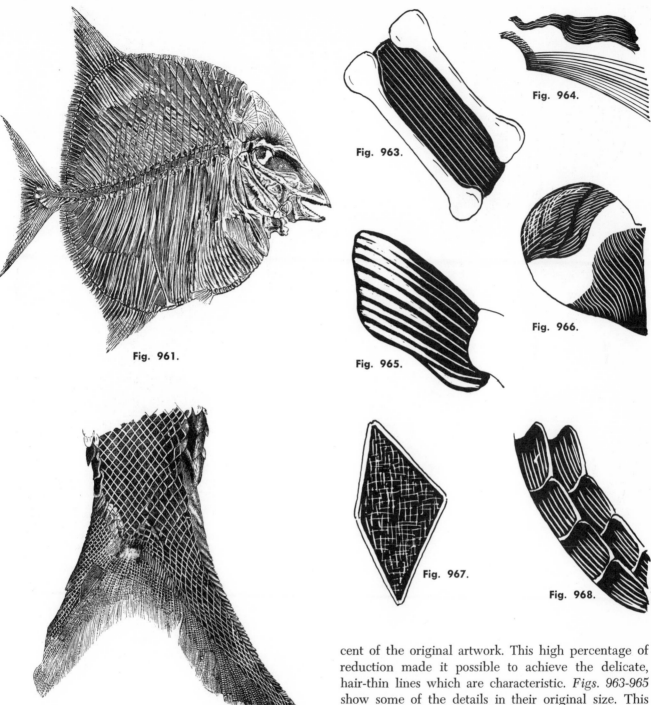

Fig. 961.

Fig. 963.

Fig. 964.

Fig. 965.

Fig. 966.

Fig. 962.

Fig. 967.

Fig. 968.

Another suitable technique, although more time-consuming, is the scratch board method. This is especially adaptive for drawing bone parts, such as the Microdon species (*Fig. 961*); reduced to 25 per cent of the original artwork. This high percentage of reduction made it possible to achieve the delicate, hair-thin lines which are characteristic. *Figs. 963-965* show some of the details in their original size. This technique lends itself to corrections and also to very effective detail and three-dimensional effects. *Fig. 962* is also reduced to 25 per cent of the original; note the detailed studies of portions of this Palaeoniscus species' tail in *Figs. 966-968*. Note the technique used to create the scaly effect and the method of representing the incomplete tail fin of the species. Compare the shading of the head area in *Fig. 961* and the over-all shading in *Fig. 962* and those with the shading used

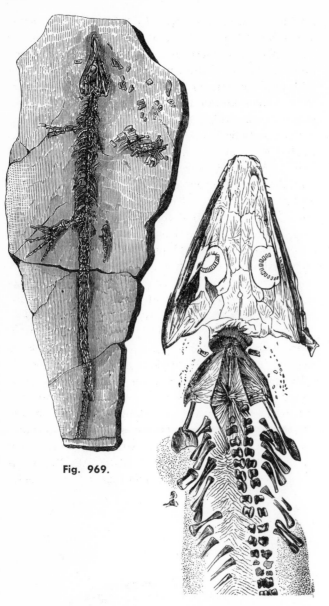

Fig. 969.

Fig. 970.

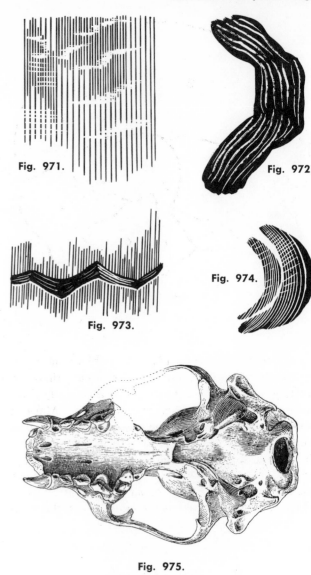

Fig. 971.

Fig. 972.

Fig. 973.

Fig. 974.

Fig. 975.

in *Fig. 969* to create this imbedded fossil's (Lepterpeton) portrait. The background in this figure is composed of solid lines broken with a scalpel (*Fig. 971*). Edges were painted black and after completely dry, lines were scraped to present the necessary shading (*Fig. 973*). *Fig. 969* is reduced to 25 per cent of the original. *Fig. 970* is an anterior portion of an Archegosaurus; it, too, is reduced to 25 per cent of the original. *Figs. 972* and *974* show the technique used in the composition of this species. Attention was given to the formation, shape and relative proportion in this illustration and a minimum of shading was used, leaving out background altogether.

More shading is used in the skull illustration of a Potamotherium sp. in *Fig. 975*; this is a drawing with crowquill pen and Pelikan India ink on semi-smooth Strathmore paper. Curved lines and darkened, cross-hatched areas create a 3-D effect; missing portion is represented with simple dotted lines. This illustration was reduced to 50 per cent of the original.

The smudging technique is excellent for illustrating paleontological species; using carbon powder and stumps on practically any type of paper. Either the three-ply Strathmore semi-smooth or the medium rough (No. 61) hot pressed illustration board is excellent for this technique. The fine texture on the surface helps achieve the required shading far easier than any of the slick surfaced drawing paper. This is

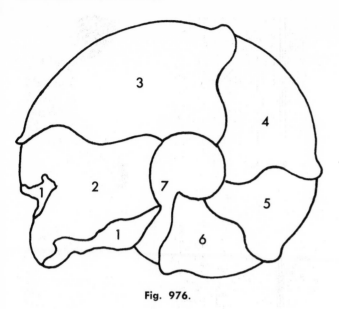

Fig. 976.

marked *1* fulfill this step). In this case these areas are chipped. Cut out the portion you have chosen for your base color; place this paper in the proper position on your final drawing paper and hold it down with masking tape on the edge of the drawing paper. With carbon powder and stump, applying varied pressures for contrasting shades, proceed to complete the cut-out portions of your drawing. If you feel the highlighted areas are too dark, lighten them with a soft eraser. When this much of the drawing is finished, tape the cut-out section back into the original outline. The next step is to cut out another area, such as in *Fig. 976*, No. 2. Place the sheet on your drawing board and with a stump or chamois skin darken the cut-out surface with carbon powder, shading as you go in order to gain a 3-D effect. When the entire section is completed to your satisfaction, replace the cut-out portion and secure it with masking tape and proceed with another portion, as in *Nos. 3, 4, 5* and *6*. After completion of *No. 6* (*Fig. 977*) the illustration, nearly complete, may be given additional details in shading; some areas lightened with an eraser, others made slightly darker. The center section (*No. 7*) was added with a finer stump, as were the lines representing the cracks. When the finishing touches are made, clean the background of excess carbon powder, fingerprints, etc., and spray artwork with a protective spray (*Fig. 978*). Illustrations made with this technique are reproducible from half-tone negatives only.

equally true if the original is to be in black and white or in color. Some helpful hints for saving time and creating impressive originals, especially if they are to be small in size are: Step one (*Fig. 976*): Make an outline and designate the various portions or areas, creating the proper proportions and dimensions as they relate to their components. If a damaged area is present, indicate this on your pencil outline. Use good-quality, smooth stationery paper (not bond). Decide where to place the base color (in *Fig. 976* the areas

Fig. 977.

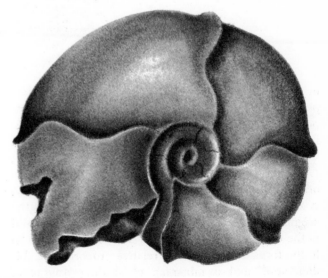

Fig. 978.

Fig. 979.

This step-by-step procedure is time-saving and produces an attractive drawing. However, it will not produce satisfactory results when fine outlines or minute details are present. In such instances details would be incorporated after the basic shading process is finished. Draw the details on your first sketch and transfer it onto the drawing board illustration with very light pressure, using a medium hard pencil (No.

2). This technique was used to create the illustration in *Fig. 979;* it is reduced 50 per cent. The original was done in full color, using pastel color on No. 61 illustration board. The basic color is brown with shades of orange and black. If done in black and white, this drawing could be reduced to 10 per cent of the original size. It is printed from a half-tone negative with the background blocked out.

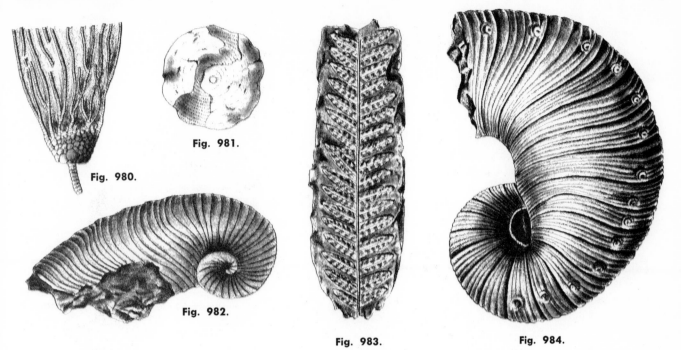

Fig. 980.

Fig. 981.

Fig. 982.

Fig. 983.

Fig. 984.

An illustrator will often experience discouragement when he sees his artwork in print. This is because the printer must work within a given space and in order to take advantage of all available room on a printed sheet, he may have to reduce an illustration greater than its reducible capacity. If time allows, the artist may redo an illustration so that it will not lose any of its detail. This loss in reduction is especially noticeable in line illustrations done on pebble or coqille board. It may be remedied by adding deeper shading with a fine carbon powder and a selection of stumps. In returning the original to the printer request that he reproduce the illustration in half-tone and opaque the background. Examples of this may be seen in *Figs. 980-984.* Compare these half-tone reproductions with line negatives presented earlier: *Fig. 980* with *956, 957* and *958; Fig. 981* with *943, 946* and *947; Fig. 982* with *951, 952; Fig. 983* with *953, 959* and *960; Fig. 984* with *941, 954, 955.* These presentations may help you to visualize the quality differnces in the two reproduction methods. A thorough knowledge of reproduction methods and illustrations most suitable to these techniques is a valuable asset to an illustrator.

Archeological Illustrations

All illustrators are interested to some degree in the history of art. It is fascinating to study the old techniques used in pictures and sculptures and to observe the high quality of skill, the keen sense of proportion and detail present even though the materials were crude and the tools primitive. Note the charcoal drawing in *Fig. 985* which is only a poor imitation drawn from a color slide of a reindeer painting done approximately 15,000 B.C. by a prehistoric man. The drawing is easily identified as a living animal. We cannot even imagine what tools might have been used to carve the outline into a rock wall, what implements may have been devised to smooth the surfaces within those true-to-life forms, nor how the colors were achieved which produced a work of art to withstand the ravages of time and weather and disaster. We can be sure that much time, patience and tenacity went into these masterpieces which we marvel at and adore.

Most archelogical illustrations must be drawn from photographs; there is seldom opportunity to see the actual objects. Many are preserved in their original locations, such as in caves or pyramids. Others are in museums in far corners of the world. An illustrator's job is made easier if he has several photographs taken at various angles from which to compose his drawing.

Fig. 985.

Fig. 986.

Fig. 987.

Fig. 988.

Fig. 989.

Fig. 990.

Fig. 991.

Fig. 992.

Oftentimes simple line drawings fulfill the need, especially in the case of carvings; *Fig. 986* is such a drawing of a mammoth. This technique may also be used in drawing tools, as in *Fig. 987*, adding a few lines to create a 3-D effect. Silhouette drawings are sometimes sufficient (*Figs. 988* and *989*), as are also the simple line drawings *Fig. 990* of the Fighting Bull; *Fig. 991* of the Farmer; and *Fig. 992* of the Fisherman.

Illustrating objects carved into rocks or wood is effectively done with the smudging technique, especially if background details are desired. Select a soft drawing paper with a rough surface. Make an outline on a sheet of tracing paper and place it over the drawing paper, keeping the clean side of the tracing paper in contact with the drawing paper. With the rounded end of a brush trace the outline, as you would with a pencil, applying heavy pressure which will make indentations or grooves in the drawing paper. Remove the tracing paper and apply charcoal powder, smearing with light strokes with a chamois skin instead of a stump. You will find that the impressed outline remains white and shows up on the darkened background; highlight the outline by applying additional shading. Work out damaged or cracked areas

with a sharpened Wolff's carbon pencil; blend these into the composition by touching lightly with a clean stump (*Fig. 993*).

If an illustrator has several objects from which to draw a series of illustrations and has a limited amount of time in which to produce them, the best method is the ink and wax pencil combination on presurfaced paper. Coquille board is available in a variety of surfaces; fine, medium, rough. The surface finish depends upon the size of the original artwork. If an artist prefers drawing large originals, he may use a rough surfaced coquille board, as was used in *Figs. 994 to 997*. The outlines are first done with light pencil lines, then inked. When illustrating arrow heads or other chipped objects (*Fig. 994*) the edges of the chipped surfaces should be outlined individually. Broken specimens are drawn the same way (*Fig. 995*); the same technique is used if the object has an ornamental or decorative appearance (*Figs. 996* and *997*). Shading is added to give a 3-D effect.

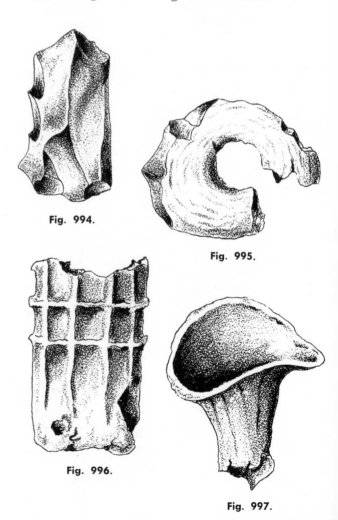

Fig. 994.

Fig. 995.

Fig. 996.

Fig. 997.

Fig. 993.

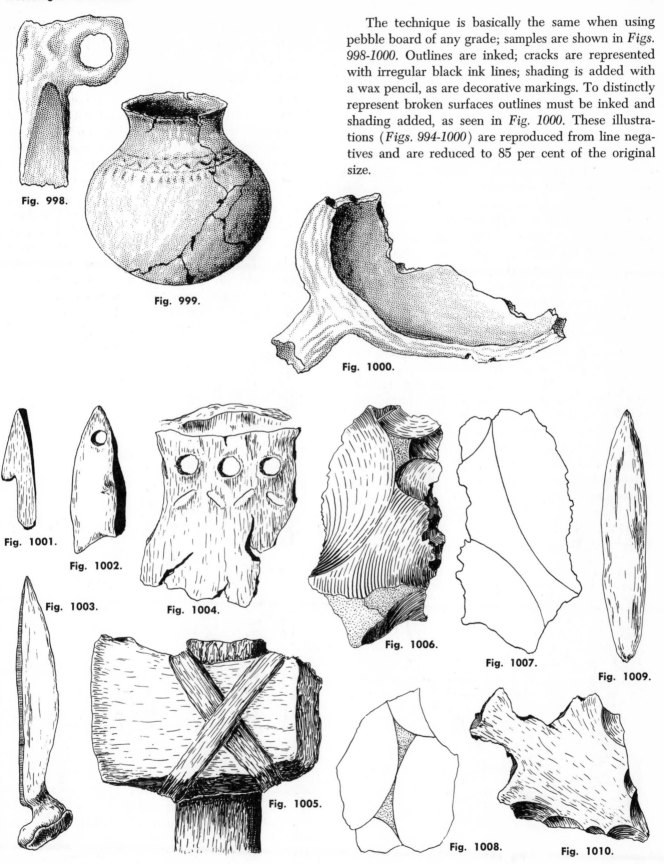

The technique is basically the same when using pebble board of any grade; samples are shown in *Figs. 998-1000.* Outlines are inked; cracks are represented with irregular black ink lines; shading is added with a wax pencil, as are decorative markings. To distinctly represent broken surfaces outlines must be inked and shading added, as seen in *Fig. 1000.* These illustrations (*Figs. 994-1000*) are reproduced from line negatives and are reduced to 85 per cent of the original size.

Fig. 998.

Fig. 999.

Fig. 1000.

Fig. 1001.

Fig. 1002.

Fig. 1003.

Fig. 1004.

Fig. 1005.

Fig. 1006.

Fig. 1007.

Fig. 1008.

Fig. 1009.

Fig. 1010.

Another excellent technique is the line drawing done with India ink. Samples may be seen in *Figs. 1001-1010.* Shading is also composed of lines of varying degrees of size and color. Strathmore two-ply drawing paper, crowquill pen and India ink were used in these figures. *Figs. 1001-1003* represent wooden objects; shading in *Figs. 1001* and *1002* was achieved with solid black areas; in *Fig. 1003* shading was accomplished with crosshatching. Earthenware objects are effectively illustrated using this technique (*Fig. 1004*); however, presurfaced paper or the smudging technique is preferable in this instance. *Figure 1005* is a quick line sketch of an ancient hatchet, employing three different grades of shading to represent the three different materials (rock, leather, wood). Split rocks (tools) are drawn easily and impressively with this technique (*Fig. 1006*). Note how the heavier shadings are represented by regulating the thickness of the individual lines. The flow and curvature of the lines helps to achieve the impression of a concave surface. Often it is necessary to illustrate such an object from two sides in order to present its true form. Usually the second view may be a simple outline, as seen in *Fig. 1007.* In *Fig. 1008* an object of similar shape is shown; chipped surfaces are left clear and unchipped portions are shaded with irregular dots. Smooth surfaced rock objects may be outlined and shaded with lines, as seen in *Fig. 1009.* Arrowheads must be illustrated with proper shading in order to register the chipped surfaces and the smooth natural characters of the rock (*Fig. 1010*). These illustrations are reproduced from line negatives, reduced to 75 per cent of the original size.

Excessive reduction of an illustration causes it to lose many of its details, especially the heavily shaded areas. The above illustrations are reproduced in *Fig. 1011* at 35 per cent reduction of the original size. Compare the individual drawings and the grade of proper shading that is necessary in order to maintain details through drastic reduction.

Half-tone reproductions are more costly; however, in some cases a publisher may apply the half-tone process to line drawings. This is permissible if the following circumstances prevail:

1. That rough surfaced coquille board is used in the original and wax pencil is used for shading (*Figs. 1012-1015*).

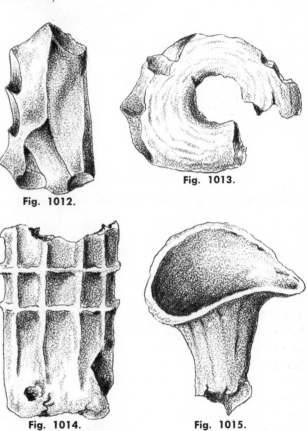

Fig. 1012.   Fig. 1013.

Fig. 1014.   Fig. 1015.

2. If pebble board is used and wax pencil for shading (*Figs. 1016-1018*). The half-tone will reproduce satisfactorily if the journal uses a good quality of paper and/or if the original must be reduced greatly. Details which may disappear in line reproduction may be preserved if the artwork is reproduced in half-tone under instances such as these. Compare the above seven figures with *Figs. 994-1000.* These half-tone reproductions are made from the same originals and are reduced to 80 per cent of the original size.

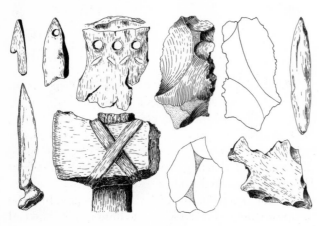

Fig. 1011.

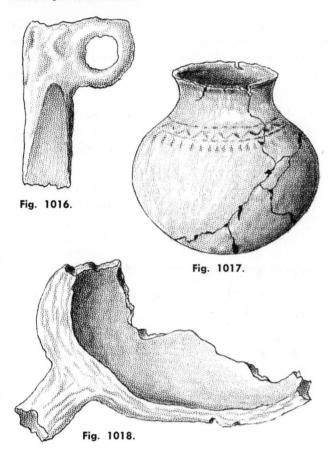

Fig. 1016.

Fig. 1017.

Fig. 1018.

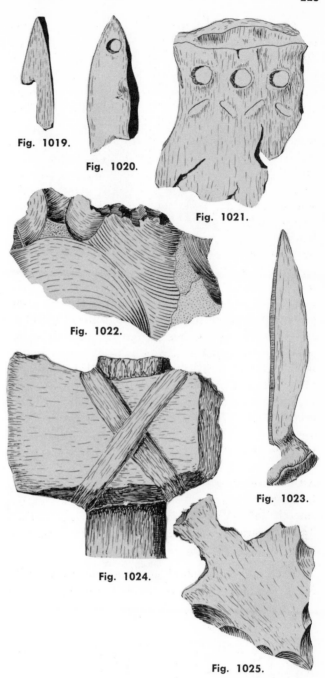

Fig. 1019.

Fig. 1020.

Fig. 1021.

Fig. 1022.

Fig. 1023.

Fig. 1024.

Fig. 1025.

In *Figs 1001-1010* we see some samples of ink line drawings reproduced from line negatives. In *Figs. 1019-1025* the same illustrations are reproduced in half-tone, the background blocked out on the negative to give the grayish overtone to the illustrations. Ink line drawings reproduced this way do not look very impressive, and their reproduction is more costly. Consequently, the illustrator must select the proper size of the original, and design the whole arrangement according to the page measurements of the journal in which the drawing will be published. If the editor receives illustrations made with this line technique, he will usually produce them in line negatives even if he must cut the negatives in pieces and arrange them differently according to the measurement of the page. This may require renumbering the illustrations which makes it confusing for the reader, especially if the numbers are not changed in the text. This is the author's problem at the time of proof reading, but the correct design, the right placement and the most suitable grade of shading are the illustrator's obligation.

Illustrating archeological (and related) specimens is best accomplished by the smudging technique. Compare *Fig. 1026* with similar ones (*Figs. 994, 1006, 1010* etc,) on the previous pages. It is a much faster technique and requires less practice, but good vision and organized thinking are required for the shading. This sample, reproduced in its original size, demonstrates the smoothness achieved with possibly the cheapest stump obtainable on medium-rough surfaced Strathmore drawing paper.

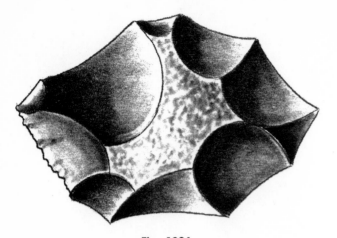

Fig. 1026.

The following illustrations are drawn with the same technique, the same stump and charcoal on the same side of the paper (two-ply Strathmore). In *Fig. 1027* and *1028* iron tools are illustrated. Outlines are done with No. 2 drawing pencil, shading with charcoal powder smeared in variable density with the stump; *Fig. 1029* also with No. 2 pencil outlines. The

dark shading inside the pot was done in two different ways: (1) inside of the opening on the top entirely with charcoal, and (2) the holes on the side were covered with India ink using a brush. The cracks on the lighter side were drawn with the same pencil as the outlines, those on the darker areas with Wolff's carbon pencil. The outline was drawn first, marking all the cracks and holes, holes were then covered with India ink. Starting on the top inside portion of the pot, shading was added from the darker areas toward the lighter, and finally, the upper, chipped edge. Then the outside, beginning with the darker side with a dull stump, working toward the lighter side with the same stump. After basic shading is completed the shading on the outside is smoothed by applying chamois skin without any carbon powder. After the shading is completed, the cracks are made more distinct with a sharp-pointed No. 2 pencil, and on the darker side with a sharp-pointed Wolff's carbon pencil. The same technique was used in *Figs. 1030-1032*. They are reduced to 74 per cent of the original size, and the background is opaqued out on the negative. The drawings have a somewhat photographic effect. They could be successfully reduced down to about 20 per cent of the original dimensions.

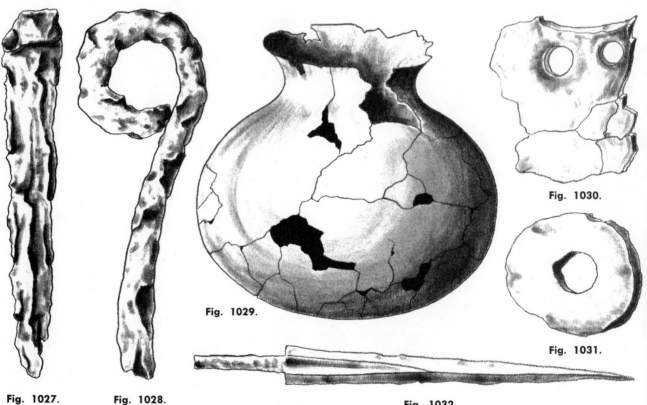

Fig. 1030.

Fig. 1029.

Fig. 1031.

Fig. 1027.   Fig. 1028.   Fig. 1032.

Archeological specimens of sculpture are the most difficult objects to properly illustrate. The illustrator must choose the technique which fits his ability and is adaptable to the structure of the specimen. Most may be illustrated very beautifully by applying the smudging technique, as we discussed in the previous captions. As an example, observe the head of Mykerinus (Egypt), where smooth lines (face) and geometric lines (ornaments) are represented with a generous supply of cracks and chipped areas. The statue is made from limestone. Now turn to *Fig. 1041* and study the details. Then turn back to *Fig. 1033*.

The following four figures are reproduced in original size to present the individual details:

Figure 1033: the upper right side of the statue. Note the energetic lines on the headdress, and their shading; the construction of the ear and that of the center of the headdress (only half of it is present). Note the grade of shading behind the ear and the highlights on the ornament. Analyze the chipped area, especially.

Fig. 1033.

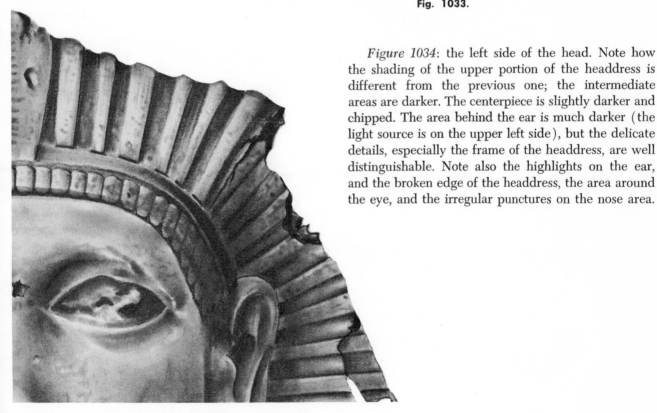

Fig. 1034.

Figure 1034: the left side of the head. Note how the shading of the upper portion of the headdress is different from the previous one; the intermediate areas are darker. The centerpiece is slightly darker and chipped. The area behind the ear is much darker (the light source is on the upper left side), but the delicate details, especially the frame of the headdress, are well distinguishable. Note also the highlights on the ear, and the broken edge of the headdress, the area around the eye, and the irregular punctures on the nose area.

Figure 1035: the lower right side. Observe the irregular outline and the manner in which the broken edges are shaded. It is obvious that part of the headdress is broken off and some parts are missing. Note the structural composition of the headdress and compare it with that of the face, neck and chin-rest. Pay special attention to the shading aspect of the chipped-out areas.

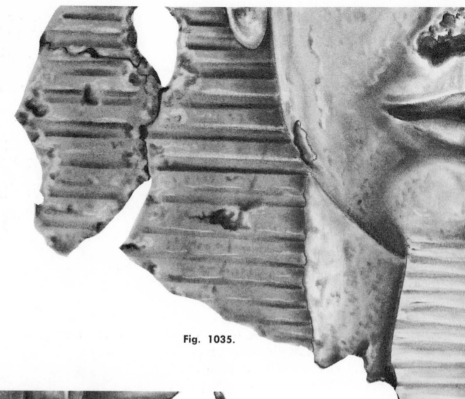

Fig. 1035.

Fig. 1036.

Figure 1036: is the lower left side of the statue. The darker, shaded side of it is presented in this figure; compare the tones with the previous illustration. Note how the broken parts fit together and how the headdress is shaded below the left ear. Chipped areas and stain marks on the cheek are well visible on this side. The chin-rest is slightly darker, the area behind it is darker yet, but the end of the headdress which tilts slightly forward is lighter.

Fig. 1037.

Fig. 1038.

Figures 1037 and *1038* (the same drawing reduced to 27 per cent of the original size) demonstrate the result of half-tone negatives made two different ways: *Fig. 1037* contains all the details on a smaller scale. The shading is effective, the light areas are not too light nor the dark ones too dark. The background would be gray in this print if it were not blocked out with opaque paint. Opaquing is usually a time-consuming process; that is why editors dislike and try to avoid it whenever possible. *Fig. 1038* demonstrates how an illustration will appear in print when the editor attempts to block out the background photographically; the result is a loss of detail, light areas appearing too light and dark ones too dark. Both reproductions are acceptable; unless the difference were explained and demonstrated side by side, undoubtedly the viewer would not detect the dissimilarity.

For the original No. 61 medium-weight, hot-pressed Hi-Art illustration board, carbon powder and different sizes of stumps, both soft and hard, were used. There are two techniques worth mentioning here: (1) observe the lower left portion of the headdress in *Fig. 1035*; the rough surface of the limestone is vividly reflected. Smudging was done with a soft-textured stump and highlights were added with a sharp-edged, soft eraser. (2) Refer to *Fig. 1036*; note the lower right-hand portion of the headdress. The texture is smooth on the wider (lighter) horizontal lines, where a hard stump was used, and the narrower, darker areas between them reflect the limestone quality. These were done with a soft stump and

slightly more powder was applied with very light pressure.

In *Fig. 1039* you see samples of Strathmore paper, medium hard stumps and charcoal powder; the upper figure was done on the smoother side of the paper, the lower on the rougher side. Both are satisfactory. A very sensitive, white clay coated paper, called Beverly Brilliant, was used in *Fig. 1040*. This paper is

Fig. 1039.   Fig. 1040.

Fig. 1041.

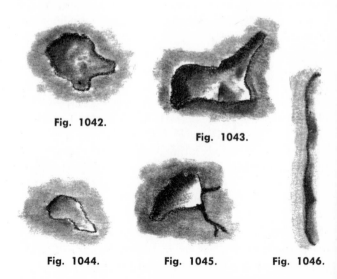

Fig. 1042.

Fig. 1043.

excellent for pastel color work but is extremely sensitive to black. Erasers may be used on both kinds of
paper. In *Figs. 1042-1045* there are some detail ideas
for shading chipped-out surfaces and also that of a
continuous crack. Some of them are shallow (*Fig.
1042* and *1044*) and others are deeper (*Fig. 1043* and
1045). Outlines are drawn with Wolff's charcoal pencil, well sharpened, and slightly smudged where
cracks must be represented (*Fig. 1046*).

Fig. 1044.   Fig. 1045.   Fig. 1046.

Fig. 1047.

Figure 1047 is another example of a charcoal illustration (Ermafrodite) which reflects the texture of stained marble. Whereas the previous sample (*Fig. 1035*) reflects the structural roughness of limestone, the smooth surface of the marble is shown here. Stain marks around the neck area and back probably originated from the chemical reaction of the soil in which this sculpture was buried for a few centuries. This illustration was drawn on Hi-Art No. 69 illustration board with charcoal powder. Chamois skin was used for shading the body; the rest of the picture was shaded with stumps of various sizes. Study the light reflection around the eye (see also Fig. *1048*), on the hair (see also *Fig. 1049*), and on the robe. Note the highlight on the right shoulder and how the light reflects from it to the lower chin and the front of the neck. The stained areas are more densely covered with charcoal and smeared with a hard stump. The white

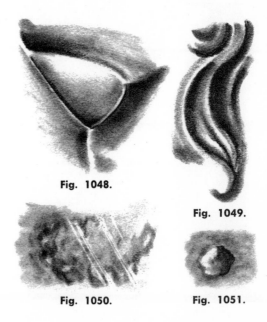

Fig. 1048.

Fig. 1049.

Fig. 1050.

Fig. 1051.

scratch marks on the surface were achieved by the use of a sharp eraser (see also *Fig. 1050*). Study the construction of the pitted areas (*Fig. 1051*), especially on the face and the right arm. In shading those areas the light reflection must be studied and the shading properly applied. This illustration is reduced to 35 per cent of the original size.

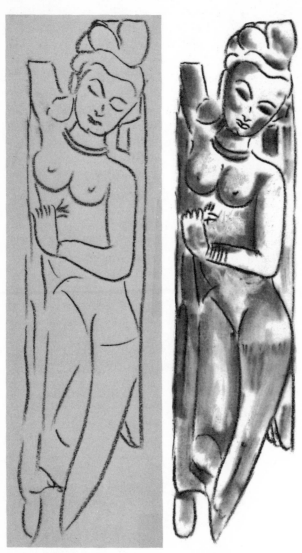

Fig. 1052.   Fig. 1053.

Fig. 1054.

The next sample is also a charcoal drawing, demonstrating the technique of illustrating a wooden structure (*Fig. 1054*). The first step, as previously explained, is the fairly accurate outline (*Fig. 1052*), followed by shading the darker areas lightly with a very soft stump. This step is important; it guides you through the entire composition and helps achieve the 3-D effect (*Fig. 1053*). The next step is to smooth out the heavy shades. Do not use a hard stump except where, sharp lines are desired. Analyze *Fig. 1055* (reduced to 60 per cent of the original size), especially the headdress, hair and neck decoration. Note the areas where the artist cut across the grain of the wood; those cross-cuts are represented by dark, irregular lines, as seen on the upper left-hand ornament in the headdress and on the under surface of the bust. If some of the shaded areas are too dark, try to avoid using an eraser; they may be lightened with a clean chamois skin applied first very lightly then with heavier pressure. The woody effect is easy to achieve. All wood has a degree of visible grain marking; cover are area with charcoal, using a soft stump. With a sharp pencil add some uneven, vertical lines which are more or less parallel (*Fig. 1056*). You now have the basic elements of the longitudinal grain marks. If the grains are cut crosswise, as the under surface of the bust (*Fig. 1057*), apply a few irregular darker lines and dots with a sharp-pointed Wolff's carbon pencil. Now go back to the longitudinal grain and make some of the lines slightly heavier. Using a sharp-edge soft eraser, erase a white line on one side of the dark line. You have now learned how to illustrate cracks on the

Fig. 1055.

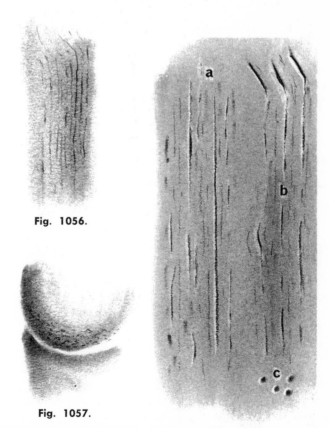

Fig. 1056.

Fig. 1057.

Fig. 1058.

surface (*Fig. 1058a*). If the cracks are deep, especially at a turned angle, use an occasional heavier dark line (*Fig. 1058b*). Wooden sculptures are frequently marred by woodborers. Such holes as these are easy to illustrate; clean a small area with a sharp pointed electric eraser, then add a dark dot, placing it off-center. The partially white margin helps create the 3-D effect even when making simple holes on a smooth surface (*Fig. 1058c*). If the cracks are deep, as on the right side of the face and across the right bust, make the dark line heavier in the middle, tapering off gradually toward the ends. The parallel white line must be thin. If the crack is long and goes through a larger portion of the sculpture, those black and white lines should follow the curvature of the surface, as seen in *Fig. 1054* (also in *Fig. 1055* in greater detail). The heavy crack on the face tapers off through the neck, widens across the left bust and below that almost disappears, then continues across the middle of the left lower arm, through the stomach and ends at the pelvic area. For practice analyze these figures and trace down the continuation of the cracks.

When the major cracks are finished, apply a sharp-pointed Wolff's carbon pencil to add to the grainy appearance of the surface (*Fig. 1058*), always following the curvature of the body. Examples may be seen on the chest area, the shoulder and above the eyes.

As mentioned earlier, working with charcoal, stumps and chamois skin is a dirty job. You must keep the paper free of fingerprints (*Fig. 883*). It takes practice to keep a uniform tone throughout the entire composition. This original drawing was 23 inches long; it required frequent checking from a distance to plan every stroke in advance. This type of illustration requires a darker background (*Fig. 1054*), which, in this case, was also done with charcoal and smeared with chamois skin.

When your artwork is completed, set it aside for a few hours or perhaps even several days. Study it periodically for details and correctness. When you are satisfied with its appearance, spray it lightly with protective (Krylon) clear spray three or four times at half-hour intervals. Illustrations made with this technique are reproducible in half-tone only. If the artwork is precise and attractive, the printed illustration will appear similar in tone quality to a sharply detailed photograph.

In examining masterpieces by scientific illustrators of the old days, we find much excellent art work, uniform shading, fine "screens" and lines. Those beauties were all hand made so masterfully that they would be very difficult to duplicate today. When the patience, enthusiasm, love and courage necessary to a great artistic undertaking started to disappear gradually, artificially prefabricated tone-types were created for the benefit of illustrators of our days who claim not to have enough patience or are pressed by the notorious shortage of time, a by-product of our rapidly developing culture.

Prefabricated tones are widely used today especially in illustrations of technical, mechanical and statistical nature. Just using two varieties of tones in a simple table-work layout (*Fig. 1059*) makes the drawing more compact and artistic. Creating a series of bar graphs, if these bars were clear, eventually only numbered (*Fig. 1060*) they would appear necked, unimpressive and flat. Adding three different tones to them (*Fig. 1061*) the illustration will be clearer, impressive and more artistic. When creating distribution maps of any kind, those tones are quite appropriate (*Fig. 1062*). In designing covers for books, or in advertising, artists commonly use this material in a great

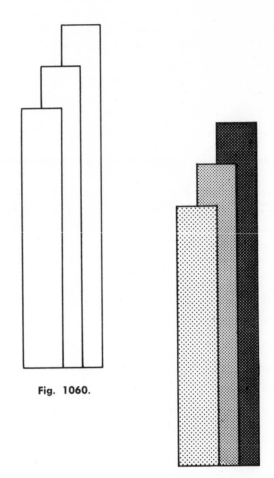

Fig. 1060.

Fig. 1061.

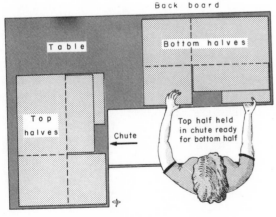

Fig. 1059.

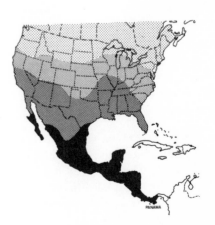

Fig. 1062.

variety of forms and shades (*Figs. 1063* and *1064*). At the end of this chapter (pages *241-244*) are some of the most commonly used tones reproduced in their original size (*Figs. 1089-1156*).

Fig. 1063.

Fig. 1064.

There are several kinds of prefabricated tones on the market today. It is hard to recommend any of them, especially because their practicality depends entirely upon the requirements and the ability of the illustrator. There are two important kinds on the market:

1. *Craf-Tone,* manufactured in the United States and available in better art stores. The patterns (tones) are printed in black or white (some in color) on thin gauge, no glare matte acetate sheets, which are adhesively backed for easy application (*Figs. 1089-1156*). The popular size is 8 x 12 inches, but larger sizes are also available. They are also produced in a heat-resistant form with adhesive back for artwork to be reproduced in the form of blueprint or to be used in an ozalid type of machine. For other sizes, tones and colors consult the manufacturer's catalog.

2. *Instantex* is printed on treated paper. As of now only 19 different patterns and black are available (*Figs. 1158-1166*). They are well designed, extremely clear in print, and the application is simple. They are made in England and available in better art stores in 10 x 15 inch sheets. The completed product (artwork) is sharp, deep black and matte in finish.

There are other makes on the market. Perhaps the best known is the *Zip-A-Tone,* which works the same way as Craf-Tone. The disadvantage is that most of the sheets still on the market have a glossy finish, which causes quite a problem in reproducing the illustration. They are good, accurate, and if the glossy sheets were to be replaced with dull finished ones, it would be a product you may well like.

The use of tones with adhesive backing is a simple process, but requires caution and some practice. The basic steps can be summarized as follows:

(1) Check artwork for cleanliness; all pencil marks, dirt, dust, powder, eraser chips, etc. have to be completely removed. If ink lettering is required, do it *before* applying the tones.

(2) Place the tone sheet on top of the required area; press gently and evenly throughout starting from the center of the surface.

(3) With a sharp blade cut the pattern sheet along the layout line. If this line is not inked in, then it must be drawn with a sharp *light blue* pencil. After the cut is made, cover the tone with a piece of tracing paper and use slightly harder pressure. Avoid wrinkling the surface.

(4) Cover the artwork with a thin sheet of paper for protection. Take a photograph of the product, and if it is satisfactory, mail it for publication. If the artwork contains great details in tones, it is better to mail the original artwork to the publisher. Keep the tone sheets and the finished artwork in a cool place unless the tones are heat-resistant. In warm air, the tones will peel and shrink to a certain degree. Do *not* use any kind of protective spray over these tones. This applies to all tones printed on acetate sheets and having adhesive backing.

Using the nonadhesive backed tones the handling is much simpler:

(1) Place the tone sheet on top of your outline, which may be an inked or a blue pencil outline. Secure the sheet to keep it from moving, then rub the area desired on the backing sheet with a smooth surfaced rounded stylus (*Fig. 1065*).

(2) Peel off the backing sheet and the pattern will stick to the drawing paper (*Fig. 1066*). It is advisable to cover the toned area with tracing paper and gently press the toned areas to the drawing paper. Spray the finished product for protection. If you have to make corrections, e.g., the tone was accidentally rubbed off outside of the required area, use any kind of eraser to remove the excess tone. Do the correction before spraying.

The *storage* of tone sheets must be mentioned: keep them in a cool place if possible. They dry out easily in constant heat and will not be usable. It is best to keep them in a tight box at least at room

temperature. Store them in separate folders according to pattern for easier handling. Do not leave them unprotected.

You must be careful when purchasing these sheets. Check them, especially those with adhesive backing, to be sure that they are still usable (not dry). Then check on the pattern: it should be uniform, with no areas where the lines are broken or the dots missing. Do not buy too many at once; whenever possible, work with fresh material. Study the manufacturer's catalog before ordering patterns. Set up a list of numbers on your original artwork then check and compare with the printed product. This way you may learn a great deal and you will be able to correct mistakes.

If you are not familiar with the use of any of the foregoing tones, let me suggest some practical samples to practice on. First go through the remaining pages of this book and make a general study of the illustrations. You may be surprised at how many different things can be created with these tones.

rub down

Fig. 1065.

Fig. 1066.

peel off

ABCDEFGHIJK
Fig. 1067.

ABCDEFGHIJK
Fig. 1068.

ABCDEFGHIJK
Fig. 1069.

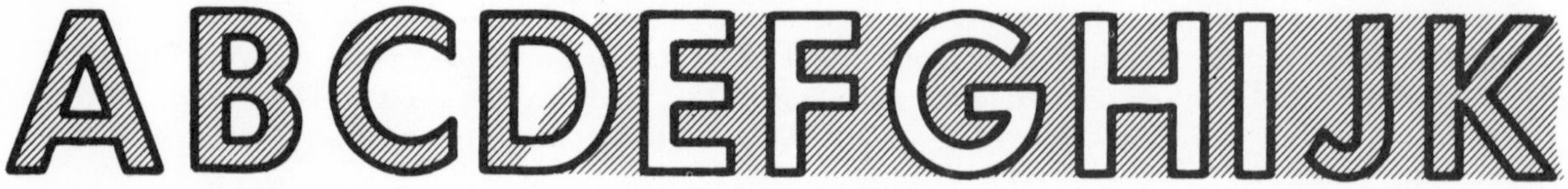

ABCDEFGHIJK
Fig. 1070.

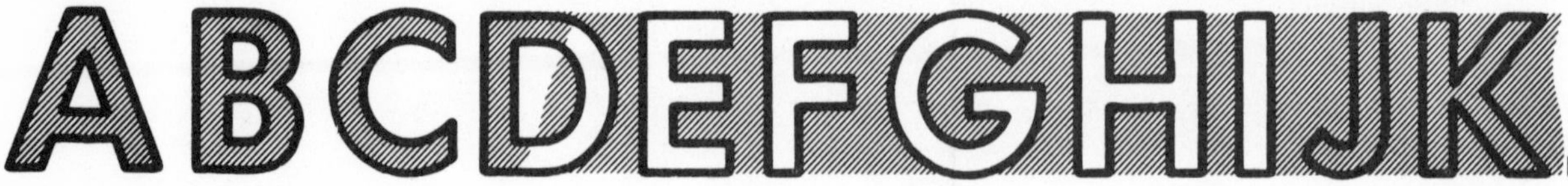

ABCDEFGHIJK
Fig. 1071.

Let us practice first with tones with *adhesive backing*. Take a piece of illustration board or three-ply Strathmore drawing paper and draw the letters of the alphabet in outlines. Use Leroy pen No. 3 or 4 according the size of your letters (*Fig. 1067*). After the ink is well dried and the drawing paper is clean, cover the letters with one type of tone. To be sure that all of them are well covered, cut the tone-strip slightly wider than the height of the letters (*Fig. 1068*) or evenly with the outer edge of the ink lines (*Figs. 1069-1071*). The cut around the letters should be made with a sharp (possibly new) single-edged razor blade so that you cut the tone approximately in the center of the ink outline by using light pressure. If the letters should be toned, peel off the acetate sheet outside of the letters (as on *ABC*) or, reversing the procedure, you will end up with light letters on shaded background (as in *EFGHI*). If you use rough tones (*Fig. 1068*) it may be possible that some of the letters, especially if they are smaller, will be hard to see (like *JK*). For this reason, it is very important to select the right size letters with outlines of various

thickness. On *Fig. 1072* the same samples are reproduced in 50 per cent reduction to demonstrate how these different tones will appear after they are reduced. Analyze and compare with density of the line shadings in the original size (*Figs. 1069-1071*) with those in the reduction.

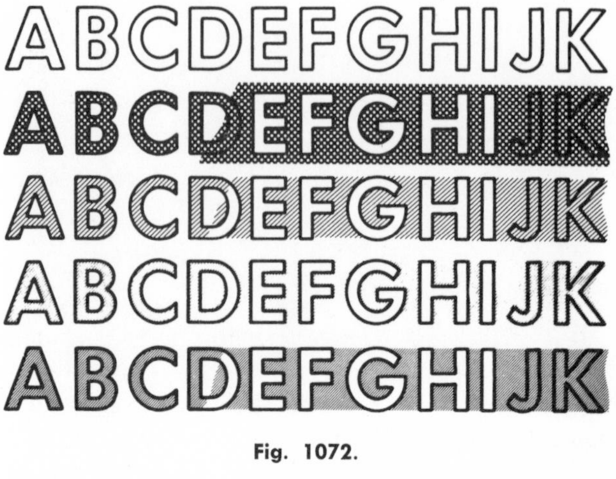

ABCDEFGHIJK
ABCDEFGHIJK
ABCDEFGHIJK
ABCDEFGHIJK
ABCDEFGHIJK

Fig. 1072.

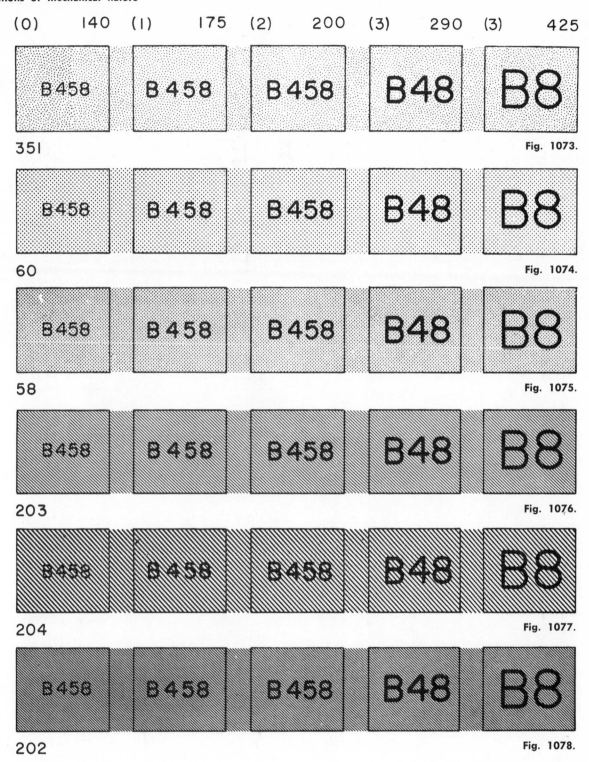

(0)   140   (1)   175   (2)   200   (3)   290   (3)   425

B458   B458   B458   B48   B8

351   Fig. 1073.

B458   B458   B458   B48   B8

60   Fig. 1074.

B458   B458   B458   B48   B8

58   Fig. 1075.

B458   B458   B458   B48   B8

203   Fig. 1076.

B458   B458   B458   B48   B8

204   Fig. 1077.

B458   B458   B458   B48   B8

202   Fig. 1078.

It is of the utmost importance to select the proper tone when single-line letters must be covered. Often the illustrator uses fine tone for the background, hoping that the small and fine letters will be well visible in print. To avoid disappointment study the samples in *Figs. 1073-1078*, and compare the 50 per cent reduction in *Fig. 1079.*

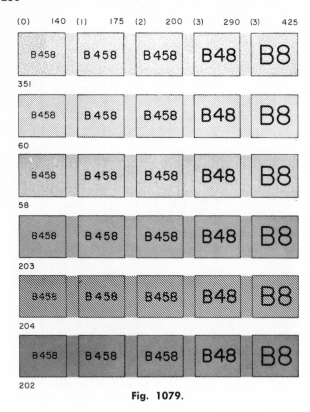

Fig. 1079.

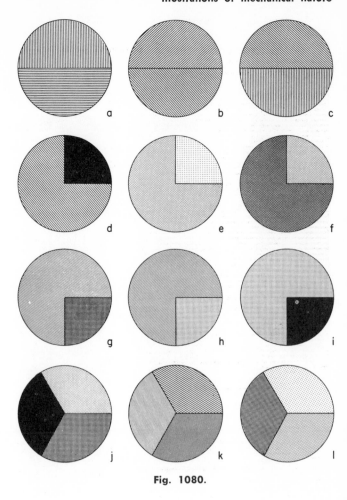

Fig. 1080.

Often the illustrator has to combine two or more tones in one figure. This is particularly true if a graph is to be prepared, whether it is of the column or circular type. On *Fig. 1080* we have a few examples of tones mixed differently for a general guide to show how the different patterns fit or do not fit together. They are reduced to 50 per cent of the original size.

Tones, especially those composed of parallel lines placed at even distances from each other, have a great many uses other than for shading backgrounds or blocking out areas within a map. One of the lesser known uses is for composing scales or rulers. In *Fig. 1081* there is a pictorial explanation showing how accurate scales (or rulers) can be composed. In this way, a tremendous amount of time is saved and accuracy is obtained with little effort. Follow the steps exactly, and check for the presentation of each step on this figure. In our sample we are going to make a centimeter scale where each millimeter, half-centimeter and centimeter is marked. Steps:

1. Set the width of the area which will be divided into the mentioned divisions (mm., 1/2 cm., cm.). Then cover the surface with parallel lined tones (in our sample, Craf-Tone, sheet No. 267), after the three

vertical lines are inked in. The three lines are the ends of

a for the millimeter lines
b for the half-centimeter lines, and
c for the centimeter lines.

Be sure that the vertical edge of the scale (at the left) is inked in also.

2. Make two cuts parallel to the vertical edge line through the parallel lines *a* and *b*. Then check that the *c*-cut is parallel to all.

3. Start peeling off the tone first in the centimeter section, are area between the *b* and *c* lines. The base of the scale (on the bottom) is line number one. Count 10 lines, and make a cut between lines 9 and 10. Now peel off the tone between lines 1 and 10. The next step is to cut between lines 10 and 11, and 19 and 20, etc. When you reach the end, the centimeter divisions are completed.

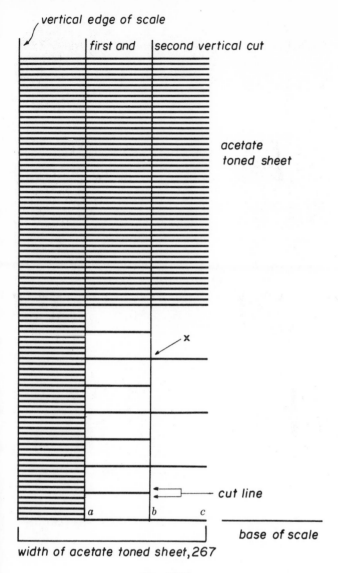

vertical edge of scale

first and | *second vertical cut*

acetate toned sheet

x

— cut line

a   b   c

base of scale

width of acetate toned sheet, 267

Fig. 1081.

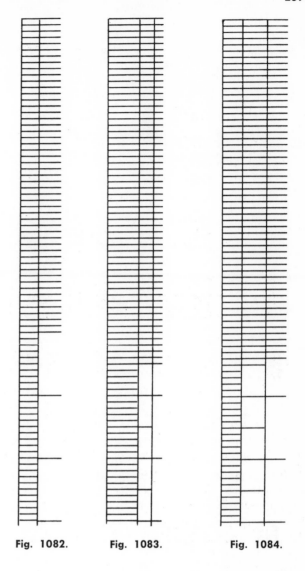

Fig. 1082.   **Fig. 1083.**   **Fig. 1084.**

The next is the half-centimeter zone, between the first (*a*) and second (*b*) vertical cuts. Count five lines; take the base scale line as line 1. Cut between lines 1 and 2, and 4 and 5. Then peel off the tone. The next is the cut between lines 5 and 6, and 9 and 10. Peel off tone. Continue the same all the way through. This will complete the half-centimeter scale. The next (left) vertical column represents the millimeters. After the required numbering is done, your job is completed. The original artwork then can be reduced photographically to the 1:1 centimeter scale or to any size scale required.

There are three styles recommended to create similar scales; these are illustrated in *Figs. 1082-1084,*

where tone sheet No. 266 was used. With this technique you are able to create any scale you need, in any size and in any division with a great variety of details and labeling or numbering.

It is also quite easy to use tones for covering background when you are using preprinted letters, such as those in the Craf-Type series. For background tones either dots (*Fig. 1085*) or lines (*Fig. 1086*) are recommended. Place the letters, which are printed on the same material as the tones itself (adhesive backing), in the right position, press hard to the paper then cover it with the desired background tone and cut gently with an extra sharp razor on the black (printed) areas of the individual letters. If you want to keep the letter white, leave the tone on the background, peel it off from inside the outline of the letter. If toned letters are desired in a white background,

Fig. 1085.

Fig. 1086.

peel off the background tone and keep the inside of the letter covered (*Fig. 1087*).

Somtimes white letters are needed. If you are not able to find white letters already printed for this purpose (as Craf-Type, or even better, Instant Lettering, which is also known as Letraset) then draw the outline of the letters, cover the whole area with red tone (Craf-Tone, red), then cut out the inside portion of the letters and peel off tone from these areas. White letters are the result. In shooting this for black and white reproduction, the red color will appear as white on the negative and will show as a black background in print (*Fig. 1088*).

Fig. 1087.

**WASHINGTON.
10.12.1942. %**

Fig. 1088.

On the following pages, in *Figs. 1089* to *1156*, is a collection of commonly used tones and styles. I recommend that you have these on hand in your studio. For detailed information on other types consult the manufacturer's catalog (Craf-Tone).

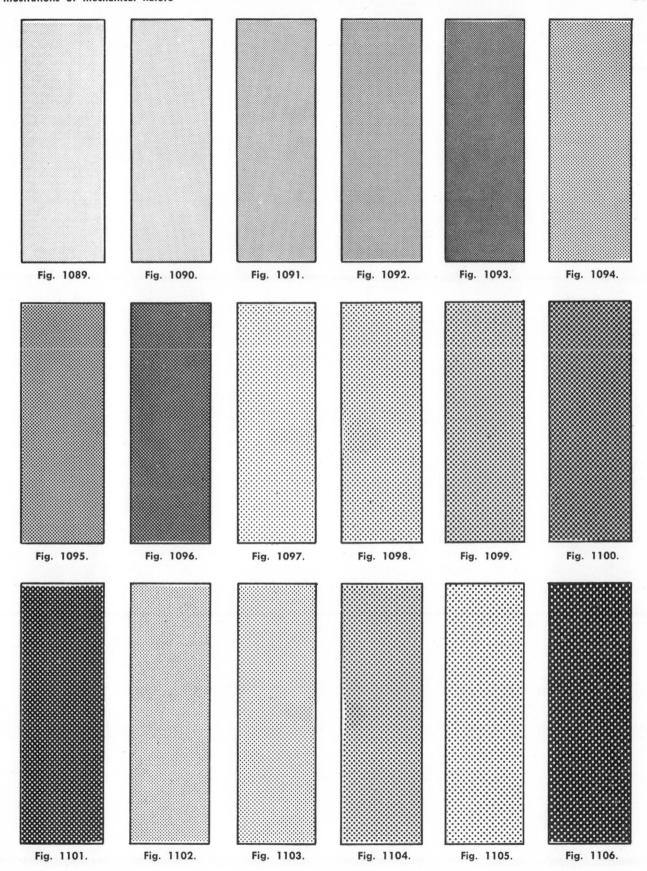

Fig. 1089. Fig. 1090. Fig. 1091. Fig. 1092. Fig. 1093. Fig. 1094.

Fig. 1095. Fig. 1096. Fig. 1097. Fig. 1098. Fig. 1099. Fig. 1100.

Fig. 1101. Fig. 1102. Fig. 1103. Fig. 1104. Fig. 1105. Fig. 1106.

Fig. 1107. Fig. 1108. Fig. 1109. Fig. 1110. Fig. 1111. Fig. 1112.

Fig. 1113. Fig. 1114. Fig. 1115. Fig. 1116. Fig. 1117. Fig. 1118.

Fig. 1119. Fig. 1120. Fig. 1121. Fig. 1122. Fig. 1123. Fig. 1124.

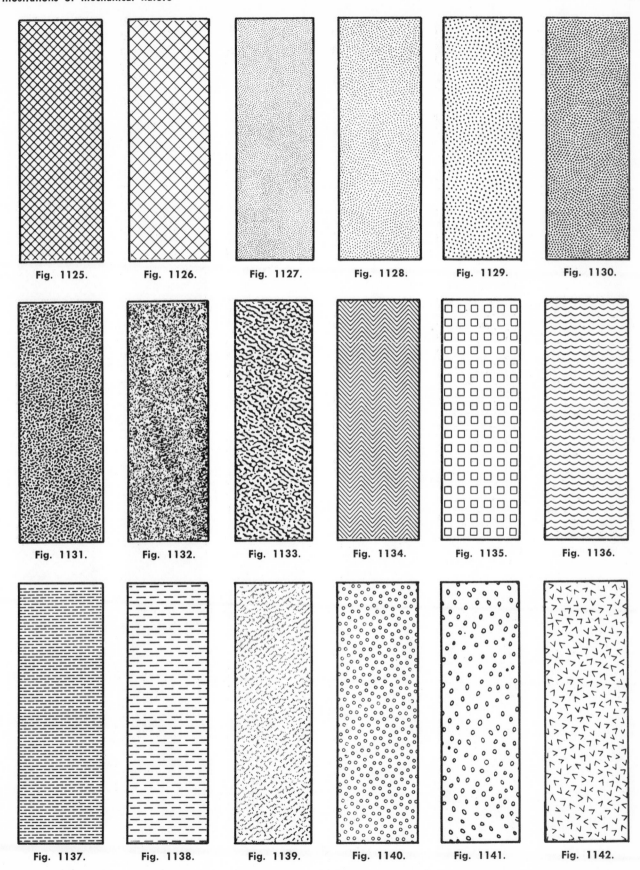

Fig. 1125.   Fig. 1126.   Fig. 1127.   Fig. 1128.   Fig. 1129.   Fig. 1130.

Fig. 1131.   Fig. 1132.   Fig. 1133.   Fig. 1134.   Fig. 1135.   Fig. 1136.

Fig. 1137.   Fig. 1138.   Fig. 1139.   Fig. 1140.   Fig. 1141.   Fig. 1142.

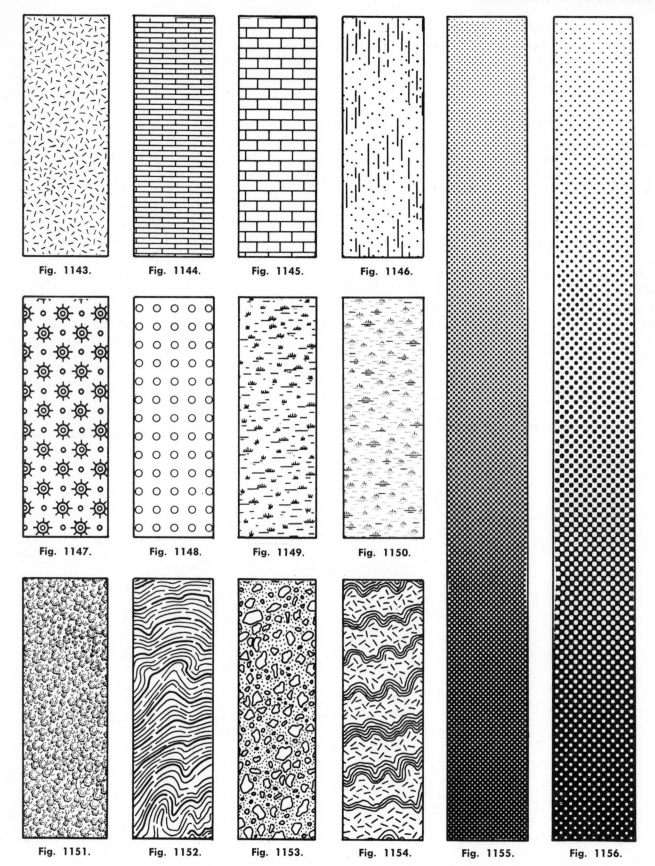

Fig. 1143.   Fig. 1144.   Fig. 1145.   Fig. 1146.

Fig. 1147.   Fig. 1148.   Fig. 1149.   Fig. 1150.

Fig. 1151.   Fig. 1152.   Fig. 1153.   Fig. 1154.   Fig. 1155.   Fig. 1156.

As mentioned eariler there is a much more impressive and easier way to work with tones. It is unfortunate that there is not a greater variety of tones distributed under the trade name *Instantex*. It is a nonadhesive type; the method of application was discussed earlier (*Figs. 1065-1066*). Being a nonadhesive type it can easily be used in true scientific illustrations, especially because the tones can be superimposed in great variety. There are twenty different tones; some of them are shown in their original size in *Figs. 1158-1166*.

On the following pages are samples of illustrations completed with the use of prefabricated tones. We must mention that these tones can be superimposed. This job is a delicate work, requires good eyesight and above all good judgment in selecting the proper tones. Superimposing means to apply layers of the same, or nearly the same, type and size tones over each other to accomplish a special effect.

Here is a sample (*Fig. 1157*) of a simple practice work, and we recommend trying it before going into a detailed work. Take any of the dotted sheets you like, similar to *Figs. 1097-1099*, or perhaps *Fig. 1105*. Have two sheets on hand. Now remove one of the sheets from its backing (protection sheet) and keeping it flat, place it randomly on top of the other sheet. Do not press, but with a gentle touch smooth the upper sheet so that you can see through it. You are superimposing two identical patterns. Now remove the top sheet and place it at a different angle. If you really want to investigate the possibilities of working with only two identical patterns, cut the top sheet into 3″ x 3″ pieces. Take the other sheet from the backing, and press it on a sheet of heavy white paper. Now use the 3″ x 3″ pieces of the first sheet to work out different patterns superimposing the small pieces in different angles. You will be surprised how many pattern variations and how many different shadings can be created. Do the same thing with another pattern.

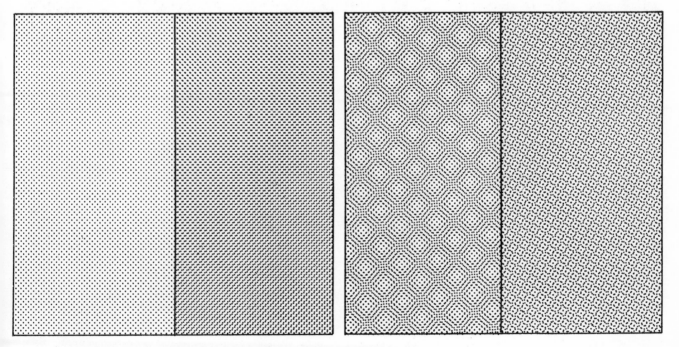

Fig. 1157.

Fig. 1158.

Fig. 1159.

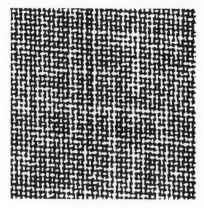

Fig. 1160.

Fig. 1161.

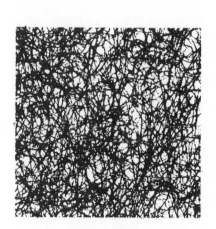

Fig. 1162.

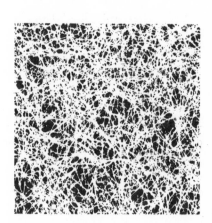

Fig. 1163.

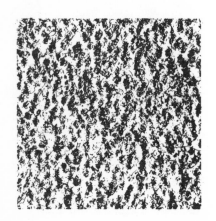

Fig. 1164.

Fig. 1165.

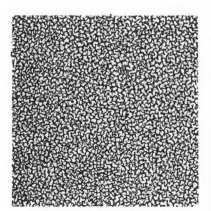

Fig. 1166.

Let's make our first adventure with these prefabricated tones. We are going to draw a pipet, a piece of equipment in laboratories. See *Fig. 1167*: make the outline with pencil on two or three-ply Strathmore paper. Then ink in the outline, clean the drawing well with a soft eraser and be sure that there are no eraser chips on the paper or its immediate area. Next, cover the drawing with the desired pattern (as in *Fig. 1094*) so that the dots are parallel with the ink line and make the following cuts:

1. Cut with sharp single-edged razor blade on the ink outline.
2. Cut another line parallel to the first, inside of the ink line about one-sixteenth of an inch.
3. Cut another line about the same distance inward.
4. Make your fourth cut about one-eighth of an inch inward.
5. Cut off the top and the bottom.
6. With sharp-pointed scalpel, or with the corner of your cutting blade, peel off the area between the second and third cut, then remove the whole sheet.

The tone will stick to the area outlined with the first, second, third and fourth cuts. Press it gently over the protective sheet with a harder object. The shading is done. Only the tapered end of the pipet is left. Shape the outside according to your outline and make a cut on the tone sheet, starting at the lower end of the wider shaded area and moving in the required angle toward the center of the tip. Your drawing is done. If you have to add scales on the pipet do it with lined tones, as mentioned before (*Fig. 1081*).

Another simple exercise is to illustrate a glass pipe or glass rod. The steps are the same, and if you examine *Fig. 1168* carefully it will not be a problem to determine the number and sizes of the cuts required.

If the pipet is to be drawn in a large size and with more shading, follow the sample presented in *Fig. 1169*. As seen at the right of the drawing, the light comes from the left. Because the pipet is larger in size, we have a better chance to decorate the drawing with more highlights. Then, for the extremely dark areas, we have to superimpose the same tone (refer to *Fig. 1157*). Use the same pattern and place another layer on top of the first one so that the dots are almost touching. Then press lightly with your fingers, and cut evenly. When all the tones are in place, cover with the original (nonsticky) protective sheet and press gently and slowly first with your finger tips,

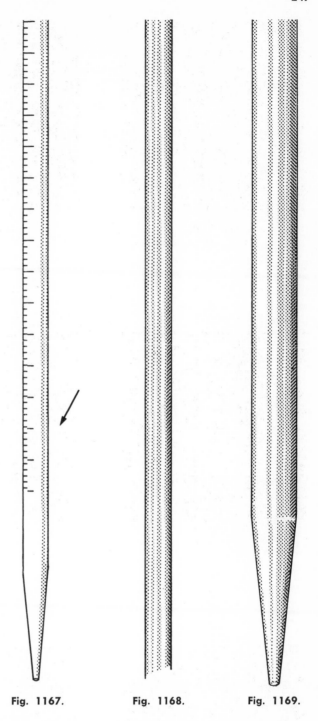

Fig. 1167.　　**Fig. 1168.**　　**Fig. 1169.**

rubbing back and forth, and then with a harder object. (For years I have been using my Zippo lighter successfully.) Do *not* press hard, because it is quite possible that these thin lines will move out of place, and you will have to redo or refit the area. Hard pressing should not be used for smaller areas such as grade-marks. (See *Fig. 1167*, arrow; the grade lines were moved as a result of hard pressing.)

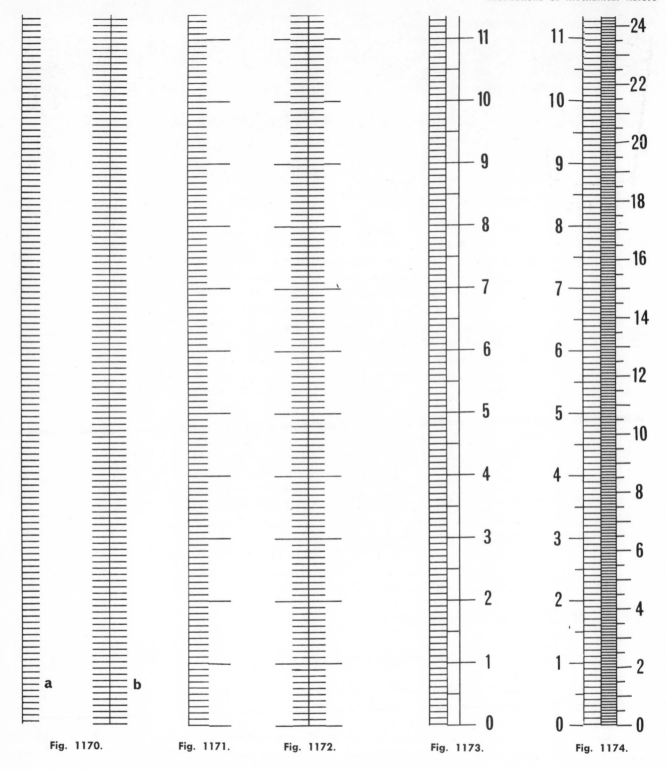

Fig. 1170.   Fig. 1171.   Fig. 1172.   Fig. 1173.   Fig. 1174.

By now the reader has an idea of how to create impressive scales and how to "dress up" a pipet with simple grading. *Figs. 1170-1174* show a few additional examples. Remember that it is easier to make these scales from tones with widespread lines (as in *Figs.* *1120-1124*). They can be reduced or enlarged to the required size very easily in the photographic process. In this way you can create scales, applying your own distances, number of divisions and labeling (or numbering).

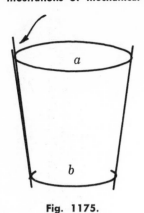

Fig. 1175.   Fig. 1176.   Fig. 1177.   Fig. 1178.

Another good way to learn how to apply these tones is to illustrate a rubber stopper. For your first attempt do not work on the smaller size (*Fig. 1178*). Make the outlines with pencil, using an elliptical template for the flat surface. Ink in the margins, first the top (*Fig. 1175, a*) then the bottom, *b*, then the sides. If you make the wrong move (see arrow), cover the wrong line with Snopake, let it dry well, and try again. After the outline is done and cleaned (*Fig. 1176*) you are ready to use the tone. The steps are the same as in our previous example (*Figs. 1167-1169*). In this case we are illustrating a rubber stopper and not a cork (*Fig. 1177*) so the texture will be entirely different. Let our sample be a black rubber stopper with the light coming from the left. As we see in the example, the right fourth of the surface is black: two wide black stripes and one narrow black stripe were made with India ink after the outlines were inked. When the ink is dry, apply the tone, cutting the highlights out. Save one narrow strip from these cut-outs, and place it near the center by superimposing on the ground tone (*Fig. 1178*).

In the following samples, after carefully analyzing details, the reader may find many technical answers. The shading of circular surfaces always creates a problem especially for the beginner in the use of prefabricated tones, but if you have the feeling for it, if you can imagine the object in three-dimensions, and if you have the necessary pattern at hand, it is quite easy. These samples are based on the same general outline, which can be drawn in order as numbered on *Fig. 1179*. Note that on some of them several patterns are used. For practice purposes it is recommended to copy these illustrations in their outlines in four or five copies, then try to shade them with the different patterns used in our samples. To achieve the same effect, the pattern identifications will be given. Our samples here are reduced to 80

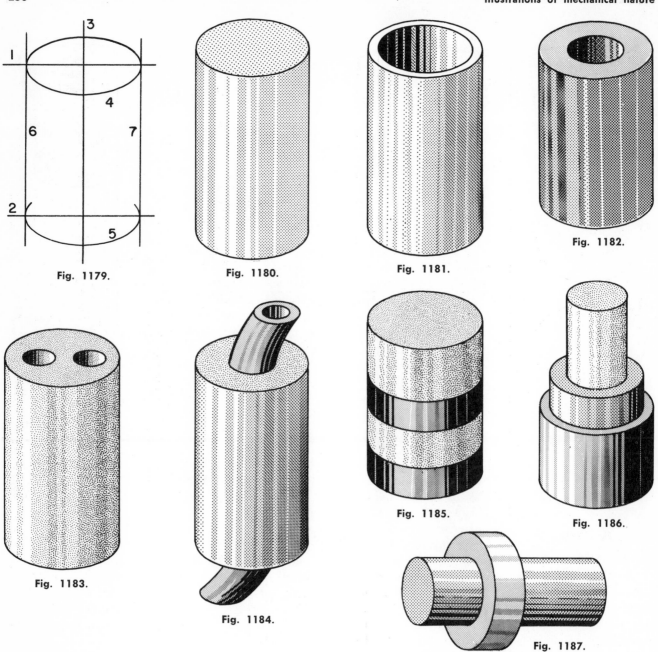

Fig. 1179.

Fig. 1180.

Fig. 1181.

Fig. 1182.

Fig. 1183.

Fig. 1184.

Fig. 1185.

Fig. 1186.

Fig. 1187.

per cent of the original size. Following is the key to the patterns used:

Fig.	Fig. of Pattern
1180	1094 and 1097
1181	1094 and 1097
1182	1094, 1096 and 1097
1183	1127 and 1128
1184	1091, 1094 and 1128
1185	1127, 1128 and 1091
1186	1128, 1094 and 1091
1187	1091 and 1094

All the black areas and the outlines were drawn with India ink, using Leroy pen No. 0. A 60 per cent reduction of these drawings can be seen in my first book.[1] These figures can be reduced to 40 per cent of the original size. When greatly reduced they resemble a half-tone reproduction.

[1]C. S. Papp: *An Introduction to Scientific Illustration,* 1963, on pages 68-70, and page 206. Copies of this book can be ordered directly from the author (P. O. Box 5042, Riverside, California 92507. $5.75 plus 35¢ postage.)

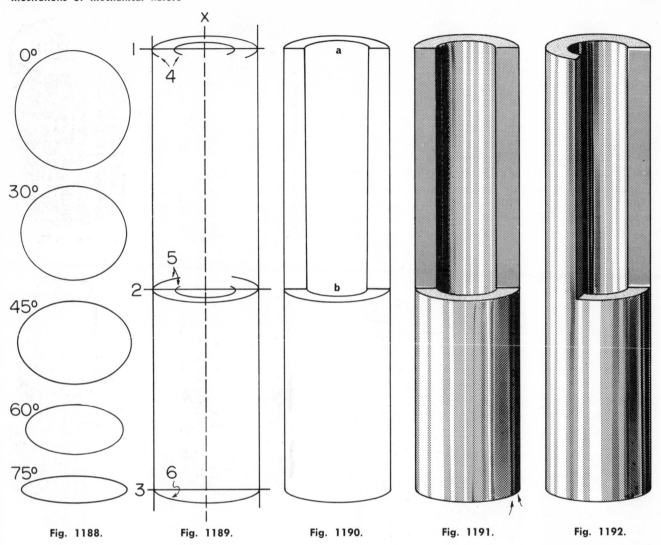

| Fig. 1188. | Fig. 1189. | Fig. 1190. | Fig. 1191. | Fig. 1192. |

Another excellent way to learn the use of pre-fabricated tones is to make a drawing of a piece of thick metal pipe with a portion cut away. The first and most important step is to determine the angle at which we want to view the pipe. In *Fig. 1188* there are five views with simple outlines. These are identified by numbers indicating the degrees of angle we look at a circle. The most commonly used angles are 60 degrees and 75 degrees. The latter one is used in our sample. The steps are as follows:

1. Make a pencil outline (*Fig. 1189*). Establish the vertical axis (x), then draw the horizontal axis of the top (*1*), then of the cutaway section (*2*) and then of the lower end (*3*). The next step, using the elliptical template, is to draw the cross sections (*4*) and (*5*), then the lower end (*6*). These ellipses should be perfectly level. To accomplish this you have to center the lines on your template which should line up with

the axes (i.e., x and *1*, x and *2*, x and *3*). When these are done, draw the outside lines connecting the three ellipses, and then the inside lines connecting the smaller ellipses which indicate the thickness of the metal pipe.

2. After the pencil outline is completed, use Leroy pen No. 0 (or No. 1, if the original is to be reduced more than 50 per cent) and start inking. First ink the ellipses, stopping at lines (*1*), (*2*) *and* (*3*), as seen in the sample (*Fig. 1190*). It is strange but true that in most cases, especially the first time, the student is bound to make a mistake so the inside diameter of the pipe is not even. This is demonstrated in *Fig. 1190*, referring to *a* and *b*. Check for these before inking. After inking is done, clean the drawing of pencil marks and you are ready to apply the tones (*Fig. 1190*).

3. Determine from which direction the light is coming. Apply India ink lines on the darkest areas. In our sample the light comes from the left, so the outside of the pipe will be darker on the right side. After the ink has dried, cover the surface with the selected tone (We used the one seen in *Fig. 1094*). Press the tone sheet gently so it sticks to the drawing paper. Cut out the area covering the external surface. Do the same with the inside and then remove the rest. Place your determined cuts on the tones and peel off the strips you want to represent the highlights. The next area is the cross section of the pipe, in which we used the tone illustrated on *Fig. 1127*, and then covered the longitudinally cut area with the tone shown in *Fig. 1093*. Refer to details in *Fig. 1191*.

It is recommended to do as many variations as possible to practice illustrating cutaways on pipes. Another example is illustrated in *Fig. 1192*. All these illustrations are reduced to 72 per cent of the original size.

We learned previously (*Figs. 1167-1169*) how to illustrate glass tubes and we mentioned that in the case of glass much lighter tones must be used than in illustrating metal. After you know the slightly complicated metal-toning, examine *Fig. 1193*. This illustration was done by applying three different tones:

1. The main tube all the way down to the ground and tapered end portion is covered with the same tone (*Fig. 1094*). On the right side of the outside and on the left side of the inside the same tone is superimposed for shading. The inside of the narrowing, concave neck part is covered with a fine tone (*Fig. 1091*) to give a slightly darker effect reflected through the outside wall. The tapered end portion has a different surface finish; it is ground to assure perfect fitting. This area is differentiated from the smooth, shining surface by using an irregularly stippled tone (*Fig. 1128*). The illustration is reproduced in its original size (*a*) and in 50 per cent reduction (*b*).

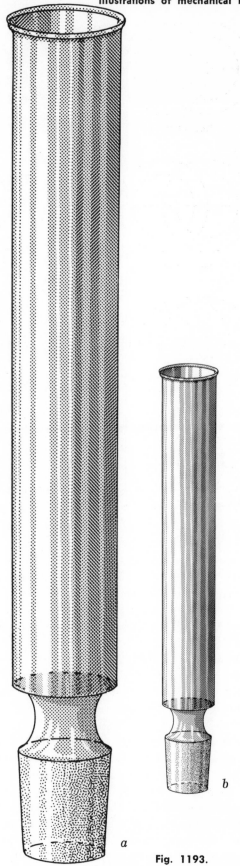

Fig. 1193.

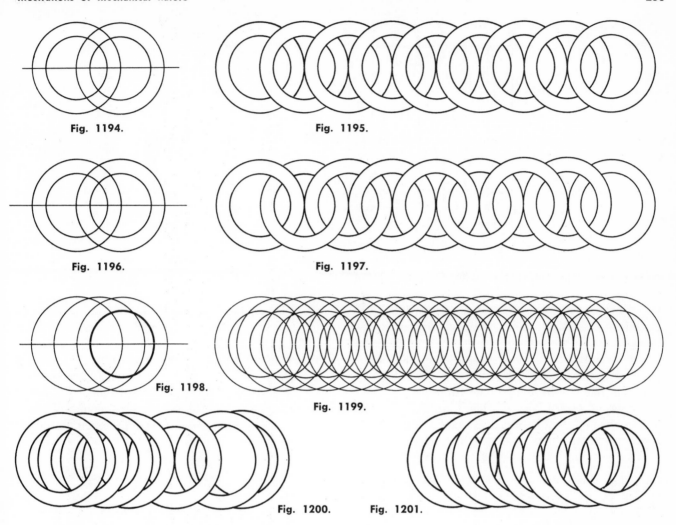

Fig. 1194.

Fig. 1195.

Fig. 1196.

Fig. 1197.

Fig. 1198.

Fig. 1199.

Fig. 1200.

Fig. 1201.

If you like to doodle with your compass, making circles of even sizes, you may try sometime to learn the basic element in creating a spiral pipe or coil or a spring. In any case draw the horizontal axis, as seen in *Figs. 1194* and *1196*. Have two compasses on hand set for the proper radius, one for the outside, another for the inside one. Place the second outside circle on a chosen distance, as in our example (*Fig. 1194*), at the point where the outside circle intercepts the horizontal axis. From the same center point draw the inside circle; continue drawing about eight to ten sets of circles. Now if you erase the pencil lines where another pair of circles overlaps, the row of circles appears as though the circles were placed on top of the other on a flat surface (*Fig. 1195*). Do the same group of circles and for a change, copy the "chain" illustrated on *Fig. 1197*. When the areas are cleared from excess pencil marks, ink in the lines. Now draw these circles closer to each other (*Fig.*

1198), always making a double circle. Continue this for about five to six inches. Your drawing will look like that in *Fig. 1199*. Now erase the excess pencil marks and ink in the lines. If the circles are not spaced evenly, the end result will resemble *Fig. 1200*; in *Fig. 1201* the circles are spaced evenly. This is an optical illusion and the first circles will appear somewhat larger than the others. These circles are placed in "space" in a somewhat three-dimensional way, and give the impression that they are behind each other. The last circle (at the right end) seems to be closest to you, and the left circle the farthest away; however, the latter should appear smaller than any other. Don't let this illusion fool you when creating a similar design in a composition.

It is quite easy to draw coil-shaped objects from the side. To grasp the general idea it is recommended to experiment with this idea first.

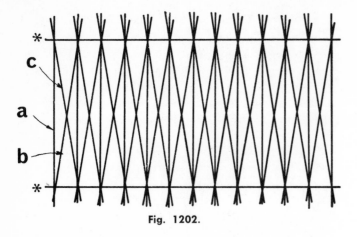

Fig. 1202.

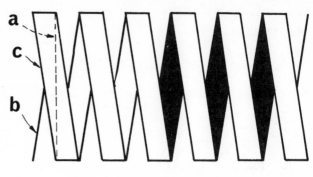

Fig. 1203.

Figure 1202 gives you a starting point. With a pencil make two parallel lines to indicate the width of the coil (*); then, with pencil draw vertical lines (*a*) the same distance apart as the width of the coiled material (assuming that the distance between "rings" is the same as the width of the material, or diameter of the tube). Then connect these lines with each other diagonally (*b* and *c*). When these lines are correct, starting on the upper line (upper *) connect every second pair of lines, i.e., line *1* and *2*, line *3* with *4*, line *5* with *6*, etc. Then do the same on the bottom, starting from the same line (*c*). The next step is to

connect those horizontal lines with each other so, that following the direction of line (*c*) from the top to the bottom, then the next, etc. When all the (*c*) lines are inked in, do the same with the (*b*) lines. The first (*b*) line goes from the center of the second (*c*) line to the upper margin, and so forth. Then you have a picture as seen in the left half of *Fig. 1203*. Now if you shade the areas between the (*b*) lines you will have a drawing as illustrated in the remaining part of *Fig. 1203*. Now you have a rough drawing of a coil in which the individual rounds are pupped out evenly and on an angle.

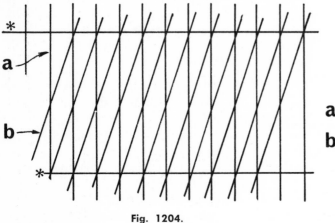

Fig. 1204.

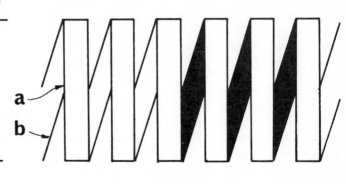

Fig. 1205.

Figure 1204 is another example, where one segment is 90 degrees on the longitudinal axis. The composition is simple, starts with the same two lines (*), then vertical lines placed the same distance from each other (*a*), the (*b*) lines connecting the previous one so that it crosses one (*a*) line every time. After inking in those lines we have an outline as seen on the left half in *Fig. 1205*. Shading can be applied the same way as in the previous example.

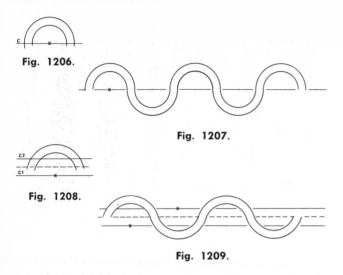

Fig. 1206.

Fig. 1207.

Fig. 1208.

Fig. 1209.

There is a very easy technique to create a 3-D illustration by using dotted tones when drawing a tightly compressed spiral pipe or tube of the kind commonly used in a distilling apparatus. The steps are illustrated in the following figures.

Figure 1210: Set the diameter of the spiral, which is the distance between (*a*) and (*b*) vertical lines. Measure the thickness (the O.D.) of the pipe, and mark those even divisions on line (*a*). After all the marks are completed, set the correct angle and draw one line across (*a*) and (*b*), followed by so many parallel lines how many divisions marked on line (*a*). Then connect the ends of those parallel lines using the proper size circular template. Then your pencil outline is complete.

Fig. 1211: Inking those lines is the next step. Note that the upper and lower ends are open, which may represent the "in" and "out" ends. Clean drawing of pencil marks and add the necessary labeling.

Figure 1212: Cover the surface with a dotted pattern. Press gently so that the adhesive sheet stays firmly on your drawing paper. Cut the tone pattern around the outline of the drawing and work out the shading effect by cutting and taking off strips of tones on the lighter side; then add some to the darker side (superimpose the same tone). Use dotted tones for this type of work. Our sample is reduced to 72 per cent of the original size. The tone pattern we used is illustrated in *Fig. 1103*.

Sometimes it happens that an evenly curved glass tube or pipe must be illustrated. It is simply and easily done by using the compass.

Figures 1206 and *1207* demonstrate the construction of an evenly wavy pipe. Note we have to work with only one axis (*c*) using two different radii from the same center (*x*). Follow the details in *Fig. 1207*. If we want to have these waves slightly shallower then we have to offset the centers by using two horizontal axes, as indicated on *Fig. 1208*, C_1 and C_2. The center points will then be placed on those axes alternately (*Fig. 1209*, marked with *x*). There is a third dashed line present to determine where the curved lines will meet. The farther you place the two center lines (*x*), the farther the wavy line will be.

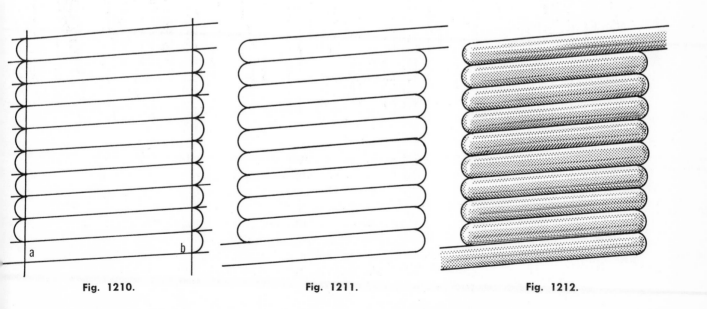

Fig. 1210.   Fig. 1211.   Fig. 1212.

A. ILLUSTRATING EQUIPMENT

Illustrations of laboratory equipment may be part of the work of the scientific illustrator, especially in smaller institutions where no specialized illustrators are employed. Such an illustrator must have an over-all talent, must be very flexible and able to do a great variety of work. Switching from one assignment to another may be boring and disconcerting at times; on the other hand it can be very relaxing and reward-ing.

The illustrator must go to the laboratory where the equipment is installed and *must see it*. It is highly recommended that the scientist explain the function of the instrument and point out all the details he may want to illustrate. It commonly happens that some portion of the equipment must be omitted from the drawing, and some parts must be emphasized. First do a true-to-scale sketch of the equipment, marking

dimensions or scale on your initial notes (*Fig. 1213*). When the equipment is grouped, do the same (*Fig. 1214*). Working from your preliminary notes you are able to build an excellent illustration.

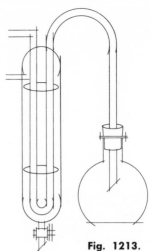

Fig. 1213.

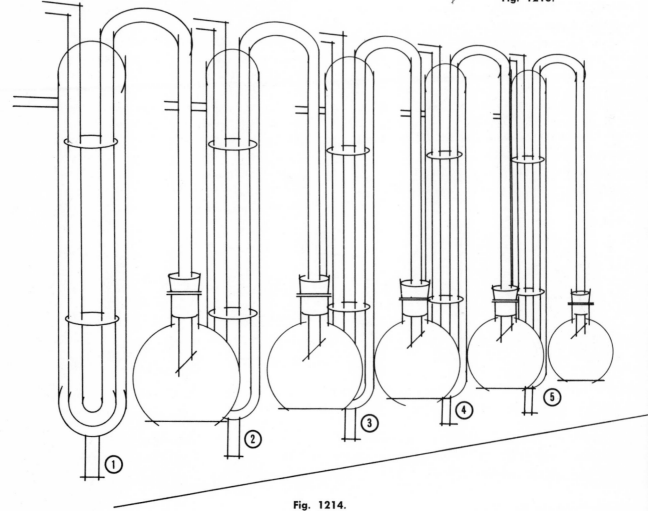

Fig. 1214.

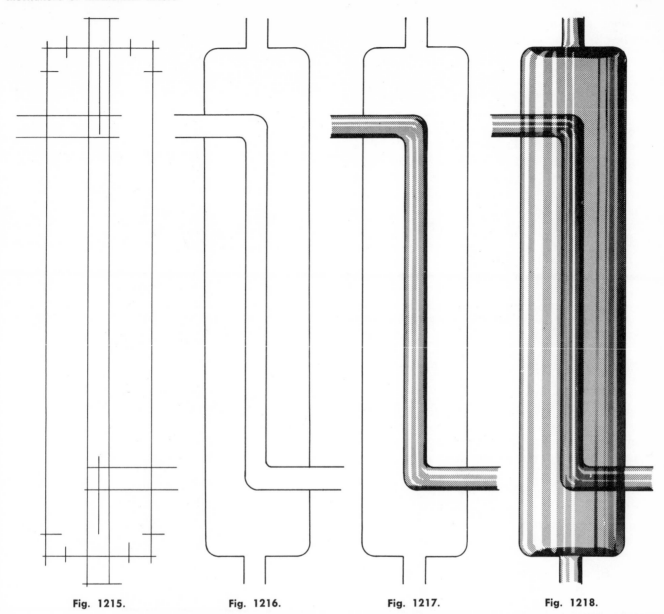

Fig. 1215.   Fig. 1216.   Fig. 1217.   Fig. 1218.

Sometimes it is a problem, especially in illustrating glass equipment, to demonstrate the presence of glass that is within a glass container. Let us demonstrate the easiest way to do it.

Figure 1215: Make a true-to-scale pencil outline of the equipment. First do the outer tube (container) then set the outline for the glass tube inside.

Figure 1216: Ink in the drawing properly. Round off the corners smoothly; use the same pen all the way through. If you make some mistakes with the ink, do not scrape. Use well diluted Snopake to cover the mistake and re-ink the area.

Figure 1217: Select the tone pattern you think is the best for reduction. Do not use a very fine dotted pattern as it may not come out well in the final print. If the original must be reduced more than 50 per cent use medium rough dot sizes, such as seen in *Figs. 1097, 1098, 1103* and *1105*. The smaller the reduction will be, the finer pattern that can be used. After the pattern is selected cover the area with the tone. Cut out around the outline of the pipe that is inside of the container, then peel off the rest. Gently press the tone to the drawing paper and start to place the shading on the pipe by cutting small areas on the lighted side, and adding those cut-out strips to the darker side. Follow the curves halfway around, then continue on the opposite side in both cases. When the shading is done you will have a picture as seen in *Fig. 1217.*

Figure 1218: Cover the entire drawing with the same tone. Secure the fitting of the sheet with slight pressure. Then cut out around the outlines of the outer tube or container and peel off the excess. Repeating the same shading procedure that you used for the inside tube will give a three-dimensional effect to the drawing. You have just made an illustration which can be nicely reproduced in line form and still give the impression of a half-tone. Do not use protective spray on this type of illustration; it is recommended to place a protective cover sheet on the top of the drawing (like tracing paper) to eliminate the chances of accidentally rubbing off small pieces of tones.

It is to your advantage to try this technique before engaging in some more expensive illustration. Strathmore two- or three-ply paper is very handy for such an illustration. If a larger original must be made (over 12 x 12 inches) use heavier illustration board.

In *Fig. 1219* there is another sample of a piece of glass laboratory equipment that contains another glass shape inside plus metal spirals and inlets and outlets. To make such illustrations the steps are the same as mentioned. After the ink outlines are done, ink in the spiral wires, then follow the same steps as outlined to place the tones properly. If you decide to use fine tones (as in *Figs. 1089* and *1090*) make your original small, so it need not to be reduced more than 10 per cent, and use fine ink lines for outlines (crow-quill pen and India ink). If this is inconvenient for you, use larger dots (tones), and make the original larger in proportion. The pattern in *Fig. 1091* is excellent if the original must be reduced to not more than 80 per cent of the original size; the pattern in *Fig. 1102* can be reduced to 60 per cent. For a larger original, which requires 50 per cent reduction, it is better to use a rougher pattern as seen in *Figs. 1097* and *1103.*

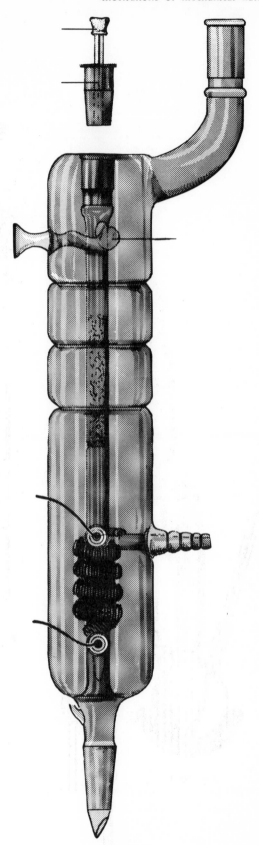

Fig. 1219.

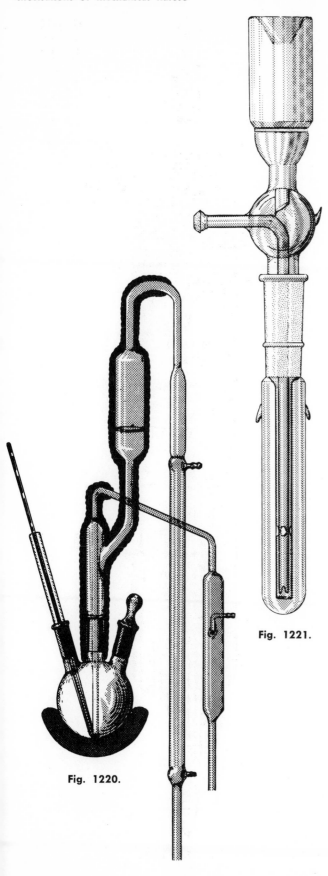

In *Fig. 1220* is a darker (black) area around certain parts of the equipment. This is the simplest way to demonstrate the presence of material used as insulation. Cover the area with India ink to achieve this effect. For the heating unit you may use a darker dotted pattern (as in *Figs. 1096* or *1101*).

Figure 1221 demonstrates another piece of glass equipment. As seen in the lower part of the drawing there are three tubes placed inside of each other. Note the neck part. To distinguish the inner surface (ground for perfect fitting) different patterns are used *(Figs. 1127* and *1128* are the best). But for the rest always use organized dotted patterns. The combination of tones in *Figs. 1127* and *1094* takes well a reduction to 75 per cent of the original size.

Metallic surfaces can also be well illustrated with prefabricated tones. The procedure is the same as for illustrating glass equipment. The only difference is using solid ink lines for the heavily shaded (dark) areas. The steps are the same: make accurate ink outlines, then shade darker areas with solid black lines that gradually narrow toward the lighter area. Then cover the whole surface with the desired tone and follow the same steps as outlined. A good example can be seen in *Fig. 1222*.

Fig. 1221.

Fig. 1220.

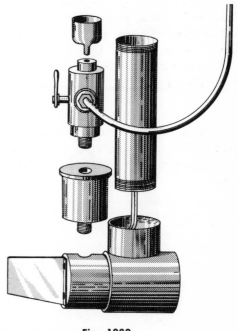

Fig. 1222.

Detailed cross sections are naturally done with uniform shading on the entire body part. Our sample in *Fig. 1224* demonstrates this well. Some unimportant parts, such as the wing-bolt, spring, etc., may be worked out in detailed shading, but the main components in the real cross section must be covered with uniform tones. Be sure to select the right density of tones for the same body part where it appears on the drawing. Note the way the spring is represented. For

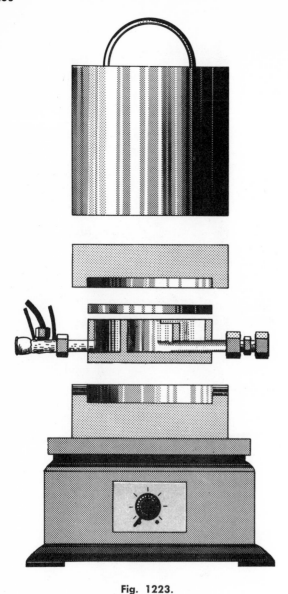

Fig. 1223.

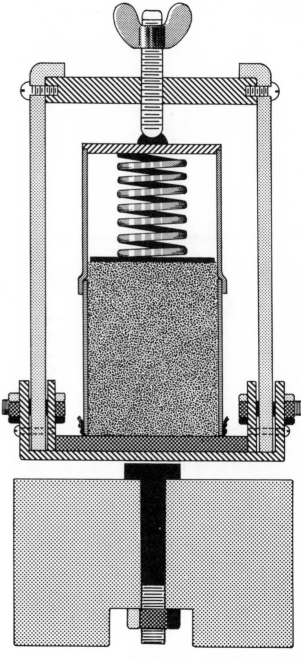

Fig. 1224.

Occasionally we have to illustrate equipment partially in cross section, as seen in *Fig. 1223*. To give a slight 3-D effect to the drawing make a cross section of the areas desired, then draw the rest as a normal 3-D illustration. In the area of the cross section, cover with a simple tone and do not put any shading on it (see *Fig. 1223*, the center portion). It is advisable to work out a 3-D effect if there are some deep cuts or other quite visible details. To present the 3-D in those illustrations we have to reverse the light: make the left side shaded, which will then indicate a circular cut-out.

its detail refer to *Fig. 1203.* Note also the shading on the wing-nut and the representation of the threaded bar. Observe how the shading is done on the common nuts on the lower portion of the figure. In the "chamber" (under the spring) the soil is represented with a granule-like tone (see *Fig. 1131*). This drawing is reduced to 80 per cent of the original size; it may be reducible to 50 per cent of the present size.

Figure 1225 shows another way to illustrate a cross section. There is no 3-D represented at all. The spring (G) is indicated only with a solid black line; the other parts are solidly toned. Note how the large tightening nut (M) is represented, covered with dense lines in two different ways. The dirt sample is indicated (C) by using the tone illustrated in *Fig. 1151.* This equipment is a long probe and to save space the not too important center portion was cut out as indicated by the two white zig-zag lines across the center. Reduced to 75 per cent of the original, it can be well reproduced at half of the present size if printed on good quality paper.

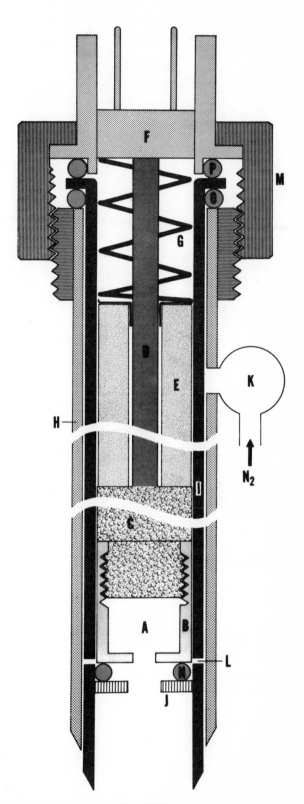

Fig. 1225.

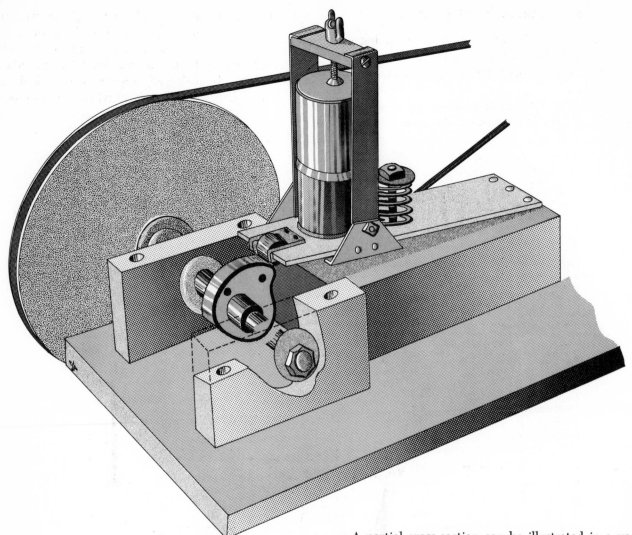

Fig. 1226.

A partial cross-section can be illustrated in a very attractive way by applying different tones. As seen in *Fig. 1226* the proper mixture of very fine and rough tones can be used to differentiate material and parts. The chamber part on this machine (seen in cross section in *Fig. 1224*) was covered with fine tones. The wooden parts are toned with material illustrated in *Fig. 1115*, a pattern which neatly represents gradual shading. Note how the shadings are worked out on the belt, and especially on the vertical wooden parts; the holes drilled to fit the tightening screws are also shaded (dark side is in reverse position). This print is a 50 per cent reduction of the original size; it may be successfully reproduced at about 75 per cent of the present size. On fine quality paper this illustration would reproduce extremely well and would resemble a neat half-tone reproduction. The proper selection of the pattern in relation to the original size and the final reproduction is extremely important.

B. ILLUSTRATING EXPERIMENTS

The use of prefabricated tones in illustrating experiments is highly recommended. Simple ink outlines can be dressed up impressively by applying one or two tones.

In *Fig. 1227* four different types of tones were used: dotted pattern to illustrate the cross section of the container (B) and (C), alternately placed dashed lines for representing the water (D), the pattern illustrated in *Fig. 1153* was used to represent the soil (N); and densely lined tone was used for the tube. The rubber tube-seals and stoppers were inked in with black India ink. For identifying the different

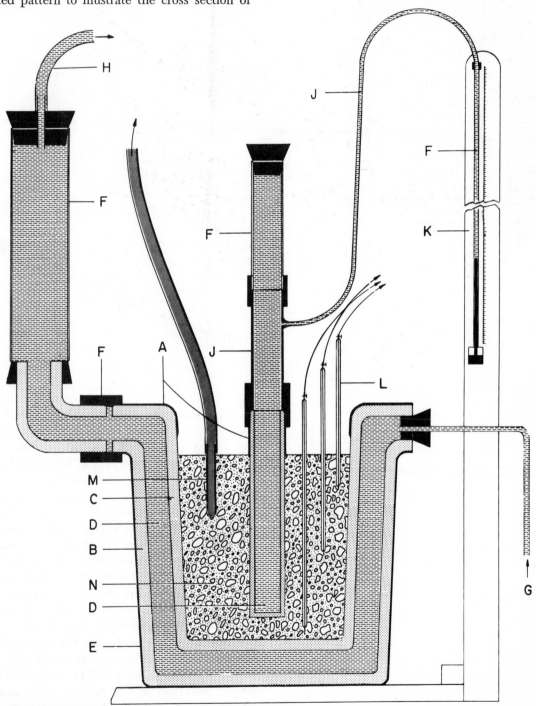

Fig. 1227.

parts the lettering system is used. Those letters need explanation which can be given in the caption to the illustration or explained in the main text.

Another example can be seen in *Fig. 1228*. The illustration explains the composition of the container, the constant water level, the position of the plant used in the experiment and the distribution of the parasite. On the side of the plastic container there is a tape which can be lifted and used for observation while the rest of the container is covered to keep light out.

For such illustrations the steps are as follows:

1. Make the correct pencil outline.

2. Ink in lines, starting first with the elliptical forms on the top and on the bottom of the container. Then finish the plant, using solid lines and just the minimum shading. Work out the soil using the stippling technique; place dots closer to each other on the darker side, and farther from each other while moving to the lighter side. Do not use too dense stippling, but indicate clearly the darkest areas. Note that on the lower portion of the soil (darker), it is indicated by darker shading as a wet part below the constant water level: make its darker side about three times wider than the dry portion above it. Draw pebbles on the bottom, but do not shade them. Cover the area between the granules (pebbles) with India ink. Add labeling.

3. Apply tones. Use an irregularly stippled pattern (*Figs. 1127, 1128* and *1129*) to cover the soil, giving a uniform shading. If you use the tone illustrated on *Fig. 1127* for the soil, use the tone illustrated on *Fig. 1128* to cover the top of the soil. Then work out the details on the container, starting with the base and then doing the plastic tube portion. Finally cover the observation strip area, shading properly the portion lifted off from the side of the container. It is advisable to study the details of this illustration and take notes on the patterns used. Make your own selection and try to design your own illustration.

The simplest way to illustrate experiments with the minimum use of tones is demonstrated in *Fig. 1229*. If you are engaged in this type of illustration and there are a great number of these to be done, it is advisable to cut your own templates. There are some templates on the market for different glasswares in the field of chemistry. They are usually too small to be used in larger illustrations. They are probably excellent to make your first pencil notes, but they are small to work with. Make the exact outlines of the different types of flasks in four or five different sizes on a sheet of paper with pencil. Place heavy gauge plastic sheet on the top of the outlines and cut it out slowly and smoothly. If you use these templates to

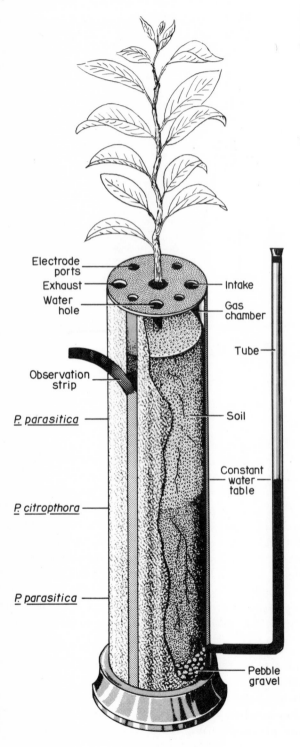

Electrode ports
Exhaust
Water hole
Observation strip
P. parasitica
P. citropthora
P. parasitica

Intake
Gas chamber
Tube
Soil
Constant water table
Pebble gravel

Fig. 1228.

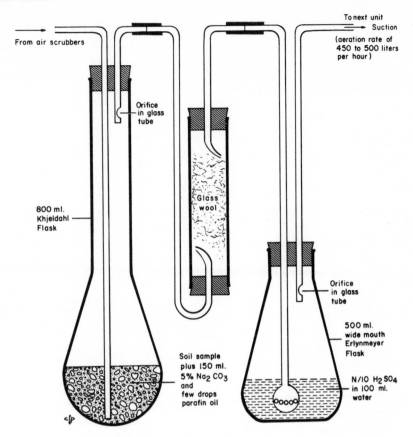

From air scrubbers

Orifice in glass tube

To next unit

Suction

(aeration rate of 450 to 500 liters per hour)

Glass wool

800 ml. Khjeldahl Flask

Orifice in glass tube

500 ml. wide mouth Erlynmeyer Flask

Soil sample plus 150 ml. 5% Na_2CO_3 and few drops parafin oil

$N/10$ H_2SO_4 in 100 ml. water

Fig. 1229.

make the pencil outlines of your illustration planned for publication, you just place the template on the drawing paper and use pencil close to the edges. When you start to ink in the penciled outlines place masking tape in two or three layers around the edges of the cut-out so that the edge of the tpe is about a quarter of an inch away from the edge of the cut-out line on the template. This creates a slight elevation, and the plastic edge of the template will not reach the drawing paper. Consequently there will be no chance to smear the ink while you are inking in the outlines. Be careful picking up the template after the ink lines are made.

Use heavier outlines for the flasks and lighter outlines for the glass tubes. Use the same pen to draw the rubber connections around the pipe-joints. If rubber stoppers have to be drawn, make their outlines with the same pen as the outlines for the glass tubes,

then cover the surface with line pattern (see *Figs. 1107* to *1112*) selecting the proper density. The rest of the drawing can be worked out simply. If soil is represented, use one of the types illustrated on *Figs. 1131, 1132* and *1151*, or *1153*. If more flasks are present and they contain different types of soil, use different tones. Liquid can be represented with dashed tones (*Figs. 1137 and 1139*) or with wavy lines, especially if the liquid is boiling (*Fig. 1136*). For representing woolen material, use a few thin lines (India ink and crow qiull pen), as seen in our sample.

As seen in *Fig. 1229* a minimum number of tones are used and the illustration is clear and neat. If labeling is required place the labels (Leroy type) before applying the tones. If you use Instant Letters, they can be applied after the tones are placed. If you are planning to use a typewriter for labeling, use it before you add the tones.

C. MAKING GRAPHS

In most institutions the making of graphs or statistical illustrations is also the job of the scientific
illustrator. With talent and imagination these simple
figures (*Fig. 1230*) can be done artistically (*Fig.
1231*). In the present book we will not give a detailed discussion of making graphs; a separate book
is designed to cover this subject and to give techniques and ideas in map making also.

No matter what type of graphs we have to make,
we must first determine the size of the original. To
do this, we have to know in which periodical and in
what size the drawing will be reproduced. Usually
originals are made too large. We have seen originals
30 x 40 inches that were to be reduced to fit a
3 1/2″ wide column!

If we can help it we like to make our originals
not larger than twice the published size. This rule of
thumb works out nicely, is well adaptable for slides,
and excellent for rough manuscript reproductions with

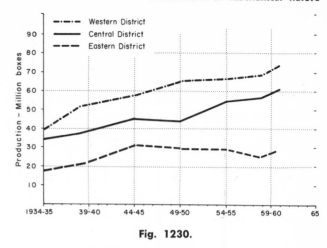

Fig. 1230.

Xerox and the original can be handeled easily within
the pages of the manuscript.

The second important decision is the type of the
graph: line (curve) or bar graph. Both are very popular. Perhaps the line graphs are more favored, but
the bar graphs are more impressive and artistic in
appearance.

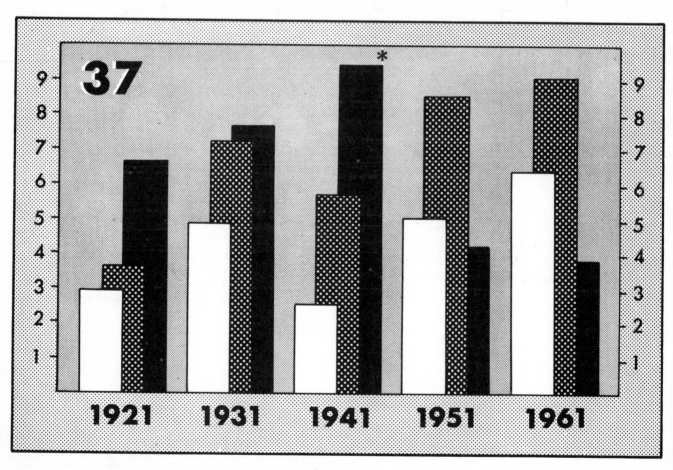

Fig. 1231.

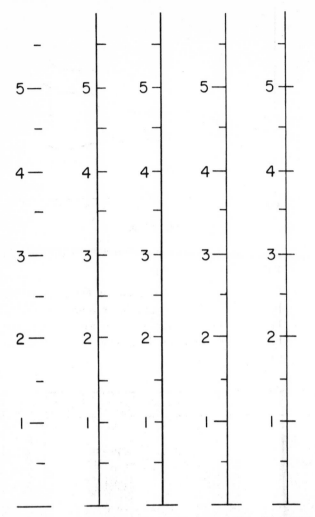

Fig. 1232.   Fig. 1233.   Fig. 1234.   Fig. 1235.   Fig. 1236.

After these preliminary and important decisions are made, the first step is to decide the division of the scales, either the vertical or horizontal ones. There are five widely used ways of illustrating scales, as demonstrated in *Figs. 1232* to *1236.* Some illustrators use only the dividing lines (*Fig. 1232*); others like to apply the vertical or base line and place the divisions inside (*Fig. 1233*) or outside (*Fig. 1234*), marking them with lines of even length and numbering each one or every second line, or making every second (numbered) marking slightly longer (*Fig. 1235*). On the other hand, numbered lines may cross the base line (*Fig. 1236*) giving more emphasis to the divisions. For an easy and accurate method of dividing lines into any given parts refer to *Fig. 1238* and to the accompanying text.[2]

Sometimes circular scales are used (*Fig. 1237*). to complete them is an elementary problem but perhaps the numbering and lettering may need some explanation. For shading graphs of this form refer to *Fig. 1080*

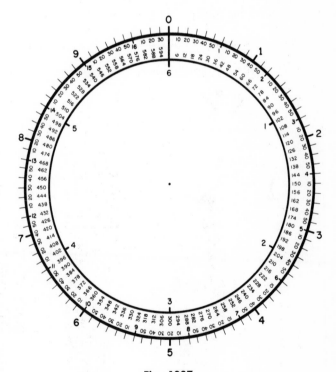

Fig. 1237.

[2]This is the DIVIDER, which comes with three holes to fit any 8 1/2 x 11″ notebook or binder. It is printed on stiff cardboard. Produced and distributed by the Charles S. Papp Scientific Art Studios, P. O. Box 5042, Riverside, California 92507. Price is $1.00 each or 10 for $8.00 plus postage. See also your own college bookstore.

The use of this divider is simple and fast. It can be learned easily by using a "very complicated" example.

Assume that there is a line 4 3/16" long and it must be divided into nine equal parts:

Have a piece of paper with a straight edge, and mark the distance above on the edge measuring from the left corner. Now place this paper on the divider so that the left corner (which is the 0"), lines up perfectly with the vertical line on the divider (line at the left side) and the edge of your paper on which the 4 3/16" distance is marked, parallel with the horizontal lines on the divider. This distance must be divided into nine parts. So keeping the 0" corner of your paper on the vertical line, move the paper up or down until the mark intercepts line No. 9 on the divider, keeping the edge of your paper parallel to the horizontal lines and the 0" on the vertical line. After you are sure that all those are right, mark the edge of the paper with pencil on the points where lines 1, 2, 3, etc. . . . 9 touches the edge of your paper. You just divided 4 3/16" line into nine even parts.

Try to figure it out mathematically, using paper and pencil. It would take you quite some time.

Set some of your examples and practice. After two or three tries you will see that it took only 15 seconds to divide a line of 3 9/16" into seven even parts.

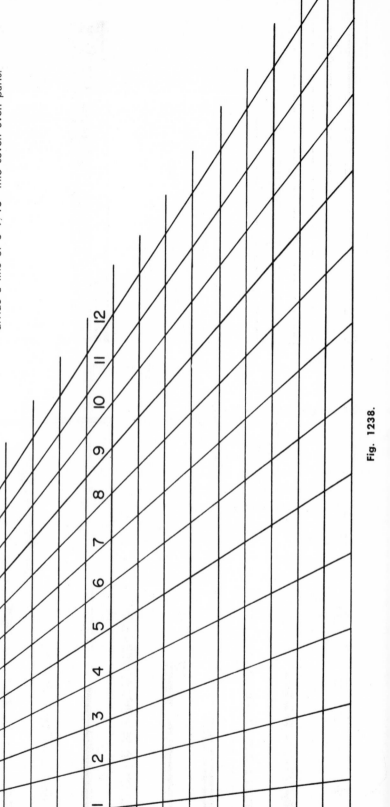

Fig. 1238.

268

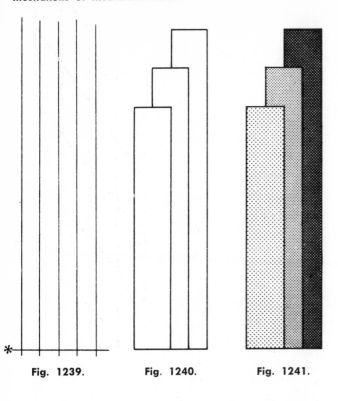

Fig. 1239.   Fig. 1240.   Fig. 1241.

1. Lay out the vertical scale and horizontal base line (*Fig. 1239*). For the vertical scale line refer to *Figs. 1232-1236*.

2. Divide the base line by the number of items or item groups, then lay out the border lines between each bar and group of bars (*Fig. 1239*).

3. Cut off the top of the bar (or bar groups) at the desired level and ink in the out line. Clean off pencil marks (*Fig. 1240*).

4. Place all the necessary lettering and numbering. After the paper is clean, cover the bars with tones (*Fig. 1241*).

It is recommended light tones be used on the first bar and darker tones for the second, etc. A very attractive combination for two bars is to use medium gray tones on the first bar (dots or lines) and black on the second (rear) bar. Black color can be replaced with red Craf-Tone material; it is easier to work with because this material is transparent and the border lines are so visible. The red photographs very well as black. If you want to make a more artistic combination refer to *Fig. 1231*, where the first bar is left white, the second shaded and the third black (red on the original art work). The immediate background within the inner border contains the scales (on both sides for easier reading) a denser tone; outside of this within the outer frame a lighter tone was used. The lettering was done with Instant Lettering. This sample is reduced to 92 per cent of the original size, but it

Bar graphs have vertical scales only and each bar, or group of bars, refers to separate information (*Figs. 1231* and *1242*). Commonly two or three bars are used in one group; when more are used they are placed side by side (*Fig. 1251*) and also toned differently. Let's learn how to design a bar graph with three bars in each group.

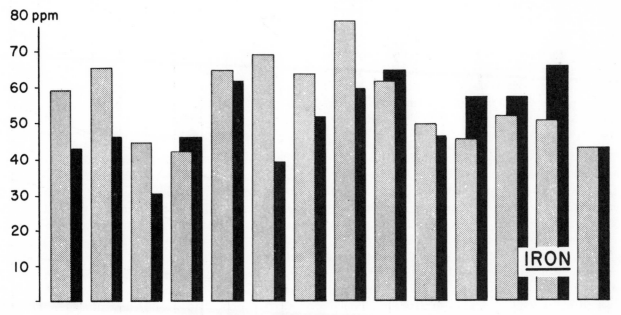

Fig. 1242.

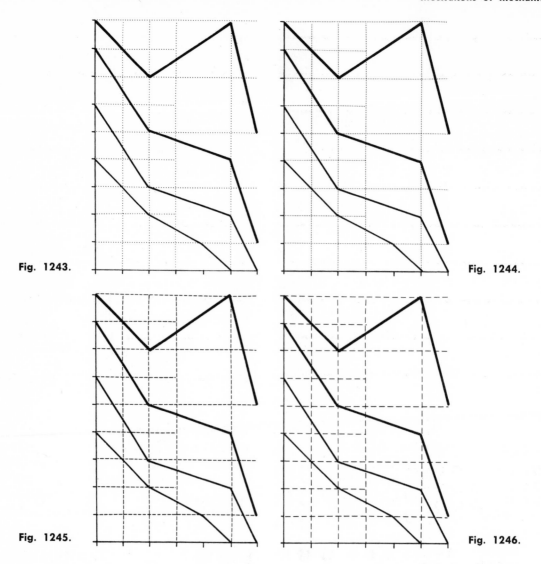

Fig. 1243.

Fig. 1244.

Fig. 1245.

Fig. 1246.

would reproduce in 50 per cent reduction very well. When the artwork is finished, cover it with a protective sheet of paper, and keep it out of direct heat or sun. It reproduces as a line-cut. If you reproduce this original in half-tone, the white area (bars left white) would have a grayish tone.

Line or curve graphs usually have two scales: horizontal and vertical. The information is plotted within the enclosed area and connected with lines. In most cases the scales are indicated on one side only; it is practical, however, to give orientation points on the opposite side too (as in *Fig. 1230*), or use dots or broken lines as a guide to help the reader. The guide lines can be completed by cutting out narrow strips of any systematically screened tone sheets (*Figs. 1097* to *1099*, and *1103* to *1105*), as demonstrated on *Figs. 1243* and *1244*. Dashed lines also are

very good, using strips cut out of tones such as those in *Figs. 1137* and *1138* and demonstrated in *Figs. 1245* and *1246*. If the divisions on the scale are far from each other, they may all be connected horizontally and vertically or just every second or third one (see *Figs. 1243* and *1246*).

The first step is, as always, the pencil outline, framework, then the scale. Plot the points (information) and connect them according to requirements, using lines of different thickness (*Figs. 1243* to *1246*) or form (*Fig. 1247*). Sometimes the scientist wants to have information of different nature plotted on the line graph, in which case different symbols must be used for each item discussed. Some of the commonly used symbols are shown in *Fig. 1248*, including arrows curving in two different directions for calling the reader's attention to certain points.

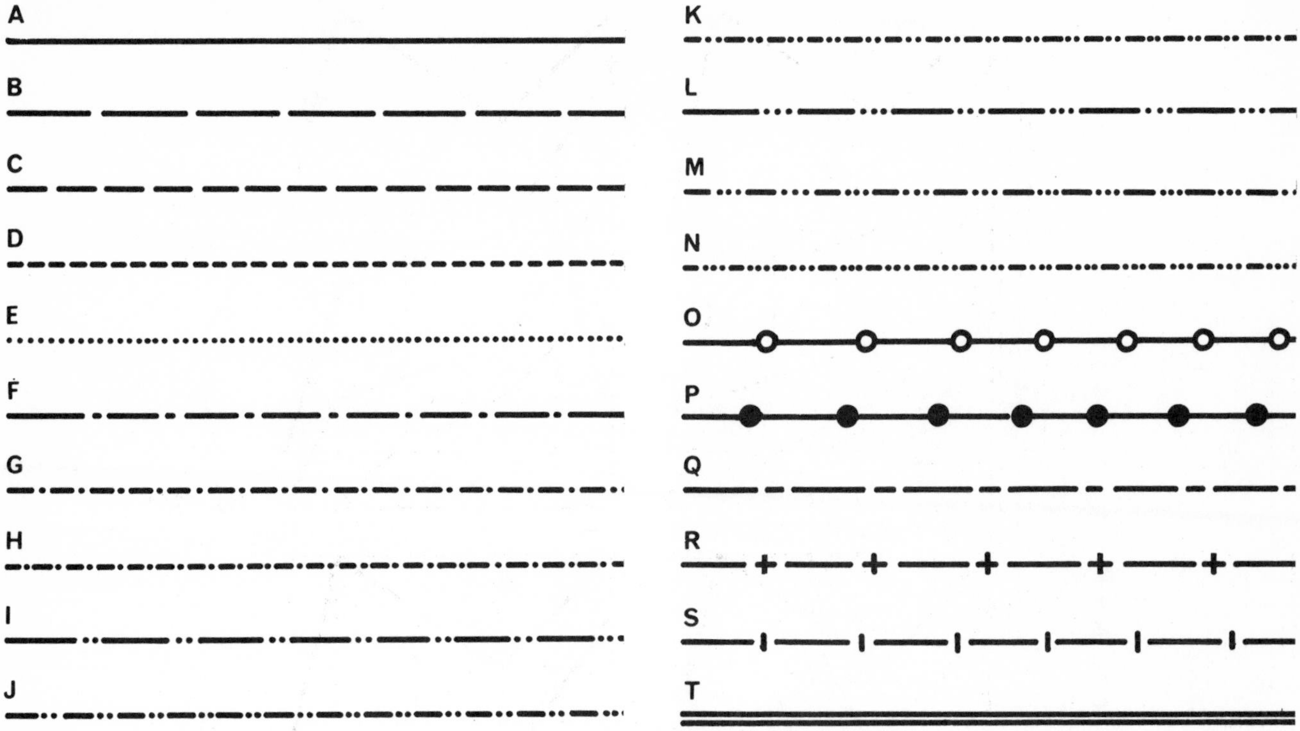

Fig. 1247.

If different types of lines are used for different items (*Fig. 1247*), a legend must be presented on the graph. If the graph is a single graph, it must be placed so that the legend does not interfere with the balance of the figure (*Fig. 1230*) If the illustration consists of several graphs grouped together, only one legend

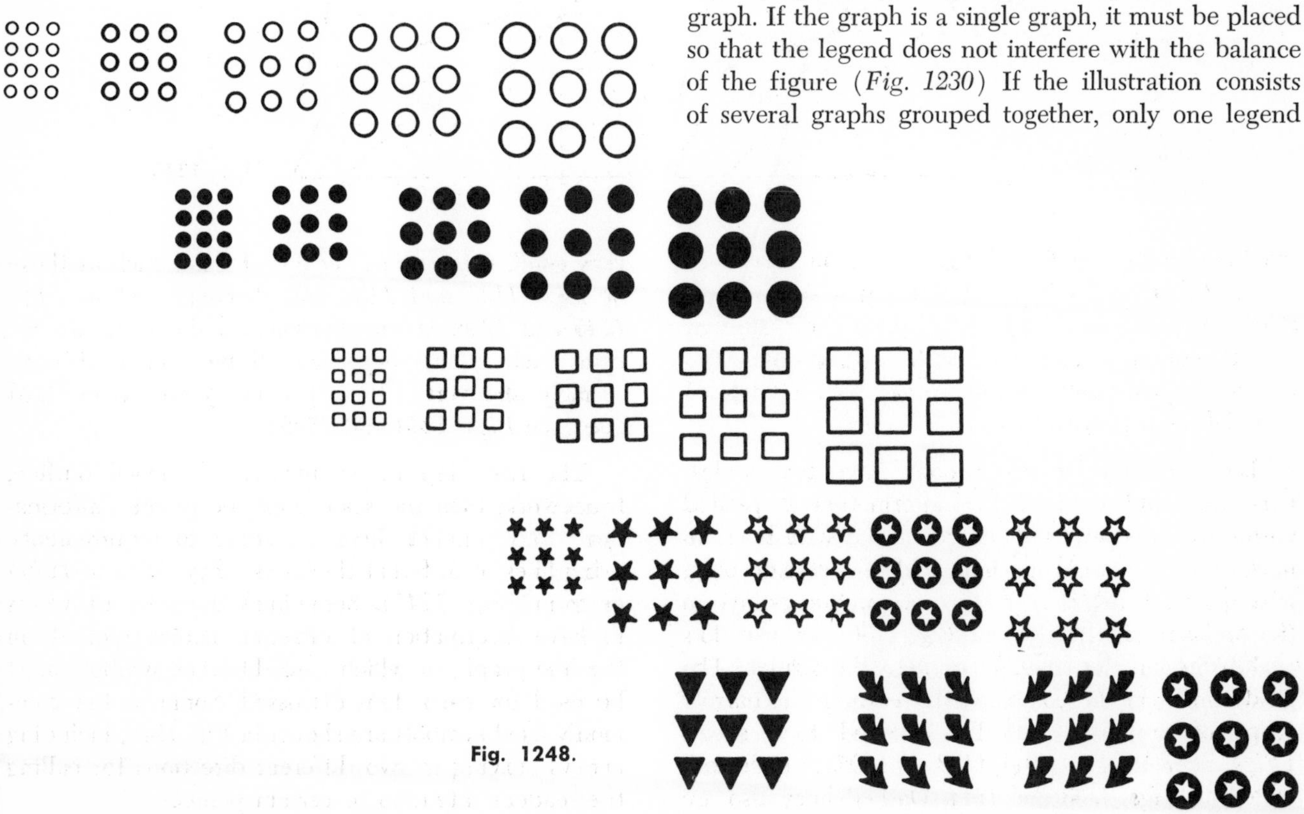

Fig. 1248.

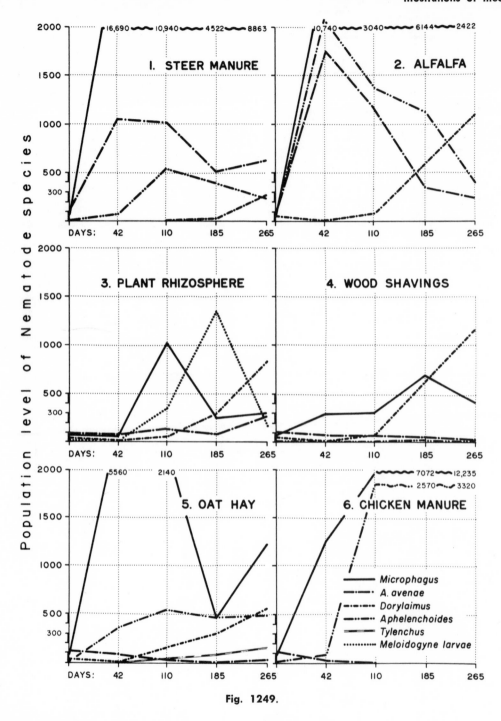

Fig. 1249.

must be used, and it must be placed properly, possibly in the lower left or right graph or within the first row (*Fig. 1249*). If possible avoid spreading out the legend through the whole composition. If you do not have enough space to explain the legend thoroughly, then make a short legend — samples of the types of lines used, with a number after each one. These numbers will then be explained in the text for the illustra-

tion or in the main text. Sometimes the legend can be omitted, however, when the individual lines are numbered on the graph, and the author can give a detailed explanation referring to these numbers in the text.

A complete explanation of the composing of graphs (and distribution maps) is given in a future publication (C. S. Papp: Making Graphs and Maps).

D. LABELING ILLUSTRATIONS

An artistically perfect illustration can be ruined with improper labeling. If you study various publications you will find examples of such work. Commonly the letters are too large: if they were to be reduced to the proper size, the illustration would suffer. Obviously it is very important to use proper letter types and sizes. The following is a brief explanation, as more detailed work is now in preparation and will be available soon (C. S. Papp: Handbook of Lettering).

The best known labeling technique is the Leroy-type of labeling. A full explanation of how to use the Leroy set is not necessary here; it is contained in the manufacturer's manual. Only one thing must be repeated: clean the lettering pens always and be sure they are washed and dried after using them. Make your letters to fit the reduction properly. It does not matter if you are using the same size letter all the way through, but in the legend use italics (tilted, as in *Fig. 1251*). If a bar graph must be labeled and the individual bars need lettering, use some other types which are easily distinguished from the base lettering. Using an inexpensive adapter to your scriber, you can change the height and the width of the letters, as demonstrated in *Fig. 1252*. If there are registered lines or pointers to be used on the illustration (as in

THE GEOGRAPHIC DISTRIBUTION OF A SPECIES POPULATION AND THE INTERRELATION OF CONDITIONING AND REGULATING FORCES.

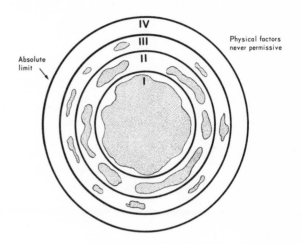

Zone I   Stable zone of permanent occupancy. Most nearly optimal physical conditions.

Zone II   Intermediate zone of permanent occupancy. Physical conditions intermediate.

Zone III   Marginal zone of permanent occupancy. Physical conditions rigorous, mostly unfavorable, at very limited places permanently permissive.

Zone IV   Zone of only temporary occupancy. Physical conditions only temporarily permissive anywhere. Dependant on immigration.

Fig. 1250.

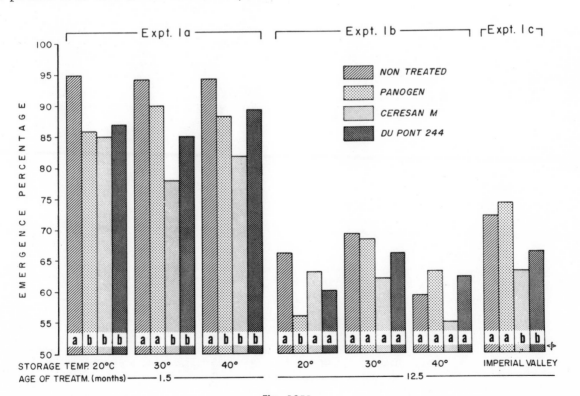

Fig. 1251.

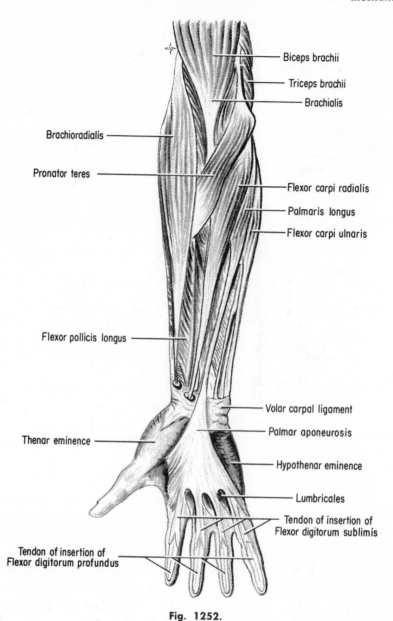

Biceps brachii

Triceps brachii

Brachialis

Brachioradialis

Pronator teres

Flexor carpi radialis

Palmaris longus

Flexor carpi ulnaris

Flexor pollicis longus

Volar carpal ligament

Palmar aponeurosis

Thenar eminence

Hypothenar eminence

Lumbricales

Tendon of insertion of
Flexor digitorum sublimis

Tendon of insertion of
Flexor digitorum profundus

Fig. 1252.

Figs. 1252 and *1253*) make them distinct, and if the background is dark, shade those lines covering one side with white ink, or press on white lines from the Instant Lettering, Sheet No. 223. For Leroy types commonly used, and their reproduction in different reductions, refer to *Figs. 1255* to *1260*.

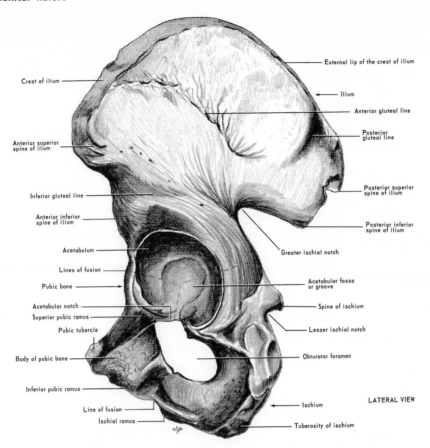

External lip of the crest of ilium

Crest of ilium

Ilium

Anterior gluteal line

Posterior gluteal line

Anterior superior spine of ilium

Inferior gluteal line

Posterior superior spine of ilium

Anterior inferior spine of ilium

Posterior inferior spine of ilium

Acetabulum

Greater ischial notch

Lines of fusion

Pubic bone

Acetabular fossa or groove

Acetabular notch

Spine of ischium

Superior pubic ramus

Lesser ischial notch

Pubic tubercle

Body of pubic bone

Obturator foramen

Inferior pubic ramus

LATERAL VIEW

Line of fusion

Ischium

Ischial ramus

Tuberosity of ischium

Fig. 1253.

A

Fig. 1254.-A

abcdefghijklmnop ABCDEFGHIJKLMNOP 1234567890
abcdefghijklmno ABCDEFGHIJKLMN 1234567890
abcdefghijklmn ABCDEFGHIJKLM 1234567890
abcdefghijklmnop ABCDEFGHIJKLMNOP 1234567890
abcdefghijklmno ABCDEFGHIJKLMN 1234567890
abcdefghijklmnop **ABCDEFGHIJKLMNOP** 1234567890
abcdefghijklmn **ABCDEFGHIJKLMN** 1234567890
abcdefghijklmnop ABCDEFGHIJKLMN 1234567890
abcdefghijklmnopqrst ABCDEFGHIJKLMNOPQRS 1234567890
abcdefghijklmnopqrs ABCDEFGHIJKLMN 1234567890

B

Fig. 1254.-B

On the following pages appear some examples of Leroy letters. For easier reference, the template numbers are given at the left and the pen numbers on the right. Each type face is available in two different styles: the top lines show thet regular (upright) face, and the lower lines show the italicized (tilted) face.

Plate

Pen

80 ABCDEFGHIJKLMNOPQRSTUVWXYZ& abcdefghijklmnopqrstuvwxyz, (%)"= 0123456789·
ABCDEFGHIJKLMNOPQRSTUVWXYZ& abcdefghijklmnopqrstuvwxyz, (%)"= 0123456789·   000

100 ABCDEFGHIJKLMNOPQRSTUVWXYZ& abcdefghijklmnopqrstuvwxyz, (%)"=
ABCDEFGHIJKLMNOPQRSTUVWXYZ& abcdefghijklmnopqrstuvwxyz, (%)"=   000
123456789   *123456789·*

100 ABCDEFGHIJKLMNOPQRSTUVWXYZ& abcdefghijklmnopqrstuvwxyz, (%)"=
ABCDEFGHIJKLMNOPQRSTUVWXYZ& abcdefghijklmnopqrstuvwxyz, (%)"=   00
123456789·   *123456789·*

100 ABCDEFGHIJKLMNOPQRSTUVWXYZ& abcdefghijklmnopqrstuvwxyz, (%)"=
ABCDEFGHIJKLMNOPQRSTUVWXYZ& abcdefghijklmnopqrstuvwxyz, (%)"=   0
123456789·   *123456789·*

120 **ABCDEFGHIJKLMNOPQRSTUVWXYZ&** abcdefghijklmnopqrstuvwxyz, (%)
ABCDEFGHIJKLMNOPQRSTUVWXYZ& *abcdefghijklmnopqrstuvwxyz, (%)*   0
123456789·   *123456789·*

120 **ABCDEFGHIJKLMNOPQRSTUVWXYZ&** abcdefghijklmnopqrstuvwxyz, (%)
ABCDEFGHIJKLMNOPQRSTUVWXYZ& *abcdefghijklmnopqrstuvwxyz, (%)*   I
123456789·   *123456789·*

140 **ABCDEFGHIJKLMNOPQRSTUVWXYZ&,**   (%)= 123456789·
ABCDEFGHIJKLMNOPQRSTUVWXYZ&,   *(%)= 123456789·*   I
abcdefghijklmnopqrstuvwxyz   *abcdefghijklmnopqrstuvwxyz*

175 **ABCDEFGHIJKLMNOPQRSTUVWXYZ&,**   = (%)   I
ABCDEFGHIJKLMNOPQRSTUVWXYZ&,   *.= (%)*
abcdefghijklmnopqrstuvwxyz   123456789·
abcdefghijklmnopqrstuvwxyz   *123456789·*

175 **ABCDEFGHIJKLMNOPQRSTUVWXYZ&,**   = (%)   2
ABCDEFGHIJKLMNOPQRSTUVWXYZ&,   *= (%)*
abcdefghijklmnopqrstuvwxyz   123456789·
abcdefghijklmnopqrstuvwxyz   *123456789·*

Fig. 1255.

Plate   Pen

200 ABCDEFGHIJKLMNOPQRSTUVWXYZ,123456789·   2
ABCDEFGHIJKLMNOPQRSTUVWXYZ,123456789·
abcdefghijklmnopqrstuvwxyz,   &" (%)
abcdefghijklmnopqrstuvwxyz,   *&" (%)*

240 ABCDEFGHIJKLMNOPQRSTUVWXYZ, &   2
ABCDEFGHIJKLMNOPQRSTUVWXYZ &
abcdefghijklmnopqrstuvwxyz, 123456789·
abcdefghijklmnopqrstuvwxyz, 123456789·

240 ABCDEFGHIJKLMNOPQRSTUVWXYZ &   3
ABCDEFGHIJKLMNOPQRSTUVWXYZ &
abcdefghijklmnopqrstuvwxyz, 123456789·
abcdefghijklmnopqrstuvwxyz, 123456789·

290 ABCDEFGHIJKLMNOPQRSTUVW   2
ABCDEFGHIJKLMNOPQRSTUVW
XYZ&,   abcdefghijklmnopqrstuvwxyz
XYZ&,   abcdefghijklmnopqrstuvwxyz
123456789 (%)"   *123456789 (%)"*

290 ABCDEFGHIJKLMNOPQRSTUVW   3
ABCDEFGHIJKLMNOPQRSTUVW
XYZ&,   abcdefghijklmnopqrstuvwxyz
XYZ&,   abcdefghijklmnopqrstuvwxyz
123456789 (%)"   *123456789 (%)"*

Fig. 1256.

Plate		Pen
80	ABCDEFGHIJKLMNOPQRSTUVWXYZ& abcdefghijklmnopqrstuvwxyz, (%)"= 0123456789	OOO
	ABCDEFGHIJKLMNOPQRSTUVWXYZ& abcdefghijklmnopqrstuvwxyz, (%)"= 0123456789	
100	ABCDEFGHIJKLMNOPQRSTUVWXYZ& abcdefghijklmnopqrstuvwxyz, (%) "=	OOO
	ABCDEFGHIJKLMNOPQRSTUVWXYZ& abcdefghijklmnopqrstuvwxyz, (%) " =	
	123456789 123456789	
100	ABCDEFGHIJKLMNOPQRSTUVWXYZ& abcdefghijklmnopqrstuvwxyz, (%) "=	OO
	ABCDEFGHIJKLMNOPQRSTUVWXYZ& abcdefghijklmnopqrstuvwxyz, (%)" =	
	123456789· 123456789·	
100	ABCDEFGHIJKLMNOPQRSTUVWXYZ& abcdefghijklmnopqrstuvwxyz, (%) "=	O
	ABCDEFGHIJKLMNOPQRSTUVWXYZ& abcdefghijklmnopqrstuvwxyz, (%)"=	
	123456789· 123456789·	
120	ABCDEFGHIJKLMNOPQRSTUVWXYZ& abcdefghijklmnopqrstuvwxyz, (%)	O
	ABCDEFGHIJKLMNOPQRSTUVWXYZ& abcdefghijklmnopqrstuvwxyz, (%)	
	123456789· 123456789·	
120	ABCDEFGHIJKLMNOPQRSTUVWXYZ& abcdefghijklmnopqrstuvwxyz, (%)	I
	ABCDEFGHIJKLMNOPQRSTUVWXYZ& abcdefghijklmnopqrstuvwxyz, (%)	
	123456789· 123456789·	
140	ABCDEFGHIJKLMNOPQRSTUVWXYZ&, (%)⁼ 123456789·	I
	ABCDEFGHIJKLMNOPQRSTUVWXYZ&, (%)⁼ 123456789·	
	abcdefghijklmnopqrstuvwxyz abcdefghijklmnopqrstuvwxyz	
175	ABCDEFGHIJKLMNOPQRSTUVWXYZ&, " (%)	I
	ABCDEFGHIJKLMNOPQRSTUVWXYZ&, . " (%)	
	abcdefghijklmnopqrstuvwxyz 123456789·	
	abcdefghijklmnopqrstuvwxyz 123456789·	
175	ABCDEFGHIJKLMNOPQRSTUVWXYZ&, " (%)	2
	ABCDEFGHIJKLMNOPQRSTUVWXYZ&, " (%)	
	abcdefghijklmnopqrstuvwxyz 123456789·	
	abcdefghijklmnopqrstuvwxyz 123456789·	

Fig. 1257.

Both can be done from the same template by adjusting the angle of the scriber. In *Figs. 1255* and *1256* the letters are reproduced in their original size; in *Figs. 1257* and *1258* they are reduced to 75 per cent, and in *Figs. 1259* and *1260* to 50 per cent of the original size.

The figures mentioned (*1255* to *1260*) show the 14 most commonly used templates. These samples are written with the most adaptable size pen for reproduction. It is extremely helpful to go through these

Plate   Pen

200   ABCDEFGHIJKLMNOPQRSTUVWXYZ, 123456789·   2
ABCDEFGHIJKLMNOPQRSTUVWXYZ, 123456789·
abcdefghijklmnopqrstuvwxyz,   & ‼ (%)
abcdefghijklmnopqrstuvwxyz,   *& ‼ (%)*

240   ABCDEFGHIJKLMNOPQRSTUVWXYZ, &   2
ABCDEFGHIJKLMNOPQRSTUVWXYZ &
abcdefghijklmnopqrstuvwxyz, 123456789·
abcdefghijklmnopqrstuvwxyz, 123456789·

240   ABCDEFGHIJKLMNOPQRSTUVWXYZ &   3
ABCDEFGHIJKLMNOPQRSTUVWXYZ &
abcdefghijklmnopqrstuvwxyz, 123456789·
abcdefghijklmnopqrstuvwxyz, 123456789·

290   ABCDEFGHIJKLMNOPQRSTUVW   2
ABCDEFGHIJKLMNOPQRSTUVW
XYZ&,   abcdefghijklmnopqrstuvwxyz
XYZ&,   abcdefghijklmnopqrstuvwxyz
123456789 (%)‼   *123456789 (%)‼*

290   ABCDEFGHIJKLMNOPQRSTUVW   3
ABCDEFGHIJKLMNOPQRSTUVW
XYZ&,   abcdefghijklmnopqrstuvwxyz
XYZ&,   abcdefghijklmnopqrstuvwxyz
123456789 (%)‼   *123456789 (%)‼*

Fig. 1258.

samples and compare each template size with the two reductions, e.g., 75 per cent and 50 per cent (*Figs. 1257-1258* and *1259-1260*). Being able to visualize the differences between these and the original size (*Figs. 1255-1256*) may be a help to the reader in selecting the proper size lettering. This is extremely important especially if the original is large. It is common mistake to use letters too small or too large. Such mistakes can be easily spotted in many scientific periodicals.

Plate		Pen
80	ABCDEFGHIJKLMNOPQRSTUVWXYZ& abcdefghijklmnopqrstuvwxyz, (%)"= 0123456789· *ABCDEFGHIJKLMNOPQRSTUVWXYZ& abcdefghijklmnopqrstuvwxyz, (%)"= 0123456789·*	000
100	ABCDEFGHIJKLMNOPQRSTUVWXYZ& abcdefghijklmnopqrstuvwxyz, (%)"= *ABCDEFGHIJKLMNOPQRSTUVWXYZ& abcdefghijklmnopqrstuvwxyz, (%)"=* 123456789 *123456789*	000
100	ABCDEFGHIJKLMNOPQRSTUVWXYZ& abcdefghijklmnopqrstuvwxyz, (%)"= *ABCDEFGHIJKLMNOPQRSTUVWXYZ& abcdefghijklmnopqrstuvwxyz, (%)"=* 123456789· *123456789·*	00
100	ABCDEFGHIJKLMNOPQRSTUVWXYZ& abcdefghijklmnopqrstuvwxyz, (%)"= *ABCDEFGHIJKLMNOPQRSTUVWXYZ& abcdefghijklmnopqrstuvwxyz, (%)"=* 123456789· *123456789·*	0
120	ABCDEFGHIJKLMNOPQRSTUVWXYZ& abcdefghijklmnopqrstuvwxyz, (%) *ABCDEFGHIJKLMNOPQRSTUVWXYZ& abcdefghijklmnopqrstuvwxyz, (%)* 123456789· *123456789*	0
120	ABCDEFGHIJKLMNOPQRSTUVWXYZ& abcdefghijklmnopqrstuvwxyz, (%) *ABCDEFGHIJKLMNOPQRSTUVWXYZ& abcdefghijklmnopqrstuvwxyz, (%)* 123456789· *123456789·*	1
140	ABCDEFGHIJKLMNOPQRSTUVWXYZ&, (%)‼ 123456789· *ABCDEFGHIJKLMNOPQRSTUVWXYZ&, (%)‼ 123456789·* abcdefghijklmnopqrstuvwxyz *abcdefghijklmnopqrstuvwxyz*	1
175	ABCDEFGHIJKLMNOPQRSTUVWXYZ&, ‼ (%) *ABCDEFGHIJKLMNOPQRSTUVWXYZ&, . ‼ (%)* abcdefghijklmnopqrstuvwxyz 123456789· *abcdefghijklmnopqrstuvwxyz 123456789·*	1
175	ABCDEFGHIJKLMNOPQRSTUVWXYZ&, ‼ (%) *ABCDEFGHIJKLMNOPQRSTUVWXYZ&, ‼ (%)* abcdefghijklmnopqrstuvwxyz 123456789· *abcdefghijklmnopqrstuvwxyz 123456789·*	2

Fig. 1259.

The perfect way to label any illustration is by using a Varityper. Either with a simple drawing (*Fig. 1250*) for slide projector or a more complicated one for publication (*Fig. 1253*), this method is the best. There is a special machine called the Varityper that is used for setting the type (*Fig. 1254-a*). The type faces are interchangeable; each type face has its own font (see arrow beside the machine in *Fig. 1254a*). These fonts make it possible to use different types, sizes and shapes, some of which are reproduced in their original size in *Fig. 1254b*. We have one in our studio and use it very satisfactorily. It is a great time-saver and makes easy the neatest possible job on the lettering.

Instant Lettering (also known as Letraset) is a much newer process. These letters are often called rub-off-letters. They are printed on transparent acetate sheets and are waxed on the back. Line-up lines are under each letter or number to help the user to place the letters. Easy to erase with any eraser, they come in most cases in black, white, red, blue, and some of them also in yellow, gold and silver. They are excellent for black and white or color reproductions. There are several imitations on the market today, but we have found no other to match the quality of the original (made in England).

Plate		Pen
200	ABCDEFGHIJKLMNOPQRSTUVWXYZ, 123456789· *ABCDEFGHIJKLMNOPQRSTUVWXYZ, 123456789·* abcdefghijklmnopqrstuvwxyz, &‼ (%) *abcdefghijklmnopqrstuvwxyz, &‼ (%)*	2
240	ABCDEFGHIJKLMNOPQRSTUVWXYZ, & *ABCDEFGHIJKLMNOPQRSTUVWXYZ &* abcdefghijklmnopqrstuvwxyz, 123456789· *abcdefghijklmnopqrstuvwxyz, 123456789·*	2
240	ABCDEFGHIJKLMNOPQRSTUVWXYZ & *ABCDEFGHIJKLMNOPQRSTUVWXYZ &* abcdefghijklmnopqrstuvwxyz, 123456789· *abcdefghijklmnopqrstuvwxyz, 123456789·*	3
290	ABCDEFGHIJKLMNOPQRSTUVW *ABCDEFGHIJKLMNOPQRSTUVW* XYZ&, abcdefghijklmnopqrstuvwxyz *XYZ&, abcdefghijklmnopqrstuvwxyz* 123456789 (%)‼ *123456789 (%)‼*	2
290	ABCDEFGHIJKLMNOPQRSTUVW *ABCDEFGHIJKLMNOPQRSTUVW* XYZ&, abcdefghijklmnopqrstuvwxyz *XYZ&, abcdefghijklmnopqrstuvwxyz* 123456789 (%)‼ *123456789 (%)‼*	3

Fig. 1260.

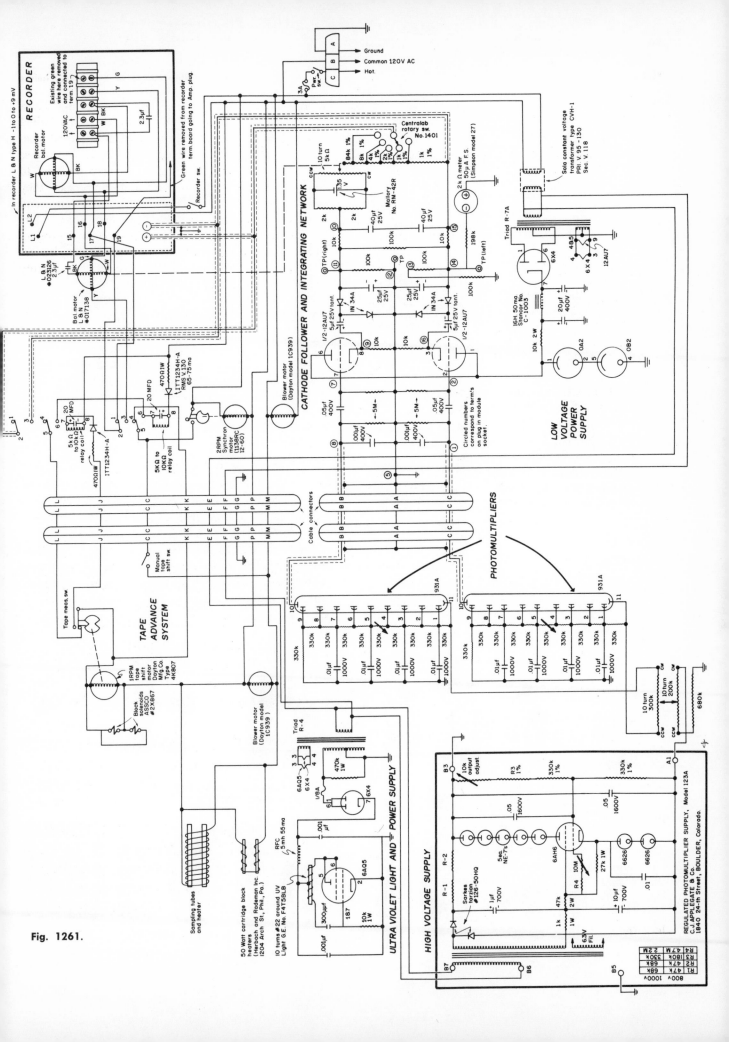

Fig. 1261.

A B Γ Δ E Z H Θ I K Λ M N Ξ O Π P Σ T Υ Φ X Ψ Ω

α β γ δ ε ζ η θ ι κ λ μ ν ξ ο π ρ σ τ υ φ χ ψ ω α ϑ φ ϛ ϭ κ ϝ ϑ ϛ

A B Γ Δ E Z H Θ I K Λ M N Ξ O Π P Σ T Υ Φ X Ψ Ω

α β γ δ ε ζ η θ ι κ λ μ ν ξ ο π ρ σ τ υ φ χ ψ ω α ϑ φ ϛ ϭ κ ϝ ϑ q

Fig. 1262.

In completing large illustrations, especially for engineering projects (as in electronics, *Fig. 1261*), in most cases the illustrator does not have much room to place the necessary lettering. If you are to design the drawing, you must have a completely labeled rough sketch to work from. You thus are able to see the difficulties in advance and, whenever possible, leave ample space for the lettering. This drawing (*Fig. 1261*) was made from a rough sketch. If the reader analyses it, he will find it very clear; the letters are quite small but legible, the headings are done with larger and heavier letters in italics for quick orientation. Heavy letters should not be used throughout on such illustrations: they would distract from the clearness of the drawing. Our sample is reduced to 50 per cent of the original.

In labeling illustrations, especially in the field of chemistry, physics and mathematics, the illustrator may have to use Greek letters. Several sizes of tem-

plates for Greek letters are manufactured by Leroy; we found it quite practical to have No. 175 on hand. The Greek alphabet is also available in Instant Lettering. The size is too small for larger originals, but if the original is not to be reduced more than 10 per cent, these instant letters are usable (*Fig. 1262*). For the smaller sizes we would not recommend any reduction at all. The Varityper also has several fonts of Greek letters and special symbols for mathematics, chemistry and physics; these are a great asset in any studio.

Once in a while some "picturesque" statistical illustrations are needed. These are used primarily on slides for projection. Instant Letters (Letraset) publishes a handy selection of figures (Sheet No. 222) which may be useful in such presentations. *Figs. 1263* to *1276* show the original size of some of those symbols. These simple figures could help create an impressive graph or other statistical illustration.

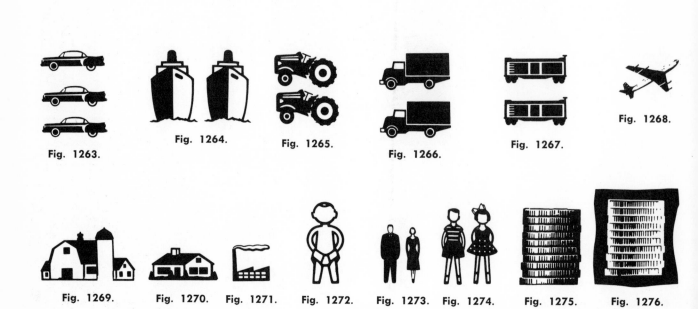

Fig. 1263.

Fig. 1264.

Fig. 1265.

Fig. 1266.

Fig. 1267.

Fig. 1268.

Fig. 1269.

Fig. 1270.

Fig. 1271.

Fig. 1272.

Fig. 1273.

Fig. 1274.

Fig. 1275.

Fig. 1276.

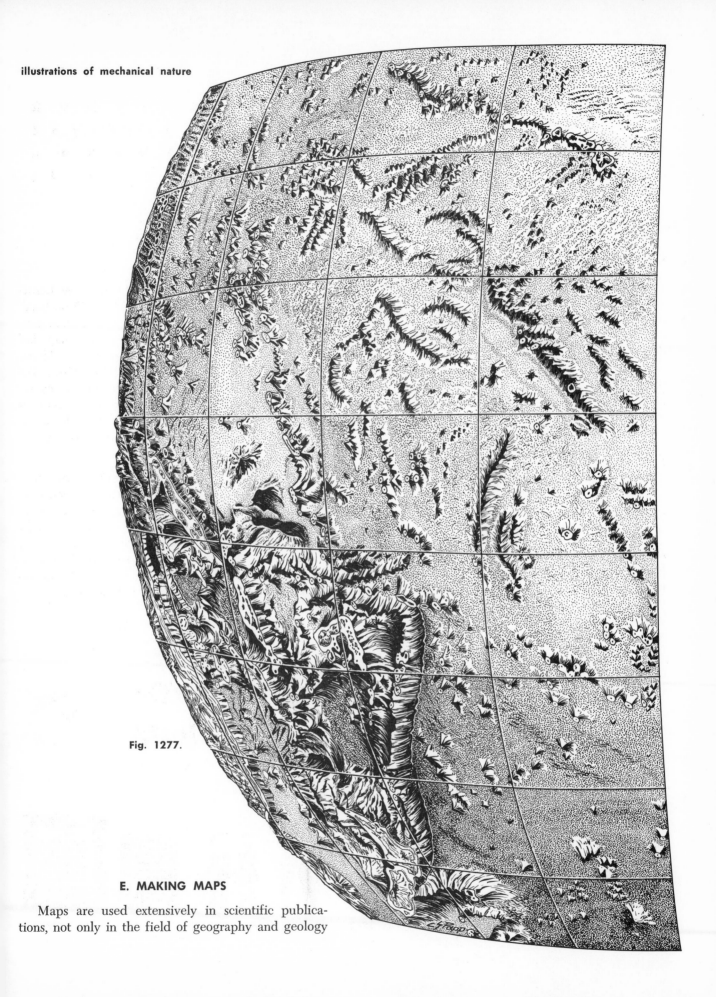

Fig. 1277.

E. MAKING MAPS

Maps are used extensively in scientific publications, not only in the field of geography and geology but also in the field of zoology and botany. A well planned map can eliminate confusion and can clarify explanations. This problem will be but briefly mentioned in this book (a through treatment of the subject is now in preparation by the author). Only a few samples are given here for those illustrators who occasionally have to do distributional maps.

Three-dimensional maps (*Fig. 1277*) are seldom used as background for distributional maps. Their preparation is very time-consuming, and the enormous amount of details would distract from the individual records and symbols. For distributional records a much more simple type of base may therefore be used. When certain areas are to be included in the distribution of certain records, as in the case of precipitation (*Fig. 1278*) a simple ink outline map can be used. If the area is larger, in our sample, the

Fig. 1279.

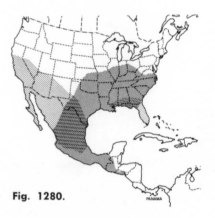

Fig. 1280.

Fig. 1281.

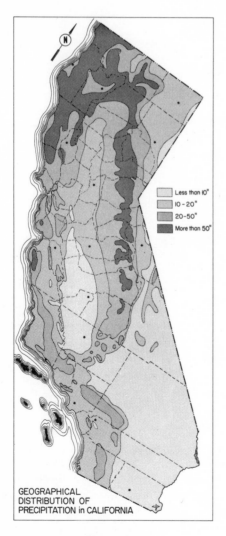

GEOGRAPHICAL DISTRIBUTION OF PRECIPITATION in CALIFORNIA

Less than 10"
10 - 20"
20 - 50"
More than 50"

Fig. 1278.

smaller units like counties are registered, together with heavier dots for some of the important cities for easier orientation. On the other hand, if prefabricated tones make the map too complicated, especially where actual finds must be located, different symbols can be used for plotting those localities, as seen on *Fig. 1279*. If the species in discussion has an over-all distribution,

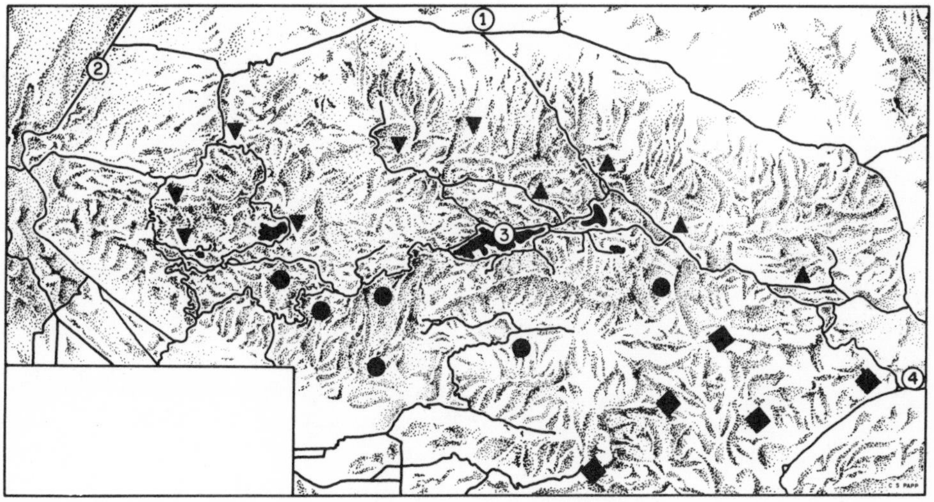

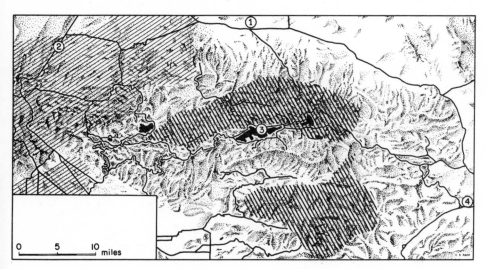

Fig. 1282.

Fig. 1283.

those tones may be applied. Using many different patterns may be permitted by the data compiled (like on *Fig. 1278*), and the printed product still would not be too confusing if the type of tones is carefully selected. It is perhaps best when tones are used not to place too much information on one map (*Fig. 1280*), especially if the illustrator does not have too many different patterns to work with. There is nothing more confusing to the reader than a badly designed tone combination, especially if the original was reduced too much (*Fig. 1281*).

Some authors prefer maps in 3-D and such maps are useful if the information is properly represented by carefully selected symbols. On maps showing mountain ranges it is very hard to choose the right pattern of prefabricated tones. It is probably best to use large dots for recording the distribution (*Fig. 1282*). The use of different tones distracts from the base map and makes the base somehow incomplete (*Fig. 1283*). In this case, it might be best to outline the distributional areas in heavier lines that will show clearly when the map is reduced (*Fig. 1284*).

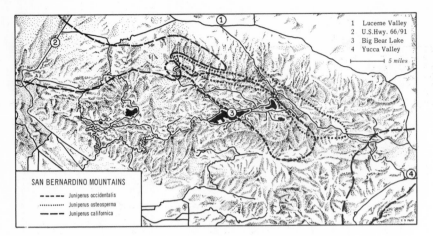

Fig. 1284.

It is common practice to make base maps of certain areas in which the scientist is engaged in research. Often such originals are far too large for fine reproduction and they usually contain small symbols and letters. An example of a complicated base map is shown in *Fig. 1277*, which is a 50 per cent reduction. This size may be usable as a base map to register localities with larger symbols. Having made the dots large enough in the original a large scale reduction is easy and pleasing (*Fig. 1285*). This is one-quarter the size of the original. Dark base maps are very seldom used, and if used the marks must be very prominent. The original map should not be more than three times the size of the published copy. It is a bad habit to make those maps unnecessarily large. It is hard to control the size of the labeling if the map is too large, and this is the reason why so many maps are unreadable.

Fig. 1285.

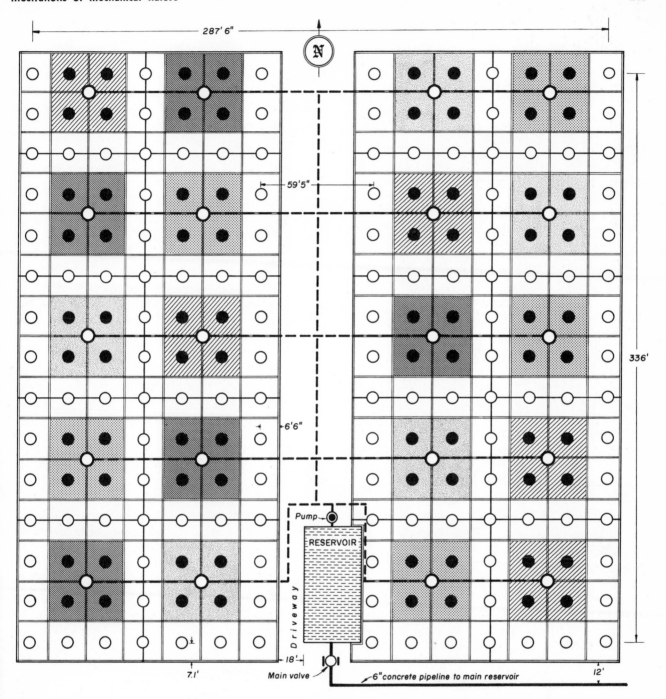

Fig. 1286.

Where field experiments are in progress the illustrator may be engaged to make field maps to aid the research staff in their work. Such a map is illustrated in *Fig. 1286*. These maps should also be small — never larger than twice the size of the finished (printed) product. They must be exact, clear, easy to read and constructed so that any changes that may occur during the experiment can be indicated.

F. REPRODUCTION TECHNIQUES

An illustrator is always interested in the final result of his work: how does the artwork appear in the publication? You may already know that the end result is not always satisfactory. Some of the illustrations may have been reduced too much, not reduced enough, or even enlarged. These are the facts that all illustrators have to face. Thanks to modern printing techniques and to the ever better quality of paper it is quite easy to reproduce illustrations properly. Despite the fact that many editors and publishers try to save space in a journal or book, the well reproduced illustrations outnumber the defective ones.

We must again stress how necessary it is that the illustrator know what size and with what technique his illustration will be reproduced. The size is always given by the editor (or author) or the publisher. The reproduction technique is determined by the illustrator when he selects the technique of his drawing. Sometimes it may happen that the illustration will not be reproduced by the best method possible. Let's look at some of these reproduction methods:

1. *Line reproduction.* Every line drawing composed of sharp and evenly black (or red) lines is reproducible with lines. If the density of the lines permits, they can be reduced to the required size or to a size which adds to the final appearance. In short, sharp dots (*Figs. 1287* and *1288*) or sharp lines (*Fig. 1289*) are prerequisites. Large dots and heavy lines make reproduction easier and provide the best chance for a larger scale reduction. The printer's job is also made easier. If the originals are composed of fine dots or fine lines (*Figs. 1290* and *1291*) there is always a chance that some of those dots and lines are not dark enough to show in the printed product. The printer makes a line negative from the original artwork; the negative is checked, so called "pinholes" are opaqued (covered with water-soluble opaque). From this line negative the plate is burned (for offset) or a cut is made (for letter press). Pinholes (from dust, etc.) are sometimes present on the negative if the illustration is not cleaned perfectly, if the glass on the shooting frame is dirty, or if the developing chemical is old. It seldom happens that the illustrator has a chance to see the negative of his line drawings. Sometimes it would help (especially in the case of illustration with labeling and register lines) if dark register lines could be scratched into the negative or some of the register lines could be lightened up (with opaque), especially if the original is reduced too much. Usually, however, a careful printer takes care of these problems.

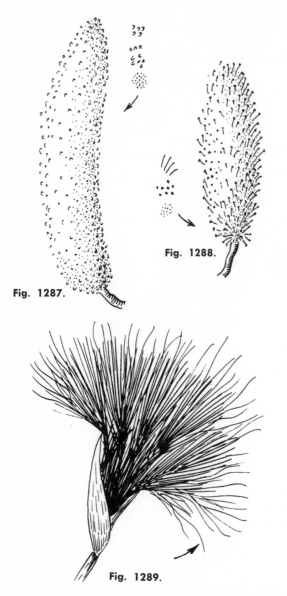

Fig. 1288.

Fig. 1287.

Fig. 1289.

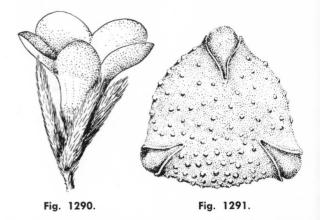

Fig. 1290.   Fig. 1291.

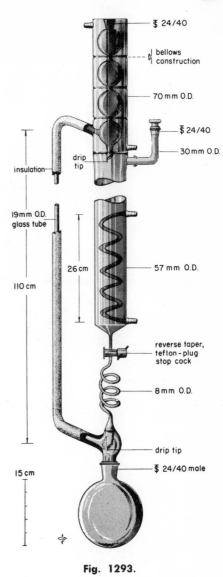

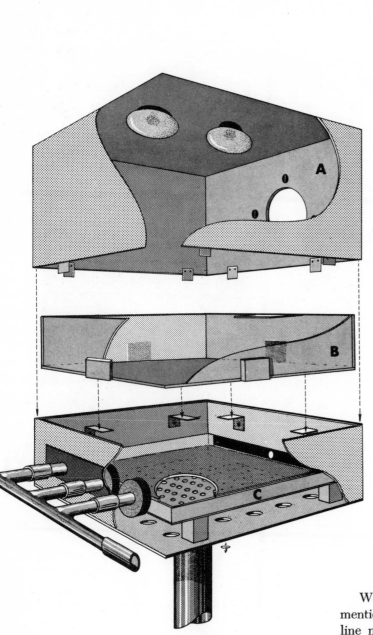

Fig. 1292.

Fig. 1293.

We learned the use of prefabricated tones and mentioned also that those tones are reproducible with line negatives. Such samples are seen here in *Figs. 1292* and *1293*, using tones of different density. At first glance they look like half-tone reproductions. We also learned that illustrations done on scratch board reproduce well in line negative (*Fig. 1294*). In the explanation of pen and wax pencil technique it was pointed out that both the outline and the shading must be dark enough for perfect reproduction. Such drawings are also excellent for line reproduction (*Figs. 1295* and *1296*).

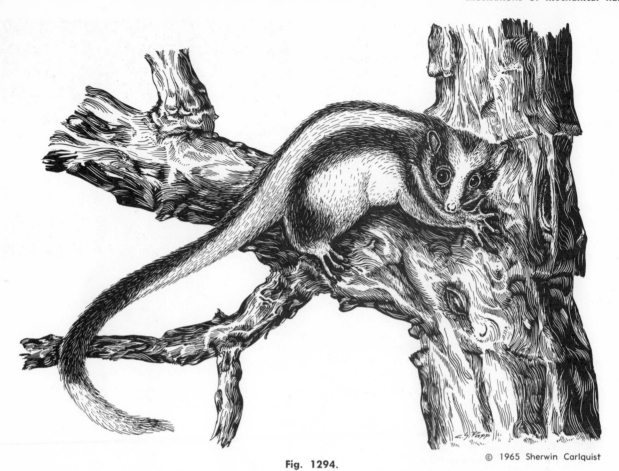

Fig. 1294.

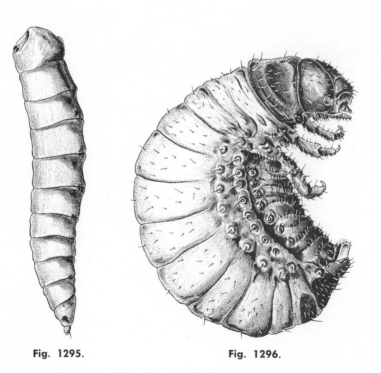

Fig. 1295.   Fig. 1296.

2. *Half-tone reproduction*. The half-tone can be easily differentiated from the line reproduction by the grayish appearance of the picture. The line reproduction is composed of solid evenly colored lines; the half-tone is composed of minute dots of various sizes. If you observe the details in *Fig. 1297* with a magnifying glass you will see minute dots, as demonstrated in *Fig. 1298*. With a powerful glass, the dots will resemble those in *Fig. 1299*. The dots are uneven and of varied sizes. Dots will appear also on the background which usually is white on the original artwork; consequently the background dots will be smaller (*Figs. 1298* and *1299*). If you want to have the artwork reproduced with its background, as in *Fig. 1297*, the printer will "frame" the negatives, making even edges around it by using opaque outline, most likely tape, when stripping the negative. The figure will then appear like our sample, in which this is the proper way of reproduction.

In most cases those background dots are not needed, however, so the printer covers them with opaque paint (water soluble). In *Figs. 1298* and *1299* this is demonstrated in part. Note how the annuli of

Fig. 1297.

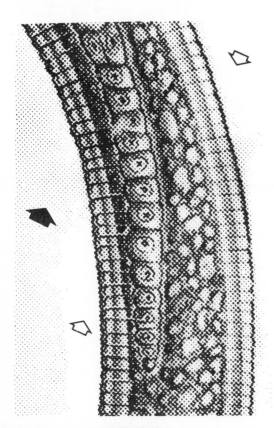

Fig. 1298.

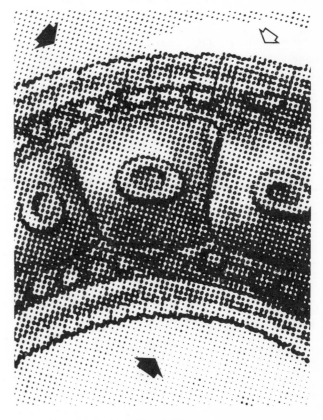

Fig. 1299.

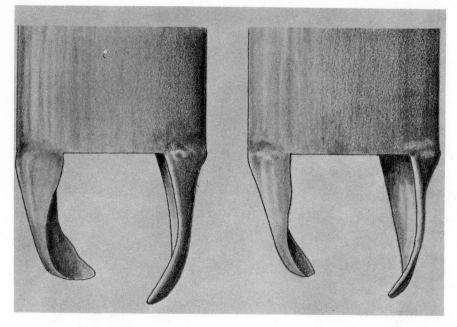

Fig. 1300.   Fig. 1301.

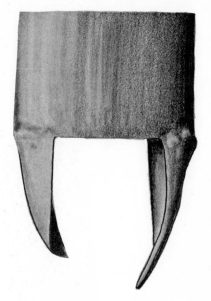

Fig. 1302.

the nematode are preserved by delicate work. White arrows indicate the opaqued area and black arrows indicate the area where the dots (screen) are still present. The presence of the screen background is sometimes disturbing, as seen in *Figs. 1300* and *1301*, especially if fine differences between species must be demonstrated. Compare the clearness of *Fig. 1302*, and how much neater the reproduction is. Those three samples were made with the smudging technique (charcoal).

As mentioned before, a line drawing is sometimes printed in half-tone. This can be satisfactory, especially if the background is opaqued as seen in *Fig. 1303* and it can be done easily on so simple a drawing.

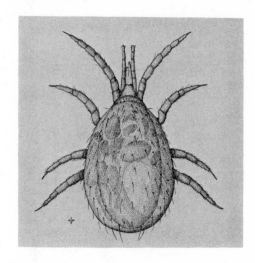

Fig. 1304.

But if the species illustrated were covered with hairs it would be quite time-consuming to opaque around those fine hairs, so the printer will leave the light tones (screen) on the background and follow the same procedure described for *Fig. 1297*. Note on the picture of the mite (*1304*) that the background is light gray. Observe the fine punctures with a magnifying glass. The original background was white. This could happen primarily with line drawings of small and fine dimensions, when line reproduction in larger reduction would not permit perfect reproduction. Again we stress that the proper size of the original artwork is important.

Fig. 1303.

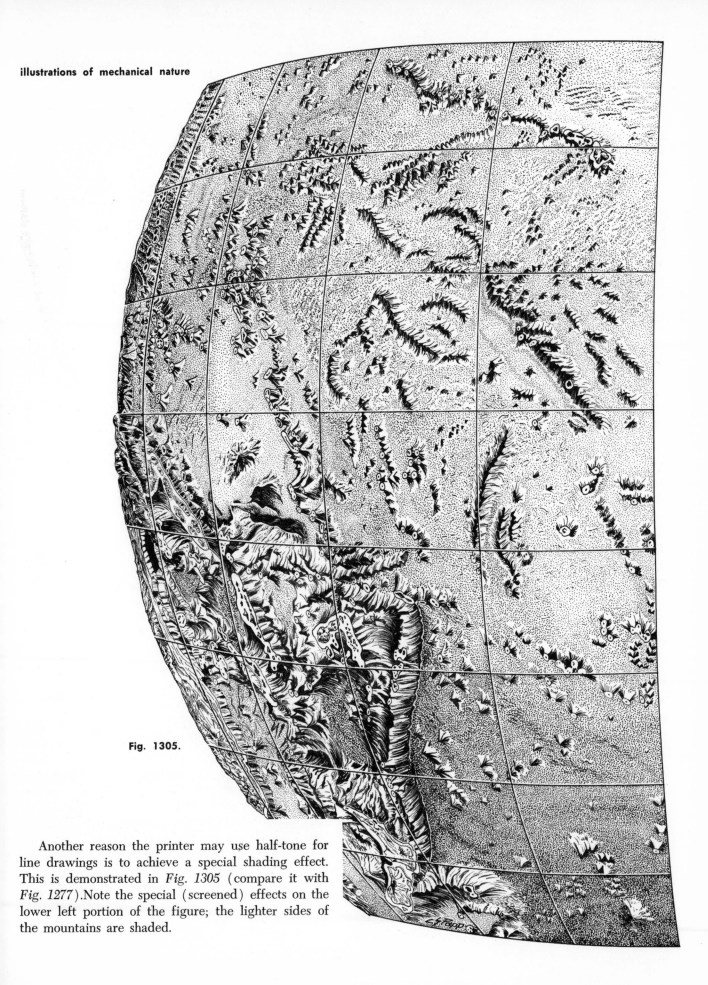

Fig. 1305.

Another reason the printer may use half-tone for line drawings is to achieve a special shading effect. This is demonstrated in *Fig. 1305* (compare it with *Fig. 1277*).Note the special (screened) effects on the lower left portion of the figure; the lighter sides of the mountains are shaded.

Fig. 1306.

Color originals can be reproduced in black and white also. It is obvious that such reproductions, especially if many colors were used on the original, will not be too good. *Fig. 1306* is such an example, reproduced from a pastel color drawing made on velour-coated paper, in 50 per cent reduction. Note how hazy the outlines are. The sharpness did not improve even by a larger reduction (25 per cent of the original in *Fig. 1307*).

Fig. 1307.

Fig. 1308.

Fig. 1309.

Often authors want to use illustrations that have been published in color. To avoid the expense of color reproductions, the printer may make a half-tone negative from the color print. The original (in this case the color print) is also a half-tone and a combination of two or more colors (in our sample four colors), but the colors will be registered on the negative only black on white. The result is demonstrated in *Figs. 1308* and *1309*. Note how the new screen added to the original (color) screen gives a special pattern to the dots. It would be far more attractive to have the "original" redrawn in black and white and have the half-tone negative made from that. The reproduction would be perfect.

Color Overlays

Color overlays are very expensive and are seldom used in scientific publications. They are found in medical books, and are occasionally used for producing maps in scientific publications or for graphs in bank reports or annual statements.

It should be understood that in order to print illustrations the printer first makes a negative; from this negative a plate (offset) or a zinc-cut (letter press) is made which can be printed in any color desired. For example an illustration made with charcoal powder using the smudging technique can be reproduced in any color. In addition of course, color overlays can be done in black and white.

Figure 1310 may look like a finished illustration; however, this is the *black* portion of a color illustration. This one was made on pebble board with wax

pencil. If it were not designed for color overlay it would be slightly more shaded in certain areas. First this base illustration must be prepared. The shading must be carefully designed and distributed so that the black portion of the illustration will not interfere with the other colors. When the drawing is completed the proper lettering (labeling) must be added. The lines must be placed properly, using sharp continuous lines clearly connecting the proper text with the proper body part. Note the shaded lines. We like to use Instant Lettering-type (Letraset) lines (Sheet No. 223), the white line placed parallel with the black line. The white line covers up the shading on one side of the black line and makes the identification lines more prominent. Then register marks are placed on the drawing (there are three of these on the sample) with instant-type (Sheet No. 554).

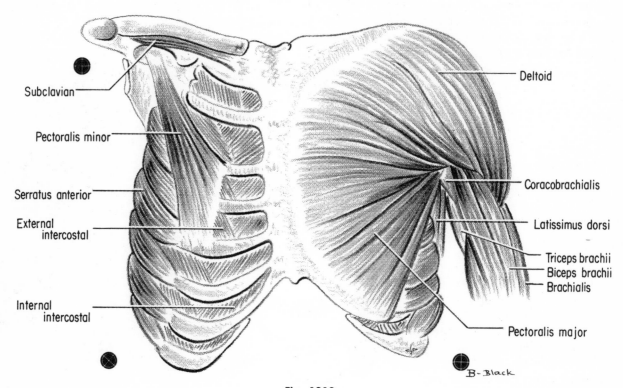

Subclavian

Pectoralis minor

Serratus anterior

External intercostal

Internal intercostal

Deltoid

Coracobrachialis

Latissimus dorsi

Triceps brachii
Biceps brachii
Brachialis

Pectoralis major

B - Black

Fig. 1310.

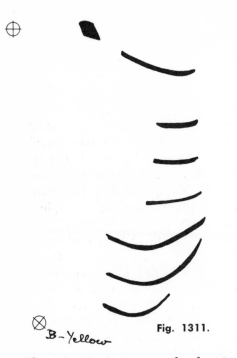

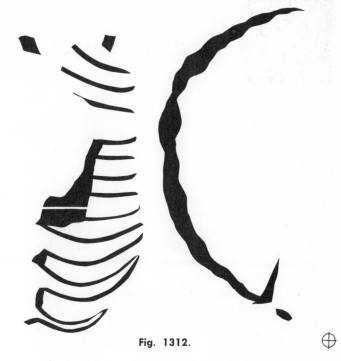

Fig. 1311.

B-Yellow

Fig. 1312.

B-Blue

The next step is to cover the drawing with a clear acetate sheet and fasten the sheet to the drawing. The positive register marks are placed on top of the negative register marks on the original drawing. The acetate sheet is covered with Pelikan India ink in the area where *yellow* color is to appear. If larger areas are to be covered, a red adhesive sheet may be used and the edge cut with a sharp scalpel. Then the sheet is marked "yellow" (*Fig. 1311*).

When the yellow is completed put another acetate sheet on top of it, place the register marks correctly and use the same process to cover the area designated for another color, such as *blue*. When completed mark it "blue" (*Fig. 1312*).

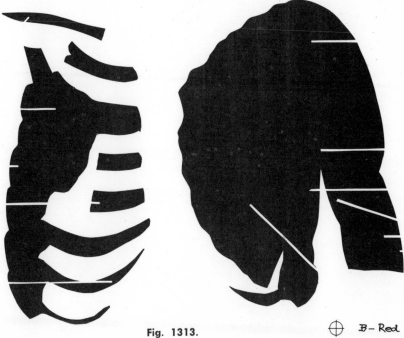

When those are completed and another color is needed, add another acetate sheet. Place the register marks after the acetate sheet is secured properly. Then cover the areas to be printed in red in the same way you did the other colors and mark it *"red"* (*Fig. 1313*).

Fig. 1313.   B-Red

If identification lines are on the illustration, as in our sample, you must cut (or leave clear) the area covered with white on the black (base) drawing on all color overlays so that those lines will appear white on the finished product. That is one of the reasons for placing the register marks properly. Now the printer will take your artwork, separate all those acetate sheets from the drawing, and make one negative. On the negative all your marks will be present — like indication of color, figure number (the B in our case) and the register marks. The next step is stripping the negatives. Each color will be stripped on a separate stripping sheet. The stripping sheet usually is an orange sheet (or acetate sheet) through which light will not penetrate. Suppose the *black* has been stripped in and is in place now. The next step is the "yellow": a new stripping sheet will be used and the negative will be lined up by using the register marks. Then the "blue" and the "red" will be stripped separately. When all the negatives are stripped, the stripping sheets will be marked with the color they represent, then all the notes and register marks will be opaqued (covered so that light will not penetrate through the area). The negatives are now prepared and the plates (or cuts) will be made from them. The next step is to "burn" the color plates. The printer covers the negative for the colors (yellow, blue and red) with a fine screen (a 20 per cent screen would be the best for this example), and burns the plates. The screen is used so that the colors will be continuous but will print light with minute dots of uniform density.

When the plates are done, the "yellow" is printed first, then the "red" and "blue," and last the *black*. Analyzing the procedure — the completion of the original artwork, stripping four negatives, burning four plates and printing four colors (between colors the press must be thoroughly cleaned) — enables the reader to understand why color reproduction, even without color separation (as in our sample) is so costly. Of course the printed product is more beautiful, more explanatory and more eyecatching than a simple black and white reproduction.

Fold Layout

Illustrators, especially those who work for smaller institutions, are frequently involved in designing folders, pamphlets, and similar institutional publications. Sometimes, to save money, the illustrator must handle every step of the job — design, paste-up, even stripping the negative. The smaller institutions usually have some sort of Multilith press and so the illustrator must supply ready material.

The most common type of folding is the one-fold. A normal (8 1/2″ x 11″) sheet folded once in the middle will produce a four page leaflet. The proper arrangement of text and pages requires special attention. See *Fig. 1314* for the first side and *Fig. 1315* for the second side of a one-fold four page publication.

Let's make another example, when eight pages are printed on one sheet. If using 17″ x 22″ size sheets, the individual pages will be 8 1/2″ x 11″. The page arrangement will be for the first side as shown on *Fig. 1316* and for the second side as on *Fig. 1317*. If you want larger page sizes you have to use larger sheets of paper.

4 pages — side 1

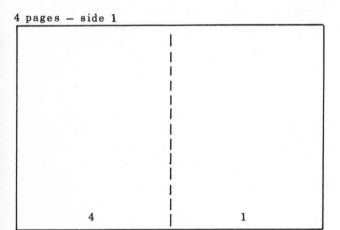

Fig. 1314.

4 pages — side 2

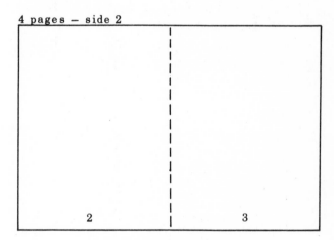

Fig. 1315.

8 pages — side 1

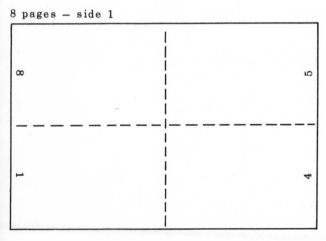

Fig. 1316.

8 pages — side 2

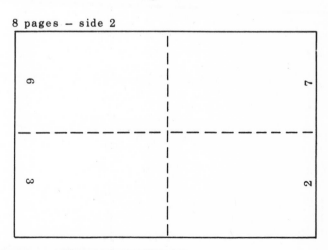

Fig. 1317.

If you want to design a 16-page brochure with 5 1/2″ x 8 1/2″ page sizes, you will lay it out on a sheet that measures 17″ x 22″. A sheet of this size will be printed on a larger press. The page layout for eight pages on side one can be seen in *Fig. 1318* and for the other eight pages on side two in *Fig. 1319.*

It is possible to print 32 pages on a sheet of the same size; naturally the page size will be different (half). The location of the pages for side one is shown in *Fig. 1320* and for side two in *Fig. 1321.*

The dashed lines on those illustrations indicate the folds. To have a four page product on one sheet, the sheet is folded once, for eight pages, twice; for 16 pages, three times; for 32 pages, four times. For a complete understanding of this procedure, which is basic to book manufacturing, it is recommended that you make up your own samples, folding a sheet several times and numbering the pages on the bottom. Then

open it up and observe how unorganized those page numbers appear on the sheet. Fold the sheet back again, staple the center fold (the vertical one) and cut the other edges. Again the pages are properly arranged.

This is important to an illustrator, particularly if he has to design a book or brochure that contains several color pictures. If all the color pictures are on one side of the sheet, the production costs are considerably lower because extra color runs are not necessary for the other side of the sheet.

If you can get acquainted with some printer in your community you can learn about all those "magic tricks" the printer has to work. Then you will gain an understanding of the production of printed materials, figures and text. Perhaps you may have a chance to see your own illustrations reproduced.

16 pages — side 1

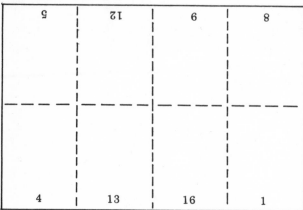

Fig. 1318.

16 pages — side 2

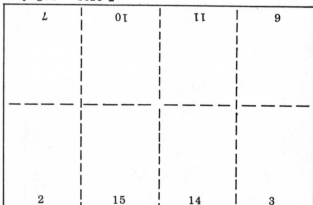

Fig. 1319.

32 pages — side 1

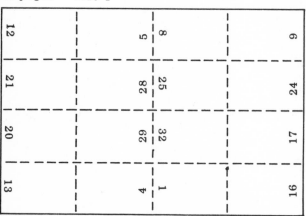

Fig. 1320.

32 pages — side 2

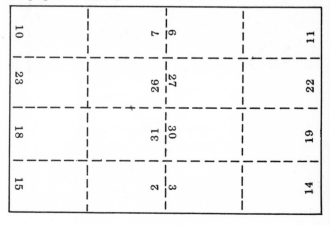

Fig. 1321.

Illustrator's Equipment

16

Most of the illustrators who work for an institution also do free-lance drawings. Institutions usually do not permit the use of their equipment for private purposes, so that the artist must have his own facilities and equipment.

The kind and quality of equipment depends entirely upon the field of specialization. This chapter lists some of the basic equipment. These are the minimum requirements even in the poorest institution. They are a "must" for the free-lance illustrator who does all sorts of biological illustrations.

Figure 1322: Camera lucida, mounted on a compound microscope. The trade name is Unitron. It is cheap and easy to handle; very useful in making pencil outlines of specimens mounted on microscope slides.

Fig. 1323.

Fig. 1322.

Fig. 1324.

Figure 1323: Compound microscope. This is a Swift scope, with tilted eye pieces and four objectives, built-in light and transformer with regulator. A vertical tube (covered in photo) enables the use of a photographic camera or the placement of a projection prism in the place of the camera to project the object on the screen. (See *Fig. 551* on page *147*).

Figure 1324: The same camera lucida mounted on a stereoscopic microscope specially set up for pencil sketches for illustrations of insects. Details are worked out by using another scope with larger magnification. It is best to have two microscopes so that the camera lucida always can be set up and ready to use. For pencil sketches we use this scope; for detailed work we use a Swift with maximum magnification of 100 x.

Figure 1325: Bio-projector. This is a very useful and inexpensive piece of equipment (Bausch and Lomb) for making correct outlines of specimens mounted on slides. If set on a table vertically, it projects the image to the table; if set horizontally, it projects onto a vertical screen. If the specimen on the table is liquid, keep the projector table in horizontal position, turn the projection mirror (*arrow*) into the path of the ray and the picture will be projected onto a vertical screen. Live specimens can be observed easily if they are microscopic in size.

Fig. 1326.

Fig. 1325.

Figure 1326: Lucigraf, an enlarger-reducer; valuable and a timesaver. Has a range of 4x in either way. Especially useful in botanical illustrations. Have extra bulbs on hand.

Figure 1327: Electric eraser. This was mentioned several times throughout the book. Especially useful in creating shades on pencil or charcoal illustrations (smudging); with extra soft refills it is good cleaning detailed artwork.

Figure 1328: A lamp magnifier is especially handy in general observation of the specimen. Lens is almost five inches in diameter and with the circular neon tube that is placed under the metal frame the light shines directly on the object. Also very useful for making fine illustrations, especially scratchboard drawings. Lenses come in 2x and 4x and are interchangeable. Table and wall models are available.

Fig. 1327.

Fig. 1328.

Fig. 1329.

Figure 1329: Opaque projector (Postoscope) of very primitive design. It could replace the Lucigraf (*Fig. 1326*) in some instances. Use is very limited for an illustrator but it is excellent for projecting your own drawings on a screen to test the details and quality of the work.

Figure 1330: Brushes are very important, especially if you work with the wash technique or in color. For general use there are two main types that every illustrator should have. The heavier type, as illustrated, holds larger amounts of paint; the red sable hairs are full-bodied in shape with sharp points. The sizes needed most are illustrated. Another type is in *Fig. 1331*.

Figure 1332: Metal palette for mixing color. These come in various sizes. You may prefer to use jars of uniform sizes. Always keep plenty of clean water on hand for final rinsing of brushes. Keep the palette clean and free of color.

Fig. 1330.

Fig. 1332.

Figure 1333: Another type of palette, called the plastic slent. It is very practical in mixing colors randomly and in smaller amounts. Have at least two of these, one for color and one for black and white. Plastic is harder to clean so wash it before the paint dries.

Fig. 1331.

Fig. 1333.

Figure 1334: Colors — most artists have their own preference. There are several types on the market. Keep the containers clean and the cap closed tightly. Protect from outside pressure and from heat.

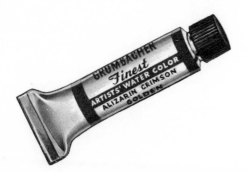

Fig. 1334.

Figure 1335: Paint storage is very important, especially if you can keep the tubes in order by color. It is a pleasing sight in a studio if all these tubes are in order and kept clean. You can store tubes in two or three drawers and use one drawer for miscellaneous tools assocaited with water-color work — a supply of scrap paper for testing color, different types of pencil, etc.

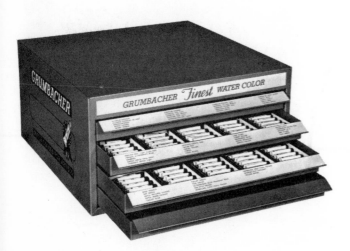

Fig. 1335.

Figure 1336: Pastel colors are another medium to work with. Select the kind you like, and stick to it. Do not mix different makes; keep them well separated from each other and in color order. Complete sets can be purchased in a metal container. If you leave part of one drawer empty, it is a good place to store used stumps or other items associated with pastel work.

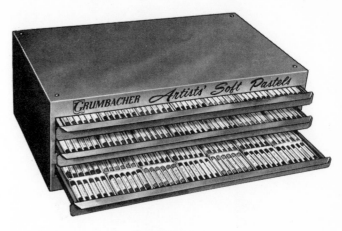

Fig. 1336.

Figure 1337: A brush for cleaning illustrations of powder or eraser chips is very useful. There are different kinds and sizes on the market. The flat type (illustrated) is very handy to brush large areas.

Fig. 1337.

Figure 1338: An acetate roll is handy especially if you do overlay work. Have clear and/or frosted type on hand. It is also good for covering (protecting) finished artwork. It is quite expensive, and is available in rolls and sheets of various sizes.

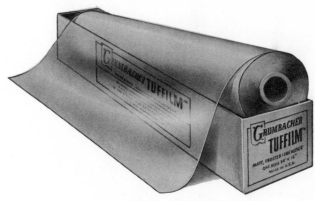

Fig. 1338.

Figure 1339: A studio easel is used especially when designing large plates. Have a sheet of formica-covered three-quarters-of-an-inch thick plywood about 40" x 30" added to the easel to place drawing papers (use tape for fastening). It can be used in the field, too.

Fig. 1339.

Fig. 1340.

Figure 1340: Powdered charcoal is very handy if you do work using the smudging technique. With a charcoal pencil it is very useful, especially in field work when you have no time to make your own powder.

Fig. 1341.

Figure 1341: A sketch box is also a very handy piece of equipment in the field. Have a sturdy one and keep it always ready to use. Do not remove any equipment from your field box for use in the studio. Keep plenty of sketching paper on hand, preferably in pads to fit your sketch box.

The photographs reproduced in *Figs. 1330* to *1341* are courtesty of M. Grumbacher and Co., New York, N.Y.

The "American Artist" (2160 Patterson St., Cincinnati, Ohio 45214) published a very useful book recently: *Art Materials Buyers Guide,* 1967 edition ($1.25.) It contains informations of various kinds of artist's materials, their manufacturers, etc. It is a very handy book to have in your studio.

Studio Plan

Every illustrator sooner or later is going to set up his own studio. *Fig. 1342* shows the floor plan of the main work room of the writer's studios.

The necessary furniture, based on the writer's own experience, would be:

1. Tables: Have plenty. Use corners for built-in tables, placing them so that you can work with daylight or with artificial light. The lights are mounted on the wall — eight foot long double tube neon lights: one such light should also be on the ceiling in the center of the room. Have an extra layout table, placed so that it is easy to reach from every direction.

2. Library: have a built-in shelf with a built-in desk under it. This desk serves as a reading corner and also could be used for storage place for paper materials.

3. Have a typewriter table as it has several uses other than holding a typewriter.

Important facts:

Select the right height for your table.

Do not buy or build anything unless you need it; a studio can be very easily overcrowded with unnecessary furniture.

Have enough chairs and plenty of light.

Formica covering is ideal for working surfaces.

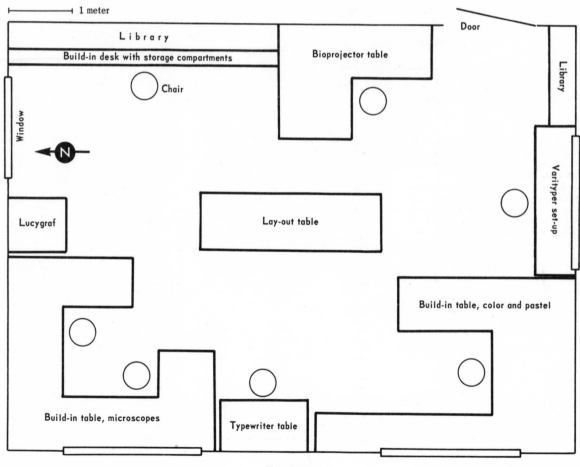

Fig. 1342.

Periodicals

In order to determine the right dimensions of the original artwork it is necessary for the illustrator to know the journal (or what size of book) in which the illustration will be published. It happens quite frequently that the author does not have all the information on hand and sometimes it is difficult to obtain a copy of the journal. The writer therefore has compiled a list of the most commonly used scientific journals and their dimensions.

Scientific journals are commonly printed in three different styles:

Figure 1343: A full page column. The width of the column is indicated below the picture (*a*).

Figure 1344: Two column page, where *a* indicates the width of the page and *b* the width of each column.

Figure 1345: A three column journal, where *a* indicates the width of the printed face, *b* the width of one column, and *c* of two columns.

The height of the page (the printed surface) is measured from the very top of the first line to the bottom of the last line. After the title of the journal there is a number in parentheses. This number indicates the number of columns per page. For example:

Journal of Economic Entomology, (2), *a* 6-1/4 x 8-5/8; *b* 3.

It means that the journal page is composed of two columns; the height of the page is 8-5/8 inches, the width is 6-1/4 inches; the width of one column is 3 inches.

Acta Agronomica, (1), 4-5/8 x 7-5/8
Acta Biologica Universitatis Szegediensis, (1), 5 x 7-1/4
Acta Zoologica Lilloana, (1), 4-1/4 x 7
Agricultural and Biological Chemistry, (2), *a* 5-7/8 x 7-1/4; *b* 2-3/4
Agricultural Chemicals, (3), *a* 7 x 10; *b* 2-1/4; *c* 4-1/2
Agricultural Gazette, (2), *a* 5-1/2 x 8-1/8; *b* 2-5/8
Agricultural Research, (1), 5-1/4 x 7-1/4

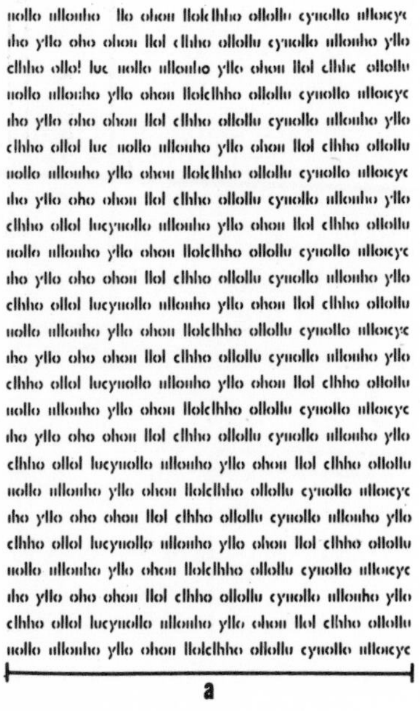

Fig. 1343.

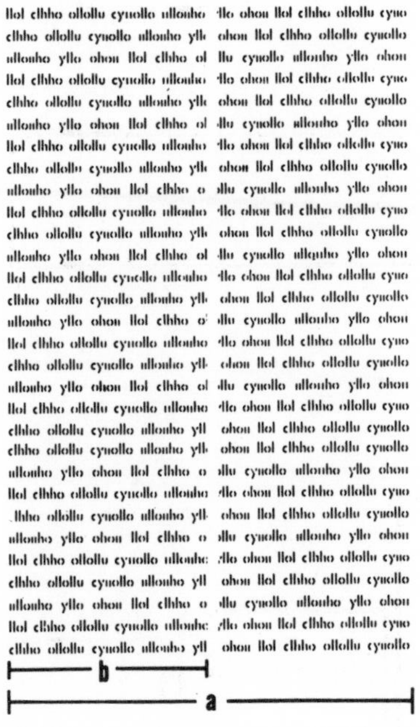

Fig. 1344.

Fig. 1345.

Agricultural Research Review, (1), 5-1/4 x 8

Agronomy Journal, (2), *a* 7 x 9; *b* 3-1/4

Al Awamia, (1), 4-1/2 x 7

Alexandria Journal of Agricultural Research, (1), 4-1/4 x 7

Aliso, (1), 5 x 7-1/4

American Journal of Botany, (2), *a* 6-1/8 x 9-1/2; *b* 3

American Journal of Tropical Medicine and Hygiene, (2), *a* 5-1/2 x 8; *b* 2-5/8

American Journal of Veterinary Research, (2), *a* 5-1/2 x 8; *b* 2-5/8

American Mineralogist, The, (1), 4-1/2 x 7

American Naturalist, The, (1), 4-5/8 x 7-1/2

American Potato Journal, (1), 4-1/2 x 7

Analyst, The, (1), 5-1/2 x 8

Analytical Biochemistry, (1), 4-1/2 x 7

Analytical Chemistry, (3), *a* 7 x 10; *b* 2-1/4; *c* 4-1/2

Angewandte Chemie, (2), *a* 6-1/4 x 10; *b* 3

Annalen der Chemie (Justus Liebig's), (1), 4-5/8 x 6-3/8

Annales Agronomiques, (1), 5 x 7-1/4

Annales Historico-Naturales Musei Nationalis Hungarici, (1), 5-1/8 x 7-1/2

Annales d. Naturhistorisches Museum, (1), 5 x 7-1/2 (Wien, Austria)

Annali del Museo Civico di Storia Naturale, (1), 4-1/2 x 7 (Genova, Italy)

Annali della Sperimentazione Agraria, (1) 4-3/8 x 7-1/4

Annals of Applied Biology, (1), 5-1/4 x 7-3/4

Annals of Botany, (1), 4-5/8 x 7-1/2

Annals and Magazine of Natural History, (1), 3-5/8 x 6-3/4

Annals of the Entomological Society of America, (2), *a* 6-1/4 x 8-1/2; *b* 3

Annals of the Missouri Botanical Garden, (1), 4-5/8 x 7-1/2

Annals of the Transwaal Museum, (1), 4-1/2 x 7-1/2

Annual Review of Entomology, (1), 4-1/4 x 7

Applied Microbiology, (2), *a* 7-7/8 x 8-1/2; *b* 3-1/2

Archives of Environmental Health, (2), *a* 5-1/2 x 8-1/4; *b* 2-5/8

Archives of Biochemistry and Biophysics, (2), *a* 5-1/2 x 8; *b* 2-5/8

Arkiv för Zoologi (also for . . . Botany, . . . Chemistry, etc.), (1), 5 x 7-1/4

Atti Accademia Nazionale dei Lincei, (1), 5 x 8

Australian Journal of Agricultural Research, (1), 5 x 7-1/2

Australian Journal of Biological Sciences, (1), 5 x 7-1/2

Australian Journal of Botany, (1), 5 x 7-1/2

Australian Journal of Marine and Freshwater Research, (1) 5 x 7-1/2

Bacteriological Proceedings, (1) 4-1/2 x 7-3/4

Bacteriological Reviews, (2), *a* 5-1/2 x 7-7/8; *b* 2-5/8

Baileya, (1), 4-1/2 x 6-1/2

Bee World, (1), 4-1/4 x 7

Behaviour, (1), 4-1/2 x 7

Beiträge zur Entomologie, (1), 4-3/4 x 7-1/2 (Berlin, Germany)

Biochimica et Biophysica Acta, (1), 5 x 7-1/2

Biochemical Journal, (2), *a* 5-3/4 x 8; *b* 2-3/4

Biochemical Pharmacology, (1), 5 x 7-3/4

Biochemistry, (2) *a* 6-7/8 x 10; *b* 3-1/4

Biologia Plantarum, (1), 5 x 7

Biometrics, (1), 4-3/8 x 7

Biometrische Zeitschrift, (1), 4-3/4 x 7-1/4

Biometrika, (1), 5-5/8 x 8-1/4

Boletim da la Sociedade Portuguesa de Ciencia Naturais, (1), 4-1/4 x 7

Botanical Gazette, (2), *a* 6-1/8 x 8-1/2; *b* 3

Botanical Review, The, (1), 4 x 6-1/2

Bragantia, (1), 4-1/2 x 7

British Journal of Industrial Medicine, (2), *a* 5-3/4 x 7-3/4; *b* 2-3/4

Brittonia, (1), 5 x 7-7/8

Bulletin of the American Museum of Natural History, (2), *a* 5-7/8 x 8; *b* 2-3/4

Bulletin, Association of Food and Drug Officials of the United States, (1), 4-1/4 x 7-1/8

Bulletin, Brooklyn Entomological Society, (1), 4 x 6-1/2

Bulletin, California State, Department of Agriculture, (2), *a* 4-3/4 x 7-1/2; *b* 2-1/4

Bulletin of Entomological Research, (1), 5 x 7-1/2

Bulletin of the Florida State Museum, (1), 4-1/4 x 7

Bulletin, Illinois Natural History Survey, (1), 4-7/8 x 7-7/8

Bulletin of the Museum of Comparative Zoology, (1), 4 x 6-1/4

Bulletin, Ohio Biological Survey, (1), 5 x 7-3/4

Bulletin, Southern California Academy of Sciences, (1), 4 x 6-3/4

Bulletin of the Research Council of Israel, (1), 5-7/8 x 7-1/4

Bulletin of the Torrey Botanical Club, (1), 4-5/8 x 7

Caldasia, (1), 4-5/8 x 7

California Agriculture, (3), *a* 7-1/4 x 9; *b* 2-3/8; *c* 4-3/4

California Fish and Game, (1), 4-3/8 x 7-3/8

Canadian Entomologist, (1), 5 x 8-1/4

Canadian Field-Naturalist, (1), 5-7/8 x 7-1/4

Canadian Journal of Animal Science, (1), 4-5/8 x 7-1/4

Canadian Journal of Biochemistry and Psychology, (1), 4-3/4 x 7-1/4

Canadian Journal of Botany, (1), 4-3/4 x 7-1/4

Canadian Journal of Chemistry, (1), 5-1/2 x 8

Canadian Journal of Genetics and Cytology, (1), 4-3/4 x 7-3/4

Canadian Journal of Microbiology, (1), 4-3/4 x 7-1/4

Canadian Journal of Physics, (1), 4-3/4 x 7-1/2

Canadian Journal of Plant Science, (1), 4-5/8 x 7-1/2

Canadian Journal of Soil Science, (1), 4-1/2 x 7-1/2

Canadian Journal of Zoology, (1), 4-3/4 x 7-1/4

Cereal Chemistry, (1), 4-1/4 x 7

Chemical Reviews, (2), *a* 6-1/2 x 9-1/2; *b* 3-1/4

Chemische Berichte, (1), 4-5/8 x 7-1/4 (Heidelberg, Germany)

Chemistry and Industry, (2), *a* 6-3/8 x 8-3/4; *b* 3-1/4

Coleopterists' Bulletin, The, (1), 4-1/2 x 7

Comparative Biochemistry and Physiology, (1), 5 x 7-1/4

Contributions from the Boyce Thompson Institute, (1), 4-5/8 x 7

Cytologia, (1), 4-7/8 x 7-3/4 (Tokyo, Japan)

Ecological Monographs, (2), *a* 6-1/8 x 8-3/4; *b* 3

Ecology, (2), *a* 6-1/4 x 8-3/4; *b* 3

Economic Botany, (2), *a* 5-1/8 x 7-5/8; *b* 2-1/2

Entomologische Berichten, (1), 4-5/8 x 7-1/2

EOS, (1), 4-1/4 x 6-3/4

Endeavour, (2), *a* 6-7/8 x 9-3/4; *b* 3-1/8

Entomologica Americana, (1), 4-1/4 x 6-1/2

Entomologia Experimentalis et Applicata, (1), 4-1/2 x 7-1/2

Entomological News, (1), 3-3/4 x 6-1/4

Entomophaga, (1), 4-3/4 x 7-1/2

Enzymologia, (1), 4-1/4 x 6-3/4

Evolution, (2), *a* 5-1/8 x 7-3/4; *b* 2-1/2

Experimental Agriculture and Animal Husbandry, (2), *a* 6-1/2 x 8-1/2; *b* 3-1/8

Experimental Cell Research, (1), 5 x 7-3/4

Experimental and Molecular Pathology, (1), 5 x 7-3/4

Experientia, (2), *a* 6-1/2 x 9-1/4; *b* 3-1/8

Fieldiana, (1), 4-1/4 x 7

Florida Entomologist, The, (1), 4-1/4 x 7

Forest Science, (1), 4-1/4 x 7

Genetical Research, (1), 5-1/8 x 7-3/4

Genetics, (1), 5 x 7-1/2

Growth, (1), 4-3/8 x 6-3/8

Helvetica Chimica Acta, (1), 5 x 7-1/2

Hereditas, (1), 4-5/8 x 7

Hilgardia, (2), *a* 5 x 8; *b* 2-3/8

Industrial and Engineering Chemistry, (2), *a* 7 x 10; *b* 3-1/4

Iowa State Journal of Science, (1), 4-1/2 x 7

Journal of Air Pollution Control, (3), *a* 7 x 9-1/2; *b* 2-1/4; *c* 4-1/2

Journal of the American Chemical Society, (2), *a* 6-7/8 x 10; *b* 3-1/4

Journal of the Association of Official Agricultural Chemists, (2), *a* 5-1/4 x 7-7/8; *b* 2-1/2

Journal of Biological Chemistry, (2), *a* 7-1/8 x 9-1/4; *b* 3-1/2

Journal of Biophysical and Biochemical Cytology, The, (2), *a* 5-1/2 x 7-7/8; *b* 2-5/8

Journal of Cell Biology, (2) 5-1/2 x 8; *b* 2-5/8

Journal of Cellular and Comparative Physiology, (2), *a* 5 x 7-3/4; *b* 2-5/8

Journal of the Chemical Society, (1), 5-1/4 x 8 (London)

Journal of the Chemical Society of America, (1), 5-1/4 x 8

Journal of Colloid Science, (1), 4-1/2 x 7-1/4

Journal of Ecology, The, (1), 5-1/8 x 7-7/8

Journal of Economic Entomology, (2), *a* 6-1/4 x 8-5/8; *b* 3

Journal of the Elisha Mitchell Scientific Society, (2), *a* 5-1/2 x 8-1/4; *b* 2-5/8

Journal of the Entomological Society of South Africa, (1), 4-5/8 x 6-3/4

Journal of Experimental Biology, The, (1), 5-1/8 x 7-3/4

Journal of Food Science, (2), *a* 5-1/2 x 8; *b* 2-5/8

Journal of General Microbiology, (1), 5 x 7-3/4

Journal of General Physiology, (1), 5 x 7-1/2

Journal of Genetics, (1), 5-1/4 x 7-3/4

Journal of Helminthology, (1), 4-1/8 x 6-5/8

Journal of Histochemistry and Cytochemistry, (2), *a* 5-3/8 x 7-7/8; *b* 3-1/4

Journal of Insect Pathology, (1), 4-1/4 x 6-1/2

Journal of Insect Physiology, (1), 5 x 7-1/4

Journal of Invertebrate Pathology, (2), *a* 5-1/2 x 7-7/8; *b* 2-5/8

Journal of the Kansas Entomological Society, (1), 4-1/8 x 6-5/8

Journal of Lipid Research, (2), *a* 6-7/8 x 8-3/4; *b* 3-1/4

Journal of the New York Entomological Society, (1), 4 x 6-3/4

Journal of Organic Chemistry, (2), *a* 6-7/8 x 9-3/4; *b* 3-1/4

Journal of Parasitology, (2), *a* 5-1/2 x 8; *b* 2-5/8

Journal of Physical Chemistry, (2), *a* 6-7/8 x 8-3/4; *b* 3-1/4

Journal of Protozoology, (2), *a* 6-1/2 x 8-5/8; *b* 3-1/8

Journal of the Royal Society of Western Australia, (2), *a* 5-3/4 x 8; *b* 2-3/4

Journal of Soil Science, (1), 4-5/8 x 7-1/2

Journal of the Washington Academy of Sciences, (2), *a* 5-1/8 x 7-3/4; *b* 2-3/8

Journal of Wildlife Management, (2), *a* 5-1/2 x 7-5/8; *b* 2-5/8

Memoires de l'Institut Scientifique de Madagascar, (1), 7-1/2 x 4

Memoirs of the New York Botanical Garden, (1), 5 x 8

Microchemical Journal, (1), 4-1/8 x 6-1/2

Mitteilungen der Münchner Entomologischen Gesell-schaft, (1), 4 x 7-1/4

Nature, (2), *a* 6-5/8 x 9-1/4; *b* 3-1/4 (London)

Nematologica, (1), 5 x 7-1/2

New Pathologist, The, (1), 5-1/4 x 8

New Zealand Journal of Science, (1), 4-1/2 x 6-7/8

Occasional Papers of the California Academy of Sciences, (1), 4-1/4 x 7

Ohio Journal of Science, The, (1), 5 x 7-1/2

Opuscula Entomologica, (1), 5 x 7-3/8

Pan-Pacific Entomologist, (1), 3-7/8 x 6-3/4

Parasitology, (1), 5-1/8 x 8

Parc National Albert, (1), 4-7/8 x 7-1/4

Physiologia Plantarum, (1), 5 x 7-1/4

Phytopathology, (2), *a* 6-1/8 x 8-1/2; *b* 3

Plant Physiology, (2), *a* 6-1/4 x 8-1/2; *b* 3

Proceedings of the Entomological Society of Washing-ton, (1), 6-3/4 x 4-1/4

Proceedings of the Entomological Society of Mani-toba, (1) 5 x 7-3/4

Proceedings of the Entomological Society of Ontario, (1), 5 x 7-5/8

Proceedings of the Hawaiian Entomological Society, (1), 4 x 6-5/8

Proceedings of the Japan Academy, (1), 4-5/8 x 7-3/4

Proceedings of the Helminthological Society of Wash-ington, (1), 4-1/4 x 7-1/2

Proceedings of the National Academy of Sciences of the United States of America, (1), 5 x 7-3/4

Proceedings of the Royal Entomological Society (Lon-don), (1), 4-3/4 x 7-1/2

Proceedings of the California Academy of Sciences, (1), 4-5/8 x 7-3/8

Proceedings of the Society for Experimental Biology and Medicine, (2), *a* 5-1/2 x 8; *b* 2-5/8

Proceedings of the United States National Museum, (1), 4-1/2 x 7-1/4

Psyche, (1), 4 x 6-1/4

Science, (3), *a* 7-1/4 x 10; *b* 2-1/4; *c* 4-3/4

Soil Science, (2), *a* 5-1/2 x 7-3/4; *b* 2-5/8

Spectrochimica Acta, (1), 5-1/4 x 7-1/2 (Berlin, Ger-many)

Talanta, (1), 5 x 7-3/4

Texas Journal of Science, The, (1), 4-1/4 x 7

Transactions of the American Entomological Society, (1), 4 x 6-1/4

Transactions of the American Geophysical Union, (2), *a* 5-1/2 x 8; *b* 2-5/8

Transactions of the British Mycological Society, (1), 4-5/8 x 7-3/8

Transactions of the New York Academy of Sciences, (1), 4-1/2 x 7

Tropical Agriculture, (1), 4-1/2 x 7-1/4 (London)

Turrialba, (2), *a* 6-3/4 x 9; *b* 4-1/8 (Costa Rica)

University of California Publications in . . . (Ento-mology, Botany, etc.), (1), 5 x 7-3/4

University of Kansas, Science Bulletin, (1), 4-1/8 x 7

University of Washington, Publications in Biology, (1), 4-1/2 x 7

University of Michigan, Miscellaneous Publications, Museum of Zoology, (1), 4-5/8 x 7-1/8

Veliger, The, (2), *a* 6-1/2 x 9; *b* 5-3/8

Virology, (2), *a* 5-1/2 x 8; *b* 2-5/8

Vitis, (1), 4-3/4 x 7-1/2 (Germany)

Wasmann Journal of Biology, (1), 4 x 6-3/4

Weeds, (2), *a* 7-1/4 x 8-3/4; *b* 3-5/8

Weed Research, (1), 5 x 7-3/4

Yearbook of the California Avocado Society, (1), 4-3/8 x 7-1/2

Zoologica, (2), *a* 5-1/2 x 8-1/4; *b* 2-5/8

Measurements

19

A. Inches into millimeters
1 inch = 25.40005 mm.

inches	mm	inches	mm	inches	mm
0.05	1.27	6.00	152.40	21.00	533.40
0.10	2.54	7.00	177.80	22.00	571.50
0.20	5.08	8.00	203.20	23.00	596.90
0.30	7.62	9.00	228.60	24.00	609.60
0.40	10.16	10.00	254.00	25.00	635.00
0.50	12.70	11.00	279.40	26.00	660.40
0.60	15.24	12.00	304.80	27.00	685.80
0.70	17.18	13.00	330.20	28.00	711.20
0.80	20.32	14.00	355.60	29.00	736.60
0.90	22.86	15.00	381.00	30.00	762.00
1.00	25.40	16.00	406.40	31.00	787.40
2.00	50.28	17.00	431.80	32.00	812.80
3.00	76.20	18.00	457.20		
4.00	101.60	19.00	482.60		
5.00	127.00	20.00	508.00		

B. Millimeters into inches
1 mm. = 0.03937 inch

mm	inches	mm	inches
10	0.3937	200	7.874
20	0.7874	300	11.811
30	1.1811	400	15.748
40	1.5748	500	19.785
50	1.9685	600	23.633
60	2.3622	700	27.559
70	2.7559	800	31.496
80	3.1496	900	35.433
90	3.5433	1000	39.378
100	3.9370		

C. Feet into meters
1 foot = 0.3048006 meter

feet	m.	feet	m.	feet	m.
1	0.305	20	6.096	200	60.96
2	0.610	30	9.144	300	91.44
3	0.914	40	12.192	400	121.92
4	1.219	50	15.240	500	152.40
5	1.524	60	18.288	600	182.88
6	1.829	70	21.336	700	213.36
7	2.134	80	24.384	800	243.84
8	2.438	90	27.432	900	274.32
9	2.743	100	30.480	1000	304.80
10	3.048				

D. Meters into feet
1 meter = 39.3700 inches = 3.280833 feet

m.	feet	m.	feet	m.	feet
1	3.28	20	65.62	300	984.25
2	6.56	30	98.42	400	1312.33
3	9.84	40	131.23	500	1640.42
4	13.12	50	164.04	1000	3280.80
5	16.40	60	196.85	2000	6561.70
6	19.68	70	229.66	3000	9842.50
7	22.97	80	262.47	4000	13123.30
8	26.25	90	295.27	5000	16404.20
9	29.53	100	328.08	10000	32808.33
10	32.81	200	656.17		

E. Miles into kilometers
1 mile = 1.609347 kilometers

miles	km	miles	km	miles	km
10	16	110	177	2000	3219
20	32	120	193	3000	4828
30	48	130	209	4000	6437
40	64	140	225	5000	8047
50	80	150	241	10000	16093
60	97	200	322	12000	19312
70	113	300	483	15000	24140
80	129	400	644	17000	27359
90	145	500	805	19000	30578
100	161	1000	1609	20000	32187

F. Kilometers into miles
1 kilometer = 0.621370 mile

km	mile	km	mile	km	mile
1	0.6	11	6.8	200	124.3
2	1.2	12	7.5	300	186.4
3	1.9	13	8.1	400	248.5
4	2.5	14	8.7	500	310.7
5	3.1	15	9.3	1000	621.4
6	3.7	20	12.4	5000	3106.8
7	4.3	30	18.6	10000	6213.7
8	5.0	40	24.9	15000	9320.5
9	5.6	50	31.1	20000	12427.4
10	6.2	100	62.1		

G. *Centigrade (C) to Fahrenheit (F)*

°C	°F	°C	°F	°C	°F	°C	°F
+102	+215.6	48	118.4	6	21.2	60	76.0
101	213.8	47	116.6	7	19.4	61	77.8
100	212.0	46	114.8	8	17.6	62	79.6
99	210.2	45	113.0	9	15.8	63	81.4
98	208.4	44	111.2	10	14.0	64	83.2
97	206.6	43	109.4	11	12.2	65	85.0
96	204.8	42	107.6	12	10.4	66	86.8
95	203.0	41	105.8	13	8.6	67	88.6
94	201.2	40	104.0	14	6.8	68	90.4
93	199.4	39	102.2	15	5.0	69	92.2
92	197.6	38	100.4	16	3.2	70	94.0
91	195.8	37	98.6	17	+1.4	71	95.8
90	194.0	36	96.8	18	−0.4	72	97.6
89	192.2	35	95.0	19	2.2	73	99.4
88	190.4	34	93.2	20	4.0	74	101.2
87	188.6	33	91.4	21	5.8	75	103.0
86	186.8	32	89.6	22	7.6	76	104.8
85	185.0	31	87.8	23	9.4	77	106.6
84	183.2	30	86.0	24	11.2	78	108.4
83	181.4	29	84.2	25	13.0	79	110.2
82	179.6	28	82.4	26	14.8	80	112.0
81	177.8	27	80.6	27	16.6	81	113.8
80	176.0	26	78.8	28	18.4	82	115.6
79	174.2	25	77.0	29	20.2	83	117.4
78	172.4	24	75.2	30	22.0	84	119.2
77	170.6	23	73.4	31	23.8	85	121.0
76	168.8	22	71.6	32	25.6	86	122.8
75	167.0	21	69.8	33	27.4	87	124.6
74	165.2	20	68.0	34	29.2	88	126.4
73	163.4	19	66.2	35	31.0	89	128.2
72	161.6	18	64.4	36	32.8	90	130.0
71	159.8	17	62.6	37	34.6	91	131.8
70	158.0	16	60.8	38	36.4	92	133.6
69	156.2	15	59.0	39	38.2	93	135.4
68	154.4	14	57.2	40	40.0	94	137.2
67	152.6	13	55.4	41	41.8	95	139.0
66	150.8	12	53.6	42	43.6	96	140.8
65	149.0	11	51.8	43	45.4	97	142.6
64	147.2	10	50.0	44	47.2	98	144.4
63	145.4	9	48.2	45	49.0	99	146.2
62	143.6	8	46.4	46	50.8	−100	−148.0
61	141.8	7	44.6	47	52.6		
60	140.0	6	42.8	48	54.4		
59	138.2	5	41.0	49	56.2		
58	136.4	4	39.2	50	58.0		
57	134.6	3	37.4	51	59.8		
56	132.8	2	35.6	52	61.6		
55	131.0	+1	33.8	53	63.4		
54	129.2	0	32.0	54	65.2		
53	127.4	−1	30.2	55	67.0		
52	125.6	2	28.4	56	68.8		
51	123.8	3	26.6	57	70.6		
50	122.0	4	24.8	58	72.4		
49	120.2	5	23.0	59	74.2		

H. Fahrenheit (F) to Centigrade (C)

F°	C°	°F	°C	°F	°C	°F	°C
+130	+54.44	72	22.22	14	10.00	44	42.22
129	53.89	71	21.67	13	10.56	45	42.78
128	53.33	70	21.11	12	11.11	46	43.33
127	52.78	69	20.56	11	11.67	47	43.89
126	52.22	68	20.00	10	12.22	48	44.44
125	51.67	67	19.44	9	12.78	49	45.00
124	51.11	66	18.89	8	13.33	50	45.56
123	50.56	65	18.33	7	13.89	51	46.11
122	50.00	64	17.78	6	14.44	52	46.67
121	49.44	63	17.22	5	15.00	53	47.22
120	48.89	62	16.67	4	15.56	54	47.78
119	48.33	61	16.11	3	16.11	55	48.33
118	47.78	60	15.56	2	16.67	56	48.89
117	47.22	59	15.00	+1	17.22	57	49.44
116	46.67	58	14.44	0	17.78	58	50.00
115	46.11	57	13.89	−1	18.33	59	50.56
114	45.56	56	13.33	2	18.89	60	51.11
113	45.00	55	12.78	3	19.44	61	51.67
112	44.44	54	12.22	4	20.00	62	52.22
111	43.89	53	11.67	5	20.56	63	52.78
110	43.33	52	11.11	6	21.11	64	53.33
109	42.78	51	10.56	7	21.67	65	53.89
108	42.22	50	10.00	8	22.22	66	54.44
107	41.67	49	9.44	9	22.78	67	55.00
106	41.11	48	8.89	10	23.33	68	55.56
105	40.56	47	8.33	11	23.89	69	56.11
104	40.00	46	7.78	12	24.44	70	56.67
103	39.44	45	7.22	13	25.00	71	57.22
102	38.89	44	6.67	14	25.56	72	57.78
101	38.33	43	6.11	15	26.11	73	58.33
100	37.78	42	5.56	16	26.67	74	58.89
99	37.22	41	5.00	17	27.22	75	59.44
98	36.67	40	4.44	18	27.78	76	60.00
97	36.11	39	3.89	19	28.33	77	60.56
96	35.56	38	3.33	20	28.89	78	61.11
95	35.00	37	2.78	21	29.44	79	61.67
94	34.44	36	2.22	22	30.00	80	62.22
93	33.89	35	1.67	23	30.56	81	62.78
92	33.33	34	1.11	24	31.11	82	63.33
91	32.78	33	+0.56	25	31.67	83	63.89
90	32.22	32	0.00	26	32.22	84	64.44
89	31.67	31	−0.56	27	32.78	85	65.00
88	31.11	30	1.11	28	33.33	86	65.56
87	30.56	29	1.67	29	33.89	87	66.11
86	30.00	28	2.22	30	34.44	88	66.67
85	29.44	27	2.78	31	35.00	89	67.22
84	28.89	26	3.33	32	35.56	90	67.78
83	28.33	25	3.89	33	36.11	91	68.33
82	27.78	24	4.44	34	36.67	92	68.89
81	27.22	23	5.00	35	37.22	93	69.44
80	26.67	22	5.56	36	37.78	94	70.00
79	26.11	21	6.11	37	38.33	95	70.56
78	25.56	20	6.67	38	38.89	96	71.11
77	25.00	19	7.22	39	39.44	97	71.67
76	24.44	18	7.78	40	40.00	98	72.22
75	23.89	17	8.33	41	40.56	99	72.78
74	23.33	16	8.89	42	41.11	−100	−73.33
73	22.78	15	9.44	43	41.67		

20 The Future in Scientific Illustrating

Because of the ever-increasing demand for illustrative material and the tremendous interest in visual education, there is probably no other profession that offers such opportunity as the field of scientific illustrating. As mentioned earlier, the public is not tired of reading books, but the increasing stress on time results in the search for methods for quick learning. "A good picture is worth a thousand words" — an old, well-established fact — is very true. The more illustrations a book has, the easier it is to understand the subject and the more copies will be read, and an increasing number of books are published each year. Scientists are preparing papers by the thousands each month. Authors are becoming increasingly aware of the need for illustrations.

How to start. The first and most important step is to decide the field in which you want to work. If you have your M.A. or M.S. degree (which is needed) in biology, specialize in botany or zoology. If you are trained in taxonomy, experiment and find out which area suits your ability best: plants or animals. Select a certain group and specialize in it — flowering plants, trees, mosses, ferns, etc., or birds, mammals, insects, worms, etc. When the territory is chosen, select the most necessary equipment and begin to buy it. Start to build up your collection of specimens (if needed), and your reference library. Start in the least expensive way; in case you change your field of interest there would be no great loss of investment. *Stay small but be good, fast and dependable in service.*

Getting customers. Word travels fast, and people will notice you sooner than you think. Start within your immediate area. College towns are excellent: teachers are working on books in almost every large college. Subscribe to four or five journals in your field and study the authors in every issue, especially in scientific journals. Write to them, and let them know about your specialty and willingness to work. Have a few, perhaps a dozen, good samples of your work printed, and send prints with your letter. Better yet, prepare a little brochure (16 pages of 5-1/2 x 8-1/2″ size), describe your specialty in a few words (one or two pages) and present some of your work on the rest of the pages. Have 200 to 300 copies printed and mail out four or five every month. If you have contracts, stop mailing the brochures. *Do not take on more work than you can handle.*

Charges. Charges will vary according to the type of work you are doing. Simple line drawings cost less than those in color or on scratchboard. The price depends also upon the quantity: a single illustration costs more than a series of drawings. If an author wants only ten drawings for an article the price per drawing would be higher than if he ordered 100 drawings for a book. Do not charge by the hour; charge by the value of the work. An hourly rate may sound preferable, but may be too expensive for the author, especially if you are slow. Set up a list of the species (object) you have to illustrate, determine the technique to be used, and set a flat rate for all the illustrations. Have a contract made according to your specifications; let the author read it and sign it. This commits you to deliver the work on time, and obliges the author to pay you the amount agreed upon. If you receive an order from an institution on an official purchase order, you can count on the payment, although a contract with the customer is still a handy paper to have. If the order is not through an institution and the client is unknown to you, draw up a contract that calls for a prepayment of 40 per cent, an additional payment of 30 per cent when three-fourths of the work is completed, and the final payment of 30 per cent when you deliver the rest of the work. In case of large orders ask your local bank for advice. The contract and payment can be arranged through your bank. In any case you may want to consult the bank with the consent of your customer. They may loan him the required amount, or he may deposit the whole amount in your bank for assurance. Roughly about 50 per cent of the authors are slow in payments (mostly miscalculation!) and about 10 per cent never pay. If you illustrate a *book* and the author has a contract from a publisher, your payment is more certain. Write to the publisher to inform them that you are doing the illustrations, (ask the author to verify this in a letter to the publisher), and know that if the author will not pay you, you will send a duplicate bill to them asking that your bill be deducted from the royalties. Illustration expenses on the part of the author are tax deductible. Your expenses (tools, materials, studio rent) are tax deductible, so keep your receipts! *Also report your income.*

Credits. Authors must give credit to the illustrator at all times. The nicest things can happen if the author includes the illustrator's name on the inside title page. Normally the artist's name is placed in the foreword, preface or in the "acknowledgments." This credit should also be specified in your contract.

Royalties. If the author pays you for the illustrations you can ask for nothing else. One copy of the book is the only thing to which you are entitled. Authors usually send a copy to the illustrator. If not, write to the publisher explaining the circumstances and they will send you a copy. If you agree to do the illustrations on a royalty basis, make your arrangements with the author, *then* have the publisher put your name on their contract. This way you have a copy of the contract and the royalties will be paid to you directly by the publisher. The percentage of the royalties depends upon the previous (and written) agreement between the author and illustrator. Until you have established yourself and have all the equipment necessary to fill any kind of order, do not take such contracts. If your studio is well equipped and the income from smaller contracts keeps you going financially, then you can undertake illustrations on the royalty basis. Always investigate the market and get the publisher's opinion about possible sales before you sign the contract.

Copyright. This is also a matter of agreement among author, illustrator and publisher.

1. Usually either the publisher or the author owns the copyright.

2. If the illustrations are done on a royalty basis, and this fact must be stated in the contract, the author and the artist may hold copyright jointly. This again depends upon the written agreement.

a) the author may hold the copyright on the text only;

b) the illustrator may hold the copyright for illustrations done by him. If illustrations from another source are included in the publication, the illustrator has no rights to these. Unless the contract precludes it, the illustrator is free to use his drawings in any

other publication of his own or to sell them to another author. The fee is due to the illustrator.

c) Both author and illustrator may be entitled to receive fees from the resale of the illustrations.

The illustrator, in case of *b*, is entitled to payment if the author uses the illustrations in another book.

These points should be covered in your written contract.

An illustrator can obtain a copyright on any of his drawings and he should have them copyrighted if he thinks they may be sold later. For a copyright, apply to the Library of Congress Copyright Office, Washington, D. C. 20540. Send two prints of the drawing with $6.00. They will send you the necessary forms and instructions.

If you make illustrations for a book and are paid for the work, generally you have no further claim on those illustrations. If you wish to use the illustrations in any published form, you must obtain permission to do so from the copyright owner.

As references. The illustrator is free to use any of his illustrations as samples of his work. It is wise to keep a list of authors, (and titles) and publishers for whom you did illustrations. Those are your recommendations and best references. Maintain a collection of those books or journals (or reprints) in which your illustrations appear. If you illustrate a book feel free to comment to the publisher on the quality of reproduction. This *is* the time when you can find new and valuable contracts. If your illustrations are good, the publisher may recommend you to other of their authors.

Remember. (1) Always do the best you can. (2) Do not be smarter than the author. (3) Ask for sufficient time to complete the drawings. (4) Never be afraid to ask for advice from the author or publisher. (5) Be confident but polite; a good relationship is important to success. (6) Your illustrations are the first thing a future book-buyer looks at; if there are many and they are good, he will buy the book. (7) Never do anything without a contract. In case of a large order ask your bank to investigate your client's credit: this is for your own protection. Keep the results strictly confidential.

You have a wonderful profession. Good luck, and plenty of work!

REFERENCES

The illustrations used in this book were made by the author. Some of them were done on commission and used in previous publications by other authors. In addition to those mentioned in the preface, the author wishes to express his most sincere thanks and appreciation to those who kindly permitted the use of illustrations for this book:

Drs. S. Stillman Berry, H. D. Chapman, F. R. Cole, Stanley E. Flanders, Verne Grant, F. A. Gunther, J. D. Kirkpatrick, J. Letey, Reinhold Mankau, G. B. Pearson, E. I. Schlinger, Henry Schneider, S. A. Sher, Ivan J. Thomason, C. R. Thompson, P. H. Timberlake, S. D. Van Gundy, and F. C. Wasek.

George T. Okumura kindly permitted the use of some illustrations of larvae that I did for his publication, sponsored at that time by the Hercules Powder Company. Kenneth Middleham (Figs. 00 00 000) and Max Badgley (Figs. 00 00 00) helped on photographs. Other photographs were made by the author or his wife. Oscar F. Clarke helped me in selecting and identifying plants for my studio herbarium. The latter part of the manuscript beginning with Chapter 13, was read by Mrs. Barbara Owens, and typed by my wife.

Sincere thanks to all.

For further references for samples on illustration techniques and reproduction it is advisable to have a copy of these books in your reference library.

Verne Grant: *The Origin of Adaptations.* (New York: Columbia University Press, 1963), 606 pp. ($12.50).

Verne Grant and Karen Grant: *Flower Pollination in the Phlox Family.* (New York: Columbia University Press, 1965), 180 pp. ($5.75).

G. B. Pearson: *Anatomy and Kinesiology.* (Greeley, Colorado: All American Productions and Publishers, P. O. Box 91). To be published with hundreds of figures, most of them in two- or four-color. Excellent example of color overlay study.

George T. Okumura: *Identification of Lepidopterous Larvae Attacking Cotton.* Special Publication No. 282. 1962. State of California, Department of Agriculture, Sacramento, Calif. 80 pp. (Free of charge.)

Sherwin Carlquist: *Island Life.* A natural history of the islands of the world. (New York: Natural History Press, 1965). 451 pp. All illustration techniques are represented in this volume. ($9.95).

ANSWERS to Figs. 105-114, on page 46:

Fig. 105: Smudging technique, reproduced in half-tone with opaqued background.
Fig. 106: India ink and wax pencil combination on rough-surfaced coquille board. Line reproduction.
Fig. 107: Pencil drawing with smudging. Half-tone reproduction, with background opaqued.
Fig. 108: India ink and wax pencil combination or presurfaced stipple board. Line reproduction.
Fig. 109: India ink. Line reproduction.
Fig. 110: Sketch board drawing with India ink. Line reproduction.
Fig. 111: India ink drawing. Half-tone reproduction with background opaqued.
Fig. 112: India ink and wax pencil combination on stipple board. Half-tone reproduction, background opaqued.
Fig. 113: India ink drawing. Line reproduction.
Fig. 114: India ink and artificial tones combination. Line reproduction.